Lottie. E. Gillett.
Keuka Lodge.
Keuka Lake.
N. Y.

BARRIERS BURNED AWAY

BY

E. P. ROE

GROSSET & DUNLAP
PUBLISHERS :: NEW YORK

This Book

IS REVERENTLY DEDICATED TO THE MEMORY OF
MY MOTHER

PREFACE TO FIRST EDITION.

I SHALL say but few words in regard to this first child of my imagination.

About one year ago our hearts were in deepest sympathy with our fellow-citizens of Chicago, and it occurred to me that their losses, sufferings, and fortitude might teach lessons after the echoes of the appalling event had died away in the press; and that even the lurid and destructive flames might reveal with greater vividness the need and value of Christian faith.

I spent some days among the smouldering ruins, and then began the following simple story, which has grown into larger proportions than I at first intended. But comparatively a small part of the narrative is occupied with the fire, for its scenes are beyond description, and too strange and terrible to be dwelt upon. Therefore the thread of my story is carried rapidly through that period of unparalleled excitement and disaster.

Nearly all the scenes introduced are historical, and are employed to give their terrible emphasis to that which is equally true in the serenest and securest times.

E. P. R.

CONTENTS

BARRIERS BURNED AWAY.

CHAPTER I.

LOVE UNKNOWN.

FROM its long sweep over the unbroken prairie a heavier blast than usual shook the slight frame house. The windows rattled in the casements, as if shivering in their dumb way in the December storm. So open and defective was the dwelling in its construction, that eddying currents of cold air found admittance at various points,—in some instances carrying with them particles of the fine, sharp, hail-like snow that the gale was driving before it in blinding fury.

Seated at one of the windows, peering out into the gathering gloom of the swiftly coming night, was a pale, faded woman with lustrous dark eyes. An anxious light shone from them, as she tried in vain to catch a glimpse of the darkening road that ran at a distance of about fifty yards from the house. As the furious blast shook the frail tenement, and circled round her in chilly currents from many a crack and crevice, she gave a short, hacking cough, and drew a thin shawl closer about her slight frame.

The unwonted violence of the wind had its effect upon another occupant of the room. From a bed in the corner near the stove came a feeble, hollow voice,—"Wife!"

In a moment the woman was bending over the bed, and in a voice full of patient tenderness answered, "Well, dear?"

"Has he come?"

"Not yet; but he *must* be here soon."

The word *must* was emphasized in such a way as to mean doubt rather than certainty, as if trying to assure her own mind of a matter about which painful misgivings could not be banished. The quick ear of the sick man caught the tone, and in a querulous voice he said, "Oh! if he should not get here in time, it would be the last bitter drop in my cup, now full and running over."

"Dear husband, if human strength and love can accomplish it, he will be here soon. But the storm is indeed frightful, and were the case less urgent, I could almost wish he would not try to make his way through it. But then we know what Dennis is; he never stops to consider difficulties, but pushes right on; and if—if he doesn't—if it is possible, he will be here before very long."

In spite of herself, the mother's heart showed its anxiety, and, too late for remedy, she saw the effect upon her husband. He raised himself in bed with sudden and unwonted strength. His eyes grew wild and almost fierce, and in a sharp, hurried voice, he said: "You don't think there is danger? There is no fear of his getting lost? If I thought that I would curse God and die."

"O Dennis, my husband, God forbid that you should speak thus! How can you feel so toward our Best Friend?"

"What kind of a friend has He been to me, pray? Has not my life been one long series of misfortunes? Have I not been disappointed in all my hopes? I once believed in God and tried to serve Him. But if, as I have been taught, all this evil and misfortune was ordered and made my inevitable lot by Him, He has not been my friend, but my enemy. He's been against me, not for me."

In the winter twilight the man's emaciated, unshorn face had the ghostly, ashen hue of death. From cavernous sockets his eyes gleamed with a terribly vindictive light, akin to insanity, and, in a harsh, high voice, as unnatural as his appearance and words, he continued: "Remember what I have gone through! what I have suffered! how often the cup of success that I was raising to my lips has been dashed to the ground!"

"But, Dennis, think a moment."

"Ah! haven't I thought till my heart is gall and my brain bursting? Haven't I, while lying here, hopelessly dying, gone over my life again and again? Haven't I lived over every disappointment, and taken every step downward a thousand times? Remember the pleasant, plentiful home I took you from, under the great elms in Connecticut. Your father did not approve of your marrying a poor school-teacher. But you know that then I had every prospect of getting the village academy, but with my luck another got ahead of me. Then I determined to study law. What hopes I had! I already grasped political honors that seemed within my reach, for you know I was a ready speaker. If my friends could only have seen that I was peculiarly fitted for public life and advanced me sufficient means, I would have returned it tenfold. But no; I was forced into other things for which I had no great aptness or knowledge, and years of struggling poverty and repeated disappointment followed. At last your father died and gave us enough to buy a cheap farm out here. But why go over our experience in the West? My plan of making sugar from the sorghum, which promised so brilliantly, has ended in the most wretched failure of all. And now money has gone, health has gone, and soon my miserable life will be over. Our boy must come back from college, and you and the two little ones, — what will you do?" and the man covered his head with the blanket and wept aloud. His poor wife, borne down by the torrent of his sorrow, was on her knees at his bedside, with her face buried in her hands, weeping also.

But suddenly he started up. His sobs ceased. His tears ceased to flow, while his eyes grew hard and fierce, and his hands clenched.

"But he was coming," he said. "He may get lost in the storm this bitter winter night."

He grasped his wife roughly by the arm. She was astonished at his sudden strength, and raised a tearful, startled face to his. It was well she could not see its terrible expression in the dusk; but she shuddered as he hissed in her ear, "If this should happen, — if my miserable death is the cause of his death, — if my accursed destiny involves him, your staff and hope, in so horrible a fate, what have I to do but curse God and die?"

It seemed to the poor woman that her heart would burst with the agony of that moment. As the storm had increased, a terrible dread had chilled her very soul. Every louder blast than usual had caused her an internal shiver, while for her husband's sake she had controlled herself outwardly. Like a shipwrecked man who is clinging to a rock, that he fears the tide will submerge, she had watched the snow rise from one rail to another along the fence. When darkness set in it was half-way up to the top rail, and she knew it was *drifting*. The thought of her ruddy, active, joyous-hearted boy, whose affection and hopefulness had been the broad track of sunlight on her hard path, — the thought of his lying white and still beneath one of these great banks, just where she could never know till spring rains and suns revealed to an indifferent stranger his sleeping-place, — now nearly overwhelmed her also, and even her faith wavered on the brink of the dark gulf of despair into which her husband was sinking. Left to herself, she might have sunk for a time, though her sincere belief in

God's goodness and love would have triumphed. But her womanly, unselfish nature, her long habit of sustaining and comforting her husband, came to her aid. Breathing a quick prayer to heaven, which was scarcely more than a gasp and a glance upward, she asked, hardly knowing what she said, "And what if he is *not* lost? What if God restores him safe and well?"

She shuddered after she had thus spoken, for she saw that her husband's belief in the hostility of God had reached almost the point of insanity. If this test failed, would he not, in spite of all she could say or do, curse God and die, as he had said? But she had been guided in her words more than she knew. He that careth for the fall of the sparrow had not forgotten His children in their sore extremity.

The man in answer to her question relaxed his hold upon her arm, and with a long breath fell back on his pillow.

"Ah!" said he, "if I could only see him again safe and well, if I could only leave you with him as your protector and support, I believe I could forgive all the past and be reconciled even to my hard lot."

"God gives you opportunity so to do, my father, for here I am safe and sound."

The soft snow had muffled the son's footsteps, and his approach had been unnoted. Entering at the back door, and passing through the kitchen, he had surprised his parents in the painful scene above described. As he saw his mother's form in dim outline kneeling at the bed, her face buried in its covering, — as he heard his father's significant words, — the quick-witted youth realized the situation. While he loved his father dearly, and honored him for his many good traits, he was also conscious of his faults, especially this most serious one now threatening such fatal consequences, — that of charging to God the failures and disappointments resulting from defects in his own character. It seemed as if a merciful Providence was about to use this awful dread of accident to the son — a calamity that rose far above and overshadowed all the past — as the means of winning back the alienated heart of this weak and erring man.

The effect of the sudden presence in the sick-room was most marked. The poor mother, who had shown such self-control and patient endurance before, now gave way utterly, and clung for a few moments to her son's neck with hysterical energy, then in strong reaction fainted away. The strain upon her worn and overtaxed system had been too severe.

At first the sick man could only look through the dusk at the outline of his son with a bewildered stare, his mind too weak to comprehend the truth. But soon he too was sobbing for joy.

But when his wife suddenly became a lifeless weight in his son's arms, who in wild alarm cried, "Mother, what is the matter? Speak to me! Oh! I have killed her by my rash entrance," the sick man's manner changed, and his eyes again became dry and hard, and even in the darkness had a strange glitter.

"Is your mother dead?" he asked, in a low, hoarse voice.

"O mother, speak to me!" cried the son, forgetting for a time his father.

For a moment there was death-like silence. Then the young man groped for an old settle in the corner of the room, laid his mother tenderly upon it, and sprung for a light, but as he passed his father's bed the same strong grasp fell upon his arm that his mother had shuddered under a little before, and the question was this time hissed in his ear, "Is your mother dead?" For a moment he had no power to answer, and his father continued: "What a fool I was to expect God to show mercy or kindness to me or mine while I was above ground! You are only brought home to suffer more than death in seeing your mother die. May that God that has followed me all my life, not with blessings —"

"Hush, father!" cried his son, in loud, commanding tones. "Hush, I entreat," and in his desperation he actually put his hand over his father's mouth.

The poor woman must have been dead, indeed, had she long remained deaf to the voice of her beloved son, and his loud tones partially revived her. In a faint voice she called, "Dennis!"

With hands suddenly relaxed, and hearts almost stilled in their beating, father and son listened for a second. Again, a little louder, through that dark and silent room, was heard the faint call, "Dennis!"

Springing to her side, her son exclaimed, "O mother, I am here; don't leave us; in mercy don't leave us."

"It was I she called," said his father.

With unnatural strength he had tottered across the room, and taking his wife's hand, cried, "O Ethel, don't die! don't fill my already full cup to overflowing with bitterness!"

Their familiar voices were the best of remedies. After a moment she sat up, and passing her hand across her brow as if to clear away confusion of mind, said: "Don't be alarmed; it's only a faint turn. I don't wonder though that you are frightened, for I never was so before."

Poor woman, amid all the emergencies of her hard lot, she had never in the past given way so far.

Then, becoming aware of her husband's position, she exclaimed: "Why, Dennis, my husband, out of your bed? You will catch your death."

"Ah, wife, that matters little if you and Dennis live."

"But it matters much to me," cried she, springing up.

By this time her son had struck a light, and each was able to look on the other's face. The unnatural strength, the result of excitement, was fast leaving the sick man. The light revealed him helplessly leaning on the couch where his wife had lain. His face was ashen in color, and he was gasping for breath. Tenderly they carried him back to his bed, and he was too weak now to do more than quietly lie upon it and gaze at them. After replenishing the fire, and looking at the little ones that were sleeping in the outer room, they shaded the lamp, and sat down at his bedside, while the mother asked her son many eager questions as to his escape. He told them how he had struggled through the snow till almost exhausted, when he had been overtaken by a farmer with a strong team, and thus enabled to make the journey in safety.

As the sick man looked and listened, his face grew softer and more quiet in its expression.

Then the young man, remembering, said: "I bought the medicines you wrote for, mother, at Bankville. This, the druggist said, would produce quiet and sleep, and surely father needs it after the excitement of the evening."

The opiate was given, and soon the regular, quiet breathing of the patient showed that it had taken effect. A plain but plentiful supper, which the anxious mother had prepared hours before, was placed upon the kitchen table, and the young man did ample justice to it; for, the moment the cravings of his heart were satisfied in meeting his kindred after absence, he became conscious of the keenest hunger. Toiling through the snow for hours in the face of the December storm had taxed his system to the utmost, and now he felt the need of food and rest. After supper he honestly meant to watch at his father's bedside, while his mother slept; but he had scarcely seated himself on the old settle, when sleep, like an armed man, overpowered him, and in spite of all his efforts he was soon bound in the dreamless slumber of healthful youth. But with eyes so wide and lustrous that it seemed as if sleep could never close them again, the wife and mother, pale and silent, watched between her loved ones. The troubled expression was gone, for the ranks of her little band had closed up, and all were about her in one more brief rest in the forward and uncertain march of life. She seemed looking intently at something far off,—something better discerned by the spiritual than by the natural eye. Disappointments had been bitter, poverty hard and grinding, but she had learned to escape into a large world that was fast becoming real to her strong imagination. While her husband was indulging in chimerical visions of boundless prosperity here on earth which he would bring to pass by some lucky stroke of fortune or invention, she also was picturing to herself grander things which God would realize to her *beyond* time and earth. When alone, in moments of rest from incessant toil, she would take down the great family Bible, and with her finger on some description of the "new heavens and new earth," as the connecting link between the promise and her strong realization of it, she would look away with that intent gaze. The new world, purged from sin and sorrow, would rise before her with more than Edenlike loveliness. Her spirit would revel in its shadowy walks and sunny glades, and as the crowning joy she would meet her Lord and Saviour in some secluded place, and sit listening at His feet like Mary of old. Thus, in the strong illusion of her imagination, Christ's words seemed addressed directly to her, while she looked up into His face with rapt attention. Instead of *reading* her Lord's familiar sayings, she seemed to *listen* to them as did the early disciples. After a little time she would close the Bible and go back to her hard practical life, awed yet strengthened, and with a hopeful expression, like that which must have rested on the disciples' faces on coming down from the Mount of Transfiguration.

CHAPTER II.

LOVE KNOWN.

HOUR after hour passed. The storm was dying away, and at times, through broken rifts in the clouds, stars would gleam out. Instead of the continued roar and rush, the wind blew in gusts at longer intervals, and nature seemed like a passionate child that had cried itself to sleep. The fitful blasts were the involuntary sobs that heave the breast, till at last quiet and peace take the place of stormy anger.

It seemed as if the silent watcher never could withdraw her gaze from the beautiful world of her vision. Never had it seemed so near and real before, and she was unconscious of the lapse of time. Suddenly she heard her name called, — "Ethel!"

If the voice had come from the imaginary world present to her fancy, it could not have startled her more for a moment. Then she realized that it was her husband who spoke. He had called her name in his sleep, and yet it seemed a call of God. At once it flashed through her mind that in dreaming of a glorious and happy future she was forgetting him and his need.

She turned the light upon his face. Never had he looked so pale and wan, and she realized that he might be near his end. In an agony of self-reproach and yearning tenderness she knelt at his bedside and prayed as she never had prayed before. Could he go home? Could he be received, feeling toward his Father as he did? He had talked of forgiving, when he stood so sorely in need of Christ's forgiveness; and she had been forgetting that need, when every moment might involve her husband's salvation. Out of his sleep he had called her to his help. Perhaps God had used his unconscious lips to summon her. With a faith naturally strong, but greatly increased by the vision of the night, she went, as it were, directly into the presence of her Lord, and entreated in behalf of her husband.

As she thus knelt at the bedside, with her face buried in the covering, she felt a hand placed softly on her head, and again her husband's voice called, "Ethel!"

She looked up and saw that he was awake now, his eyes fixed on her with an expression of softness and tenderness that she had not seen for many a long day. The old restless, anxious light had gone.

"What were you doing, Ethel?" he asked.

"Praying that you might see that God loved you, — that you might be reconciled to Him."

Two great tears gathered in the man's eyes. His lips quivered a moment, then he said, brokenly, "Surely God must love me, or He would never have given me — a wife — who would watch and pray for me — the long winter night."

"O Dennis, forgive me; I cannot deceive you; for a time I forgot you, I forgot everything, and just wandered through Paradise alone. But in your sleep you called me to your help, and now it seems as if I could not be happy even there without you. I pray you, in Christ's stead, be reconciled to God," she pleaded, falling into the familiar language of Scripture, as she often did under strong emotion. Then, in low, thrilling words, she portrayed to him the "new earth" of her vision, wherein "God shall wipe away all tears, and there shall be no more death, neither sorrow nor crying, neither shall there be any more pain." She showed him that all might still be well, — that eternity was long enough to make up for the ills of our brief troubled life here. But his mind seemed preoccupied. These future joys did not take that hold upon him that she earnestly desired. His eyes seemed to grow dim in tender, tearful wistfulness, rather than become inspired with immortal hopes. At last he spoke : —

"Ethel, it seemed as if I heard some one calling me. I woke up — and there you — were praying — for me. I heard my name, — I heard God's name, — and I knew that you were interceding for me. It seemed to break my hard heart right up like the fountains of the great deep to see you there, — praying for me, — in the cold, cold room." (The room was not cold; it was not the winter's chill that he was feeling, but a chill that comes over the heart even in the tropical summer.) "Then, as you prayed, a great light seemed to shine into my soul. I saw that I had been charging God unjustly with all my failures and misfortunes when I had to thank myself for them. Like a wilful child, I had been acting as if God had but to carry out my wild schemes. I remembered all my unreasonable murmurings and anger; I remembered the dreadful words I was on the point of uttering to-night, and for a moment it seemed as if the pit would open and swallow me up."

He paused for breath, and then went on : —

"But as my despairing eyes glanced restlessly around, they fell upon the face of my son, noble and beautiful even in sleep, and I remembered how God had brought him safely back. Then your low, pleading tone fixed my attention again. It seemed to me that God's love must be better and stronger than human love, and yet you had loved me through all my folly and weakness; so perhaps had He. Then I felt that such a prayer as you were offering could not remain unheard, you seemed to pray so earnestly. I felt that I ought to pray myself, and I commenced calling out in my heart, 'God be merciful to me—a sinner.' Then, while I prayed, I seemed to see my Saviour's face right above your bowed head. Oh, how reproachfully He looked at me! and yet His expression was full of love, too. It was just such a look, I think, that He fixed on Peter when he denied Him. Then it seemed that I fell down at His feet and wept bitterly, and as I did so the look of reproach passed away, and only an expression of love and forgiveness remained. A sudden peace came into my soul which I cannot describe; a rush of tears into my eyes; and when I had wiped them away, I saw only your bowed form praying,—praying on for me. And Ethel, dear, my patient, much-enduring wife, I believe God has answered your prayer. I feel that I am a new man."

"God be praised!" exclaimed his wife, with streaming eyes. Then in a sudden rush of tenderness she clasped her husband to her heart, her strong love seeming like the echo of God's love, the earnest here on earth of that above, where all barriers shall pass away.

The sound of their voices toward the last had awakened their son, and he now stood beside them with wet eyes and heaving breast.

When the wife rose from her embrace, she saw that her husband was very weak. For a few moments he gasped for breath. Then, getting a little easier, he looked up and saw his son, and exclaimed: "Thank God—my boy,—thank God—you are here. Ah, my son,—I have learned much—since we spoke together last. I have seen that—I have much more—need of forgiveness than—to forgive. Thanks to your—mother's prayers,—I believe,—I feel sure that I am forgiven."

"More thanks to God's love, Dennis," said his wife. "God wanted to forgive you all the time more than we wanted Him to. Thank God, who is rich in mercy, for His great love wherewith He loved us. He is longsuffering to usward, not willing that any should perish."

"Those are sweet words, wife, and I have found them true."

For a little time they sat with clasped hands, their hearts too full to speak. Faint streaks along the eastern horizon showed that the dawn was near. The sick man gave a slight shiver, and passed his hands across his eyes as if to clear away a mist, and then said, feebly: "Dennis, my son,— won't you turn up the lamp a little — and fix the fire? The room seems getting so cold — and dark."

The wife looked at her son in quick alarm. The stove was red-hot, and the lamp, no longer shaded, stood openly on the table.

The son saw that he must take the lead in the last sad scene, for in the presence of death the heart of the loving, constant woman clung to her husband as never before. Throwing herself on her knees by his side, she cried with loud, choking sobs, "O Dennis, — husband, — I fear — you are leaving me!"

"Is this death?" he asked of his son, in an awed tone.

"I fear it is, father," said the young man, gently.

After a moment his father said, composedly: "I think you are right. I feel that — my end is near, Ethel, — darling, — for my sake — try to be calm — during the last few moments I am with you."

A few stifled sobs and the room was still.

"I have but little time to — put my house — in order, — and if I had months — I could not do it. Dennis, I leave you — little else — than debts, — embarrassments, and the record of many failures. You must do — the best you can. I am not able to advise you. Only never love this world as I have. It will disappoint you. And, *whatever happens, never lose faith in the goodness of God.* This has been my bane. It has poisoned my life here, and, had it not been for this dear wife, it would have been my destruction hereafter. For long years — only her patient love — has stood between me and a miserable end. Next to God — I commit her and your little sisters to your care. Be true to this most sacred trust.

"Ethel, dear, my more than wife, — my good angel, — what shall I say to you?" and the man's lip quivered, and for a time he could say no more. But an unwonted composure had come into his wife's manner. The eyes were gaining that intent look which was their expression when picturing to herself scenes in the life beyond.

"O Dennis, we seem just on the confines of a glorious world, — it is so near, so real, — it seems as if but a step would take us all into it. Oh! if you could but see its beauties, its glories, — if you could hear the music, you would not fear to enter. It seems as if we were there together now."

"O Ethel, come back, come back," cried her husband, piteously. "I am not worthy of all that. I have no heart for glory now. I can see only my Saviour's face looking — at me — with love and forgiveness. That is heaven enough for me, — and when you come — my cup will be more than full. And now — farewell — for a little while."

For a few moments they clung to each other. Then the little girls were brought, and their father pressed his cold lips to their warm, fresh young faces. They wondered at a scene they could not understand, and were tearful because of the tears of others.

He was now going very fast. Suddenly he turned to his son and said, "Dennis, repeat to me that verse, 'This is a faithful saying —'"

With a voice hoarse and broken by emotion, his son complied: "**This is a faithful saying, and worthy of all acceptation, that Christ Jesus came into the world to save sinners.**"

"Of whom I am chief," said his father, emphatically. "And yet," — his face lighting up with a wan smile, like a sudden ray of light falling on a clouded landscape before the sun sinks below the horizon, — "and yet forgiven."

By and by he again whispered, "Forgiven!"

Then his eyes closed, and all was still. They thought he was gone. But as they stood over him in awed, breathless silence, his lips again moved. Bending down, they heard in faint, far-away tones, like an echo from the *other side*, "*Forgiven!*"

CHAPTER III.

LAUNCHED.

SCARCELY was the last word spoken when a sudden glory filled the room. So brilliant was the light that mother and son were startled. Then they saw what had been unnoted before, that day had broken, and that the sun, emerging from a single dark cloud, was shining, full-orbed, into the apartment with a light that, reflected from myriads of snowy crystals, was doubly luminous. Nevertheless it seemed to them a good omen, an earnest, an emblem of the purer, whiter light into which the cleansed and pardoned spirit had entered. The snow-wrapped prairie was indeed pure and bright, but it was *cold*. The Father's embrace, receiving home the long-absent, erring, but forgiven child, would be warm indeed.

Though the bereaved wife believed that a brighter dawn than that which made the world resplendent around her had come to her husband, still a sense of desolation came over her which only those can understand who have known a loss like hers. For years he had filled the greater part of time, thought, and heart. As she saw her first and only love, the companion of a life which, though hard, still had the light and solace of mutual affection, — as she saw him so still, and realized that she would hear him speak no more, — *complain* no more (for even the weaknesses of those we love are sadly missed after death), — a flood of that natural sorrow which Christianity consoles, but was never designed to prevent, overwhelmed her, and she gave way utterly.

Her son took her in his arms and held her silently, believing that unspoken sympathy was worth more at such a time than any words.

After the convulsive sobbing had somewhat ceased, he struck the right chord by saying: "Mother, father is not lost to us. He himself said good-by only for a little while. Then you have us to love and think of; and remember, what could we do without you?"

The unselfish woman would have tried to rise from a bed of death to do anything needed by her loved ones, and this reminder of those still dependent on her care proved the most potent of restoratives. She at once arose and said: "Dennis, you are right. It is indeed wrong for me to give way thus, when I have so much to be thankful for,—so much to live for. But, O Dennis! you cannot understand this separation of husband and wife, for God said, 'They twain shall be one flesh;' and it seems as if half my very life had gone,—as if half my heart had been wrenched away, and only a bleeding fragment left."

The patter of feet was heard on the kitchen floor, the door opened, and two little figures in white trailing nightgowns entered. At first they looked in shy wonder and perplexity at their tall brother, whom they had not seen for months, but at his familiar voice, recalling many a romp and merry time together, they rushed to his arms as of old.

Then they drew near the bed to give their father his accustomed morning kiss; but, as they approached, he seemed so still that awe began to creep over their little faces. A dim recollection of the farewell kiss given a few hours before, when they were scarcely awake, recurred to them.

"Father," said the elder (about five), "we want to give you good-morning kiss."

Seldom had their father been so sick or irritable but that he reached out his arms to his little ones and gave them a warm embrace, that did him more good than he realized. The influence of trusting children is sometimes the most subtile oil that can be thrown on the troubled waters of life.

But as the little ones saw that their father made no response to their approach and appeal, they timidly drew a step nearer, and looked into his wasted, yet peaceful face, with its closed eyes and motionless repose, and then, turning to their mother, said in a loud whisper, with faces full of perplexity and trouble, "Is papa asleep?"

The little figures in their white drapery, standing beside their dead father, waiting to perform the usual, well-remembered household rite, proved a scene too touching for the poor mother's self-control, and again she gave way to a burst of sorrow. But her son, true to his resolution to be the stay and strength of the family, hastened to the children, and, taking them by the hand, said, gently: "Yes, little ones, papa is asleep. It may be a long time before he wakes, but he surely will by and by, and then he will never be sick any more. Come, we will go into the other room and sing a pretty hymn about papa's sleep."

The thought of hearing their brother sing lured them away at once, for he had a mellow tenor voice that seemed to the little girls sweeter than a bird's. A moment later the widow's heart was comforted by hearing those words that have been balm for so many wounds:—

"Asleep in Jesus! blessed sleep!
From which none ever wakes to weep."

Then, putting on his sisters' flannel wrappers, he set them down by the fire, telling stories in the mean time to divert their thoughts from the scene they had just witnessed.

Thus no horror of death was suffered to enter their young minds. They were not brought face to face with a dreadful mystery which they could not understand, but which would have a sinister effect for life. Gradually they would learn the truth, but still the first impression would remain, and their father's death would ever be to them a sleep from which he would wake by and by, "never to be sick any more."

Dennis set about preparations for their simple morning meal so deftly and easily as to show that it was no unaccustomed task. A sister older than himself had died while yet an infant, leaving a heartache till he came, — God's best remedy. Then two sisters had died after his day, and he had been compelled to be to his mother daughter as well as son, to make himself useful in every household task. His father had been wrapped up in useless inventions, vain enterprises, and was much away. So mother and son were constantly together. He had early become a great comfort and help to her, God blessing her in this vital respect, though her lot seemed hard in other ways. Thus, while he had the heart and courage of a man, he also had the quick, supple hand and gentle bearing of a woman, when occasion required. As proof of his skill, a tempting meal from the simplest materials was placed smoking on the table, and the little girls were soon chatting contentedly over their breakfast. In the mean time the wife within had drawn near her dead husband and taken his cold hand. For a while she dwelt on the past in strong and tearful agony, then, in accordance with long-established habit, her thoughts went forward into the future. In imagination she was present at her husband's reception in heaven. The narrow, meagre room melted away, and her feet seemed to stand on the "golden pavement." The jubilant clash of heavenly cymbals thrilled her heart. She seemed taking part in a triumphal march led by celestial minstrelsy toward the throne. She saw her husband mount its white, glistening steps, so changed, and yet so like his former self when full of love, youth, and hope. He appeared overwhelmed with a sense of unworthiness, but his reception was all the more kind and reassuring. Then as he departed from the royal presence, crowned with God's love and favor forever, though he had all heaven before him, he seemed looking for her as that he longed for most, and her strong effort to reach his side aroused her from her revery as from a dream. But her vision had strengthened her, as was ever the case, and the bitterness of grief was passed. Imprinting a long kiss on her husband's cold forehead, she joined her family in the outer room with calm and quiet mien. Her son saw and understood the change in his mother's manner, and from long experience knew its cause.

We need not dwell on what followed, — preparations for burial, the funeral, the return to a home from which one who had filled so large a place had gone, — a home on which rested the shadow of death. These are old, familiar scenes, acted over and over every day, and yet in the little households where they occur there is a terrible sense of novelty as if they then happened for the first time. The family feel as if they were passing through a chaotic period, — the old world breaking up and vanishing, and a new formation and combination of all the elements that make up life taking place.

Many changes followed. Their farm was sold. Part of a small house in the village of Bankville was rented as their future residence. A very small annuity from some property in the East, left by Mrs. Fleet's father, was, with Dennis's labor, all the family had to depend on now, — a meagre prospect.

But Dennis was very sanguine; for in this respect he had his father's temperament. The world was all before him, and Chicago, the young and giant city of the West, seemed an Eldorado, where fortune, and perhaps fame, might soon be won. He would not only place the family beyond want, but surround them with every luxury.

Dennis, wise and apt as far as his knowledge went, was in some respects as simple and ignorant as a child. There were many phases and conditions of society of which he had never dreamed. Of the ways of the rich and fashionable, of the character of artificial life, he had not the remotest experience. He could not see or understand the distinctions and barriers that to the world are more impassable than those of ignorance, stupidity, and even gross immorality. He would learn, to his infinite surprise, that even in a Western democratic city men would be welcomed in society whose hand no pure woman or honorable man ought to touch, while he, a gentleman by birth, education, and especially character, would not be recognized at all. He would discover that wealth and the indorsement of a few fashionable people, though all else were lacking, would be a better passport than the noblest qualities and fine abilities. As we follow him from the seclusion of his simple country home into the complicated life of the world, all this will become apparent.

Long and earnest was the conversation between mother and son before they separated. Pure and noble were the maxims that she sought to instil into his mind. They may not have been worldly wise, but they were heavenly wise. Though some of her advice in the letter might avail little, since she knew less of the world than did her son, still in its spirit it contained the best of all wisdom, profitable for this life and the life to come. But she sent him forth to seek his fortune and theirs with less solicitude than most mothers have just cause to feel, for she knew that he had Christian principle, and had passed through a discipline that had sobered and matured him far beyond his years. She saw, however, in every word and act his father's sanguine temperament. He was expecting much, hoping far more, and she feared that he also was destined to many a bitter disappointment. Still she believed that he possessed a good strong substratum of common-sense, and this combined with the lessons of faith and patience taught of God would prove the ballast his father had lacked.

She sought to modify his towering hopes and rose-colored visions, but to little purpose. Young, buoyant, in splendid health, with a surplus of warm blood tingling in every vein, how could he take a prudent, distrustful view of the world? It seemed to beckon him smilingly into any path of success he might choose. Had not many won the victory? and who ever felt braver and more determined than he, with the needs of the dear ones at home added to his own incentives and ambitions? So, with many embraces, lingering kisses, and farewell words, that lost not their meaning though said over and over again, they parted. The stage carried him to the nearest railway station, and the express train bore him rapidly toward the great city where he expected to find all that a man's heart most craves on earth.

Sanguine as his father, constant as his mother, with a nature that would go right or wrong with tremendous energy, as direction might be given it, he was destined to live no tame, colorless life, but would either enjoy much, or else suffer much. To his young heart, swelling with hopes, burning with zeal to distinguish himself and provide for those he was leaving, even the bleak, snow-clad prairie seemed an arena in which he might accomplish a vague something.

CHAPTER IV.

COLD WATER.

THE train, somewhat impeded by snow, landed Dennis in Chicago at about nine in the evening. In his pocket he had ten dollars, — ample seed-corn, he believed, for a golden harvest. This large sum was expected to provide for him till he should find a situation and receive the first instalment of salary. He would inform his employer, when he found him, how he was situated, and ask to be paid early and often.

Without a misgiving he shouldered the little trunk that contained his worldly effects, and stalked off to a neighboring hotel, that, from its small proportions, suggested a modest bill. With a highly important man-of-the-world manner he scrawled his name in an illegible, student-like hand on the dingy, dog-eared register. With a gracious, condescending air he ordered the filthy, tobacco-stained porter to take his trunk to his room.

The bar-room was the only place provided for strangers. Regarding the bar with a holy horror, he got away from it as far as possible, and seated himself by the stove, on which simmered a kettle of hot water, for the concoction of punches, apparently more in demand at that hotel than beds. Becoming disgusted with the profanity and obscenity downstairs, he sought refuge in the cold, miserable little room assigned to him. Putting on his overcoat, he wrapped himself up in a coverlet and threw himself down on the outside of the bed.

dow, frowned, and curtly said, "No!" and then went on counting what seemed to poor Dennis millions of money. The man had no right to say yes or no, since he was a mere official, occupying his own little niche, with no authority beyond. But an inveterate feud seemed to exist between this man and the public. He acted as if the world in general, instead of any one in particular, had greatly wronged him. It might be a meek woman with a baby, or a bold, red-faced drover, a delicately-gloved or horny hand that reached him the change, but it was all the same. He knitted his brows, pursed up his mouth, and dealt with all in a quick, jerking way, as if he could not bear the sight of them, and wanted to be rid of them as soon as possible. Still these seem just the peculiarities that find favor with railroad corporations, and the man would probably vent his spite against the public throughout his natural life.

From him, however, Dennis received his first dash of cold water, which he minded but little, and went on his way with a good-natured laugh at the crusty old fellow.

He was soon in the business part of the city. Applying at a large dry-goods store, he was told that they wanted a cash boy; "but he would not do; one a quarter his size would answer."

"Then I will go where they want the other three fourths and pay accordingly," said Dennis, and stalked out.

He continued applying at every promising place, but to no purpose. It was midwinter; trade was dull; and with clerks idling about the shops employers were in no mood to add to their number.

At last he found a place where an assistant book-keeper was wanted. Dennis's heart leaped within him, but sunk again as he remembered how little he knew of the art. "But I can learn quickly," he thought to himself.

The man looked carelessly at his poor little letter, and

The night passed slowly. He was too uncomfortable, too excited, to sleep. The scenes of the past blended confusedly with visions of the future, and it was nearly morning when he fell into an unquiet slumber.

When at last aroused by the shriek of a locomotive, he found that the sun was up and shining on the blotched and broken wall above him. A few minutes sufficed for his toilet, and yet, with his black curling hair, noble forehead, and dark, silken upper lip, many an exquisite would have envied the result.

His plan was simple enough, — dictated indeed by the necessities of the case. He must at once find a situation in which he could earn sufficient to support his mother and sisters and himself. Thence he could look around till he found the calling that promised most. Having left college and given up his chosen profession of the law, he had resolved to adopt any honest pursuit that seemed to lead most quickly to fortune.

Too impatient to eat his breakfast, he sallied forth into the great city, knowing not a soul in it. His only recommendations and credentials were his young, honest face, and a letter from his minister, saying that he was a member of the church in Bankville, "in good and regular standing," and, "as far as he knew, a most worthy young man," — rather meagre capital amid the competitions of a large city. But, with courage bold and high, he strode off toward the business part of the town.

As he passed the depot it occurred to him that an opening might exist there. It would be a good post of observation, and perhaps he would be able to slip home oftener. So he stopped and asked the man in the ticket-office, blandly, "Do you wish to employ a young man in connection with this depot or road in any capacity?"

The ticket-man stared at him a moment through his win-

then said, in a business-like tone, "Show me a specimen of your handwriting."

Poor Dennis had never written a good hand, but at college had learned to write a miserable scrawl, in rapidly taking notes of lectures. Moreover, he was excited, and could not do himself justice. Even from his sanguine heart hope ebbed away; but he took the pen and scratched a line or two, of which he himself was ashamed. The man looked at them with an expression of mild disgust, and then said, "Mr. Jones, hand me your ledger."

The head book-keeper passed the volume to his employer, who showed Dennis entries looking as from copper-plate, and quietly remarked: "The young man we employ must write like that, and thoroughly understand book-keeping. Good-morning, sir."

Dennis walked out, feeling almost as crestfallen as if he had been convicted of stealing, but the noon-day sun was shining in the sky, the streets were full of life and bustle, and hope revived.

"I shall find the right niche before long," he said to himself, and trudged on.

Some time after he entered a retail dry-goods store.

"Yes, they wanted a young man there, but he was rather old."

Still as the merchant saw that Dennis was fine-looking, would appear well behind the counter, and make a taking salesman with the ladies, he stopped to parley a moment more.

"Do you understand the business?"

"No, sir; but I can soon learn, for I am young and strong."

"Strength is not what is needed, but experience. Ours is not the kind of work for Paddies."

"Well, sir," said Dennis, rather shortly, "I'm not a Paddy."

The dapper little retailer frowned slightly at Dennis's tone, and continued: "You spoke as if main strength was the principal thing. Have you had any experience at all?"

"No, sir."

But seeing intelligence in the young man's face, and scenting a sharp bargain, he said, "Why, then, you would have to begin at the very beginning, and learn the name of everything, its quality, etc."

"Yes, sir; but I would do my very best."

"Of course, of course, but nothing can take the place of experience. I expect, under the circumstances, you would look for very little remuneration the first year?"

"How much could you give?"

The man named a sum that would not have supported Dennis alone.

He replied that, though his services might not be worth more than that, he was so situated that he could not take a very small salary.

"Then bring something besides ignorance to the market," said the man, turning on his heel.

Dennis was now hungry, tired, and disappointed. Indeed the calls of appetite became so clamorous that he sought a cheap restaurant. After demolishing a huge plate of such viands as could be had at little cost, he sat brooding over a cup of coffee for an hour or more. The world wore a different aspect from that which it had presented in the morning, and he was lost in a sort of dull, painful wonder.

But the abundant meal and slight element of coffee that colored the lukewarm water quite heartened him again. He resolved to go back to his hotel and find a more quiet and comfortable place in which to lodge until something permanent offered. He made what he considered sufficient inquiry as to the right direction, and resolved to save even the car-fare of five cents by walking the distance.

But whether he had not understood the directions rightly, or whether, brooding over the events of the day, his mind had been too preoccupied to heed them, he found to his great disgust, after walking two or three miles, that he had gone away from his destination instead of toward it. Angry with himself, out of humor with all the world, he began to give way to the latent obstinacy of his nature. Though everything went "contrairy," there was one thing under his control, — himself, — and he would make that do the bidding of his will.

Turning on his heel, he resolved with dogged resolution to walk back the whole distance. He would teach himself a lesson. It was fine business, just when he needed his wits so sorely, to commence blundering in this style. No wonder he had failed during the day; he deserved to fail in other respects, since in this one he had not shown the good sense of a child.

When people are "out of sorts," and things are going wrong, the disposition to blame somebody or something is almost universal. But we think that it will be found a safe general rule, that the nobler the nature, the less worthy of blame, the greater the tendency to blame self rather than anything else. Poor Dennis had no great cause for bitter self-reproaches, and yet he plodded on with an intense feeling of self-disgust.

To think that after New-England schools and three years in college he should write such a hand and have no definite knowledge of book-keeping! "What have I learned, I'd like to know?" he muttered. Then to go and lose his way like a country bumpkin! and he gnawed his lips with vexation.

The street-cars glided often and invitingly by, but he would not even look at them.

At last, foot-sore and fairly aching with cold and fatigue,

he reached the little hotel, which appeared more miserable, obscure, and profane than ever. But a tempting fiend seemed to have got into the gin and whiskey bottles behind the red-nosed bartender. To his morbid fancy and eyes, half-blinded with wind and cold, they appeared to wink, beckon, and suggest: "Drink and be merry; drink and forget your troubles. We can make you feel as rich and glorious as a prince, in ten minutes."

For the first time in his life Dennis felt a strong temptation to drink for the sake of the effects. When was a man ever weak that the devil did not charge down upon him?

But the evil and ruin wrought in one case proved another's safeguard, for the door opened and a miserable wreck of a man entered. As Dennis looked at his blotched, sodden face, trembling hand, shuffling gait, and general air of wretchedness, embodying and suggesting the worst ills of humanity, he decided not to drink for the sake of the effects.

Then came another rush of self-disgust that he had ever entertained such a temptation, and he flung himself off supperless to bed.

As he bowed that night he could not pray as usual. For anger, passion with one's self, as well as with any one else, renders true prayer impossible. But he went through the form, and then wrapped himself up as before. The wearied body soon mastered the perturbed mind, and he fell into a heavy sleep that lasted till morning.

CHAPTER V.

A HORNET'S NEST.

DENNIS awoke greatly refreshed and strengthened. For half an hour he lay quietly thinking over the scenes of the preceding day; something of his old anger returned, but he compressed his lips, and, with a face expressing the most resolute purpose, determined that the day before him should tell a different story. Every faculty and energy he possessed should be skilfully bent to the attainment of his objects. Wise deliberation should precede everything. He would write a few lines to his mother, decide as to a lodging-place, and then seek better success in another part of the city. He went to the bar and inquired as to his bill, and found that so far as bed and meals were concerned, such as they were, he could not find anything cheaper in the city, the house evidently not depending on these for its revenue. Disgusted as he was with his surroundings, he resolved to lose no time in looking for a new boarding-place, but, after writing to his mother, to start off at once in search of something permanent. He was in no mood to consult personal wishes, and the saving of tim and money settled the question.

Where should he write? There was no place save a desk at the end of the bar. Looking askance at the half-filled, villanous-smelling bottle at his elbow, he wrote in a hand stiff and unnatural (for he had resolved to change his scrawl to a business hand at once), the following note: —

"CHICAGO, ILL., Jan. 10th.

"DEAR MOTHER:—I arrived safely, and am very well. I did not, yesterday, find a situation suited to my taste, but expect better success to-day. I am just on the point of starting out on my search, and when settled will write you full particulars. Many kisses for yourself and the little girls. Your affectionate son, DENNIS."

"There! there is nothing in that to worry mother, and soon I shall have good news for her." (If he had seen its reception, he would have learned his mistake. The intuitions of love are keen, and this formal negative note in the constrained hand told more of his disappointment than any words could have done. While he knew it not, his mother was suffering with him. In reply she wrote a letter full of general sympathy, intending to be more specific when he gave her his confidence.)

Dennis folded the letter most carefully and mailed it—for he was now doing the least thing with the utmost precision—with the air of one who meant to find out the right thing to do, and then to do it to a hair's breadth. Nothing should go wrong that day. So at an early hour he again sallied forth.

Not far from the hotel there was a new grocery store about to be opened by two young men, formerly clerks, but now setting up for themselves. They stood at the door receiving a cart-load of goods as Dennis approached. He had made up his mind to ask at every opportunity, and to take the first thing that promised fairly; he would also be very polite. Touching his hat to the young men,—a little act pleasing to them in their newly acquired dignity as heads of a firm which as yet had no subordinates,—Dennis asked if they would need any assistance. Graciously replying to his salutations, they answered, yes; they wanted a young man.

Dennis explained that he was from the country, and

showed the ministerial letter. The young grocers looked wise over it, seemed pleased, said they wanted a young fellow from the country, that was not up to city tricks. Chicago was a hard place on young men, — spoiled most of them. Glad he was a member of the church. They were not, but believed a man must be mighty good to be one. As the young man they hired must sleep in the store, they wanted one they could trust, and would prefer a church member.

The salary they offered was not large, but pretty fair in view of his having so much to learn, and it was intimated, that if business was good, and he suited, it would be increased. The point uppermost in their minds was to find some one with whom they could trust their store and goods, and this young man from the country, with a letter from a minister, seemed a godsend.

They engaged him, but just as he was starting, with heart swelling with self-satisfaction and joy, one of the firm asked, carelessly, "Where are you staying?"

"At Gavin's Hotel."

The man turned sharply, and looked most suspiciously at him, and then at his partner, who gave a low whistle of surprise, and also eyed the young man for a moment askance. Then the men stepped aside, and there was a brief whispered consultation. Dennis's heart sunk within him. He saw that something was wrong, but what, he had not the least idea. The elder member of the embryo firm now stepped up and said, decidedly, "Good-morning, young man; we shall not need your services."

"What do you mean?" cried Dennis, in a voice of mingled dismay and indignation.

The man's face was growing red with anger, but he said, coldly, "You had better move on. *We* understand."

"But *I* don't understand, and your course toward me is most unjust."

"Look here, young man, we are too old birds to be caught by any such light chaff as you have about you. You are a pretty church member, you are! You are a smart one, you are; nice boy, just from the country; suppose you do not know that Gavin's Hotel is the worst gambling hole in the city, and every other man that goes there a known thief. Come, you had better move on if you do not want to get into trouble. You will make nothing here."

"But I tell you, gentlemen —" cried Dennis, eagerly.

"*You* may tell what you please. *We* tell you that we would not believe any one from that den under oath. Now you leave!"

The last words were loud and threatening. The attention of passers-by was drawn toward them, and Dennis saw that further words were useless. In the minds of shrewd but narrow business men, not over-honest themselves, more acquainted with the trickery of the world than with its virtues, suspicion against any one is fatal, and most assuredly so against a stranger with appearances unfavorable.

With heart well-nigh bursting with anger, disappointment, and shame, Dennis hastened away. He had been regarded as a thief, or at best a blackleg, seeking the position for some sinister purpose. This was the opening scene of the day on which he had determined that no mistakes should be made, and here at the outset he had allowed himself to be identified with a place of notorious ill-repute.

Reaching the hotel, he rushed upstairs, got his trunk, and then turned fiercely on the red-nosed bartender, — "Why did you not tell me the character of this place?"

"What kind of a place is it?" asked that functionary, coolly, arms akimbo.

"You know well enough. You knew I was not one of your sort."

"You don't mean to say that this is a bad place, do you?" said the barkeeper, in mock solemnity.

"Yes, the worst in Chicago. There is your money."

"Hold on here, my small chicken; there is some money, but not enough by a jugful. I want five dollars out of you before you take that trunk off."

"Why, this is sheer robbery," exclaimed Dennis.

"Oh, no; just keeping up the reputation of the house. You say it is the worst in Chicago: must try and keep up our reputation."

"Little fear of that; I will not pay it;" and Dennis started for his trunk.

"Here, let that trunk alone; and if yer don't give me that five dollars cussed quick, I'll put a head on yer;" and he of the red nose put his hands on the bar in readiness to spring over.

"I say, young feller," said a good-natured loafer standing by, "you had better gin him the five dollars; for Barney is the worst one in all Chicago to put a head on a man."

"And will you stand by and see this outrage?" said Dennis, appealing to him.

"O gosh!" said the man, "I've got quarrels 'nough of my own without getting my head broke for fellers I don't know."

Dennis was almost speechless from indignation. Conscious of strength, his strong impulse for a moment was to spring at the throat of the barkeeper and vent his rage on him. There is a latent tiger in every man. But a hand seemed to hold him back, and a sober second thought came over him. What! Dennis Fleet, the son of Ethel Fleet, brawling, fighting in a bar-room, a gambling-den, and going out to seek a situation that required confidence and fair-appearing, all blackened, bruised, and bleeding! As the truth flashed upon him in strong revulsion of feeling he fairly turned pale and sick.

"There's the money," said he, hoarsely, "and God forgive you."

In a moment he had taken his trunk and was gone. The barkeeper stared after him, and then looked at the money with a troubled and perplexed face.

"Wal," said he, "I'm used enough to havin' folks ask God to damn me, but I'm blessed if I ever had one ask Him to forgive me, before. I be hanged," said he, after a moment, as the thought grew upon him, — "I be hanged if I wouldn't give him back the money if he hadn't gone so quick."

With heart full of shame and bitterness, Dennis hastened down the street. At the corner he met a policeman, and told him his story. All the satisfaction he got was, "You ought not to go to such a place. But you're lucky if they only took five dollars from you; they don't let off many as easy as that."

"Can I have no redress?"

"Now look here; it's a pretty ticklish thing to interfere with them fellers. It'll cost you plaguey sight more'n that, and blood, too, like enough. If you'll take my advice, you won't stir up that hornet's nest."

CHAPTER VI.

"STARVE THEN!"

DENNIS now followed the natural impulse to go to some distant part of the city, entirely away from the region that had become so hateful to him. Putting the trunk on the front of a street-car, he rode on till he was in the heart of the south-side district, the great business centre. He took his trunk into a roomy hardware store, and asked if he might leave it there awhile. Receiving a good-natured permission, he next started off in search of a quiet, cheap boarding-place. His heart was heavy, and yet he felt thankful to have escaped as he had, for the thought of what might have been his experience if Barney had tried to fulfil his threat sickened him. The rough was as strong as he, and scenes of violence were his delight and daily experience. He rather gloried in a black eye, for he always gave two in exchange, and his own bruised, swollen member paved the way gracefully for the telling of his exploits, as it awakened inquiry from the lesser lights among whom he shone. But what would Dennis have done among the merchants with "a head on him," as the barkeeper understood the phrase? He would have had to return home, and that he felt would be worse than death. In fact, he had come nearer to a desperate struggle than he knew, for Barney rarely resisted so inviting an opportunity to indulge his pugilistic turn, and had he not seen the policeman going by just at that time, there would have been no idle threats in the case.

Dennis set his teeth with dogged resolution, determined, if necessary, to persevere in his search till he dropped in the street. But as he remembered that he had less than five dollars left, and no prospect of earning another, his heart grew like lead.

He spent several weary hours in the vain search for a boarding-house. He had little to guide him save short answers from policemen. The places were either too expensive, or so coarse and low that he could not bring himself to endure them. In some cases he detected that they were accompanied by worse evils than gambling. Almost in despair, tired, and very hungry (for severe indeed must be the troubles that will affect the appetite of healthful youth on a cold winter day), he stopped at a small German restaurant and hotel. A round-faced, jolly Teuton served him with a large plate of cheap viands, which he devoured so quickly that the man, when asked for more, stared at him for a moment, and then stolidly obeyed.

"What do you ask for a small room and bed for a night?" said Dennis.

"Zwei shillen," said the waiter, with a grin; "dot ish, if you don't vant as pig ped as dinner. Ve haf zwei shillen for bed, and zwei shillen for efery meal, — von dollar a day, — sheap!"

The place was comparatively clean. A geranium or two bloomed in the window, and lager instead of fiery whiskey seemed the principal beverage vended. Dennis went out and made inquiries, and every one in the neighborhood spoke of it as a quiet, respectable place, though frequented only by laboring people. "That is nothing against it," thought Dennis. "I will venture to stay there for a night or two, for I must lose no more time in looking for a situation."

He took his trunk there, and then spent the rest of the

day in unavailing search. He found nothing that gave any promise at all. In the evening he went to a large hotel and looked over the files of papers. He found a few advertisements for clerks and experts of various kinds, but more from those seeking places. But he noted down everything hopeful, and resolved that he would examine the morning papers by daylight for anything new in that line, and be the first on hand. His new quarters, though plain and meagre, were at least clean. Too weary to think or even to feel more than a dull ache in his heart, he slept heavily till the dawn of the following day. Poor fellow! it seemed to him that he had lived years in those two days.

He was up by daylight, and found a few more advertisements that looked as if they might lead to something. As early as it was possible to see the parties, he was on the ground, but others were there as soon as himself. They had the advantage of some knowledge and experience in the duties required, and this decided the question. Some spoke kindly, and suggested that he was better fitted for teaching than for business.

"But where am I to find a position at this season of the year, when every place is filled?" asked Dennis. "It might be weeks before I could get anything to do, and I must have employment at once."

They were sorry, hoped he would do well, turned away, and went on doing well for themselves; but the majority merely satisfied themselves that he would not answer their purpose, and bade him a brief, business-like good-morning. And yet the fine young face, so troubled and anxious, haunted a good many of those who summarily dismissed him. But "business is business."

The day passed in fruitless inquiry. Now and then he seemed on the point of succeeding, but only disappointment resulted. There were at that season of the year few situations offering where a salary sufficient for maintenance was paid, and for these skilled laborers were required. Dennis possessed no training for any one calling save perhaps that of teacher. He had merely the fragment of a good general education, tending toward one of the learned professions. He had fine abilities, and undoubtedly would in time have stood high as a lawyer. But now that he was suddenly called upon to provide bread for himself and those he loved, there was not a single thing of which he could say, "I understand this, sir, and can give you satisfaction."

He knew that if he could get a chance at almost anything, he could soon learn enough to make himself more useful than the majority employed, for few had his will and motive to work. But the point was to find some one who would pay sufficient for his own and his mother's support while he learned.

It is under just such circumstances that so many men, and especially women, make shipwreck. Thrown suddenly upon their own resources, they bring to the great labor-market of the world general intelligence, and also general ignorance. With a smattering of almost everything, they do not know practically how to do *one thing well.* Skilled hands, though backed by neither heart nor brains, push them aside. Take the young men or the young women of any well-to-do town or village, and make them suddenly dependent upon their own efforts, and how many could compete in any one thing with those already engaged in supplying the market? And yet just such helpless young creatures are every day compelled to shift for themselves. If to these unfortunates the paths of honest industry seem hedged and thorny, not so those of sin. They are easy enough at first, if any little difficulty with conscience can be overcome; and the devil, and fallen humanity doing his work, stand ready to push the wavering into them.

At the close of the next day, spent in weary search, Dennis met a temptation to which many would have yielded. As a last resort he had been going around among the hotels, willing to take even the situation of porter, if nothing better offered. The day was fast closing, when, worn out and dejected, he entered a first-class house, and made his usual inquiry. The proprietor looked at him for a moment, slapped him on the back, and said: "Yes, you are the man I want, I reckon. Do you drink? No! might have known that from your face. Don't want a man that drinks for this place. Come along with me, then. Will give you two and a half a day if you suit, and pay you every night. I pay my help promptly; they ain't near so apt to steal from you then."

And the man hurried away, followed by Dennis with beating heart and flushed, wondering face. Descending a flight of stairs, they entered a brilliantly lighted basement, which was nothing less than a large, elegantly arranged bar-room, with card and lunch tables, and easy-chairs for the guests to smoke and tipple in at their leisure. All along one side of this room, resplendent with cut glass and polished silver, ran the bar. The light fell warm and mellow on the various kinds of liquor, that were so arranged as to be most tempting to the thirsty souls frequenting the place.

Stepping up to the bulky man behind the bar the landlord said: "There, Mr. Swig, is a young man who will fill capitally the place of the chap we dismissed to-day for getting tight. You may bet your life from his face that he don't drink. You can break him in in a few days, and you won't want a better assistant."

For a moment a desperate wish passed through Dennis's mind, "Oh that wrong were right!" Then, indignant with himself, he spoke up, firmly,—"I think I have a word to say in this matter."

"Well, say on, then; what's the trouble?"

"I cannot do this kind of work."

"You will find plenty harder."

"None harder for one believing as I do. I will starve before I will do this work."

The man stared at him for a moment, and then coolly replied, "Starve then!" and turned on his heel and walked away.

Dennis also rushed from the place, followed by the coarse, jeering laugh of those who witnessed the scene. In his morbid, suffering state their voices seemed those of mocking demons.

The night had now fallen. He was too tired and discouraged to look any farther. Wearily he plodded up the street, facing the bitter blast filled with snow that had begun to fall.

This then was the verdict of the world, — "Starve!" This was the only prospect it offered, — that same brave world which had so smilingly beckoned him on to great achievements and unbounded success but a few days since, — "Starve!" Every blast that swept around the corners howled in his ears, "Starve!" Every warmly clad person hurrying unheedingly by seemed to say by his indifference, "Starve! who cares? there is no place for you, nothing for you to do."

The hard, stern resolution of the past few days, not to yield an inch, to persist in hewing his way through every difficulty, began to flag. His very soul seemed crushed within him. Even upon the threshold of his life, in his strong, joyous youth, the world had become to him what it literally was that night, a cold, wintry, stormy place, with a black, lowering sky and hard, frozen earth.

His father's old temptation recurred to him with sudden and great power. "Perhaps father was right," he mused.

"God was against him, and is also against me, his son. Does He not visit the iniquity of the fathers upon the children unto the third and fourth generation? Not but that He will save us at last, if we ask Him, but there seems some great wrong that must be severely punished here. Or else if God does not care much about our present life, thinking only of the hereafter, there must be some blind fate or luck that crushes some and lifts up others."

Thus Dennis, too sad and morbid to take a just view of anything, plodded on till he reached his boarding-place, and stealing in as if he had no business to be there, or anywhere else, sat down in a dusky corner behind the stove, and was soon lost to surrounding life in his own miserable thoughts.

CHAPTER VII.

A GOOD SAMARITAN.

DENNIS was too good a Christian, and had received too deep a lesson in his father's case, to become bitter, angry, and defiant, even if he had believed that God was against him. He would have felt that it was simply his duty to submit, — to endure patiently. Somehow until today his heart had refused to believe that God could be against any of His creatures. In fact, it was his general impression that God had everything to do with his being a good Christian, but very little with his getting a good place. The defect in his religion, and that of his mother too, was that both separated the spiritual life of the soul too widely from the present life with its material, yet essential, cares and needs. At this point they, like multitudes of others, fell short of their full privilege, and enjoyment of God's goodness. His mother had cheered and sustained her hard lot by hopes and visions of the better life beyond, — by anticipating joys to come. She had never fully learned how God's love, like the sunlight, could shine upon and brighten the thorny, rocky way, and cause the thorns to blossom, and delicate fragrant flowers to grow in the crevices and bloom in shaded nooks among the sharp stones. She must wait for her consolation. She must look out of her darkness to the light that shone through the portals of the tomb, forgetting that God caused His servants to sing at midnight, in the inner prison, the deepest dungeon, though scourged and bleeding.

Unconsciously her son had imbibed the same ideas. Most devoutly he asked every day to be kept from sin, that he might grow in the Christian life; but he did not ask or expect, save in a vague, general way, that help which a wise, good, earthly father would give to a young, inexperienced child, struggling with the hard, practical difficulties of this world. As the days grew darker and more full of disappointment, he had asked with increasing earnestness that he might be kept from sin, — from falling before the many and peculiar temptations that assailed him; and we have seen how God answered his prayer, and kept him where so many would have fallen. But God meant to show him that His goodness extended farther than he thought, and that He cared for His children's well-being now as truly as in the hereafter, when He gathered them home into His immediate presence. But Dennis could not see this now. As far as he thought at all on the subject, he had the vague feeling that God was either trying his faith or meting out some righteous judgment, and he must do the best he could, and only see to it that he did not sin and give way morally.

Yet, in the thick night of his earthly prospects, Dennis still loved and trusted God. He reasoned justly, that if at last brought to such a place as heaven, no matter what he suffered here, he had only cause for unbounded gratitude. And he felt sure that all would be right in the end, but now feared that his life would be like his father's, a tissue of disappointments, and that he, an unsuccessful voyager, storm-tossed and shipwrecked, would be thrown upon the heavenly shore by some dark-crested billow of misfortune.

Thus Dennis sat lost in gloomy musings, but too wearied in mind and body to follow any line of thought long. A few stern facts kept looming up before him, like rocks on which a ship is drifting. He had less than a dollar in his pocket. It was Friday night. If he did not get anything to do on Saturday, how was he going to live through Sunday and the days that followed? Then his dependent mother and sisters rose up before him. They seemed to his morbid fancy hungry and cold, and their famine-pinched faces full of reproach. His head bowed lower, and he became the very picture of dejection.

He was startled by a big, hearty voice at his side, exclaiming: "What makes yer so down in the mouth? Come take a drink, and cheer up!"

Raising his eyes, he saw a round, red face, like a harvest moon, shining full upon him. It was somewhat kindly in its expression, in keeping with the words. Rough as was the courtesy, it went straight to the lonely, discouraged heart of the young man, and with moistened eyes he said, "I thank you for speaking to me in a tone that has a little human touch in it, for the last man that spoke to me left an echo in my ear that I would gladly get out of it."

"Bad luck to him, then! Give us yer hand; there!" with a grip like a vise. "Bill Cronk never went back on a man he took to. I tell yer what, stranger," said he, becoming confidential, "when I saw yer glowering and blinking here in the corner as if yer was listening to yer own funeral sermon, I be —— if I could take a comfortable drink. Come, now, take a good swig of old rye, and see how things will mellow up."

Our good Samaritan in this case was a very profane and disreputable one, as many are in this medley world. He had a great, kindly nature, that was crawling and grovelling in all sorts of low, unseemly places, instead of growing straight up toward heaven.

"I hope you will think me none the less friendly if I decline," said Dennis. "I would drink with you as quick as with any man living, but it is a thing I never do."

"Oh, you're temperance, are yer? Well, I don't think

none the wuss of yer for standing by yer colors. Between us, it would be better for me if I was a little more so. Hang it all! I take a drop too much now and then. But what is a fellow to do, roughing it up and down the world like me? I should often get lonely and mope in the corner as you did, if I didn't get up steam. When I am down in the mouth I take a drink to 'liven me up, and when I feel good I take a drink to make me feel better. When I wouldn't take a drink on my own hook, I meet somebody that I'd ought to drink with. It is astonishing how many occasions there are to drink, 'specially when a man's travelling, like me."

"No fear but what the devil will make occasions enough," said Dennis.

"What has the devil got to do with it?" asked the man, gruffly.

Just then the miserable wretch entered who, appearing opportunely in Gavin's Hotel, had cured Dennis of his desire to drink, when weary and despondent, for the sake of the effects. For a moment they looked at the blear-eyed, trembling wreck of a man, and then Dennis asked, "Had God any hand in making that man what he is?"

"I should say not," said Bill Cronk, emphatically.

"Well, I should say the devil had," said Dennis; "and there behind the bar are the means used, — the best tool he has, it seems to me; for with it he gets hold of men with some heart and soul in them, like you."

The man winced under the words that both conscience and experience told him were true; at the same time he was propitiated by Dennis's good opinion of him. He gave a big, good-natured laugh, slapped Dennis on the shoulder, and said: "Wal, stranger, p'raps you're right. 'Tain't every temperance lecturer though that has an awful example come in just at the right time so slick. But you've stood by yer colors, and we won't quarrel. Tell us, now, if it ain't private, what you're so chopfallen about."

Dennis told his story, as grateful for this rough sympathy as a thirsty traveller would be in finding a spring though surrounded by thorns and rocks.

The round, jolly face actually grew long and serious through interest in the young man's tribulations.

After scratching a shaggy but practical head for a few moments, Bill spoke as follows : —

"Seems to me the case is just this : here you are, a young blooded colt, not broken to either saddle or thills, — here you are whinnying around a market where they want nothing but dray-hosses. People look shy at you, — usually do at a strange hoss. Few know good p'ints when they see 'em. When they find you ain't broke in to nothin', they want you to work for nothin'. I see how you can't do this. And yet fodder is runnin' short, and you must do somethin'."

Bill, having dealt in live-stock all his life, naturally clothed his thoughts in language drawn from familiar objects, and Dennis, miserable as he was, half smiled at the close parallel run between him and a young, useless colt; but he only said, "I don't think there is a cart-horse in all Chicago that feels more broken down and dispirited than I do to-night."

"That may all be, too," said Bill; "but you'd feel a little oats mighty quick, and a cart-hoss wouldn't. But I know the p'ints, whether it's a man or a hoss : you'd take kindly to work of the right sort, and it would pay any one to take you at yer own terms, but you can't make 'em see it. If I was in a situation to take you, I'd do it in a minute. Hang it all ! I can't do much for you, either. I took a drop too much in Cleveland t'other night, and some of the folks in the house looked over my pocket-book and left me just enough to get home with."

Dennis shook his head reproachfully and was about to speak.

"I know what you're going to say," said Bill, heading off

another temperance lecture. "I'll take a drink by and by, and think over what you've said, for I can't think much until I get a little steam up. But now we must try and see some way out of the fog for you;" and again in absence of the wonted steam he scratched the shaggy head vigorously.

"Seems to me the best thing for you is to do as I did when I first broke the home pasture and started out on a rampage. I just grabbed the fust job that come along, good, bad, or indifferent, — always kept doing something. You can look for a bird in a bush quite as well when you've got one in the hand as when you hain't. To be sure I wasn't as squeamish as you are. I'd jumped at the offer you had this afternoon; but I reckon I'd taken toll too often to be very profitable. But in this way I always kept a-goin' — never got down underfoot so the stronger ones could tread on me. When it comes to that, I want to die. Now if you've got plenty of clear grit — Leetle disposed to show the white feather though, to-night, ain't yer?"

Dennis flushed up, and was about to speak, almost angrily.

"There! there!" said his new friend. "I said yer wasn't a cart-hoss: one touch of the spur and up goes tail and ears, and then look out. Are yer ashamed to do any kind of honest work? I mean kinder pious work, that hasn't any smack of the devil you're so afraid of in it?"

"No! work is just what I want."

"Would you black boots, now?"

Dennis winced, thought a moment, and then, with a manly flush, said, "Yes, before I would take a cent of charity from any living soul."

"Give us yer hand again. You're the kind of critter I like to invest in; for you'd improve on a feller's hands. No fear about you; the only thing is to get you in harness before a load that will pay to haul."

Suddenly he got up, strode to the bar-room door, looked out into the night, and came back again.

"I think I know of a way in which you can make two or three dollars to-morrow."

"How?" exclaimed Dennis, his whole face lighting up with hope.

"Go to a hardware store, invest in a big wooden snow-shovel, and clean off sidewalks before stores. You can pick up a good many quarters before night, like enough."

"I will do it," said Dennis, heartily, "and thank you warmly for the suggestion, and for your kindly interest generally;" and he looked up and felt himself another man.

"Gosh! but it takes mighty few oats to set you up! But come, and let us have a little plain, substantial fodder. I will drink nothing but coffee, to-night, out of compliment to you."

Cheered, comforted, and hopeful, Dennis sat down with his good Samaritan, and made a hearty supper, after which they parted with a strong friendly grip, and sincere good wishes, Cronk, the drover, going on farther west, and Dennis to the rest he so sorely needed.

CHAPTER VIII.

YAHCOB BUNK.

BEFORE retiring, Dennis as usual took his Bible from his trunk to read a chapter. He was now in a very different mood from that of a few hours ago. The suggestion of his bar-room acquaintance was a light upon his way. And with one of Dennis's age and temperament, even a small hope is potent. He was eager for the coming day, in order to try the experiment of wringing bread and opportunity for further search out of the wintry snows.

But that which had done him the most good — more than he realized — was the kindness he had received, rough though it was, — the sympathy and companionship of another human being; for if he had been cast away on a desert island he could not have been more isolated than in the great city, with its indifferent multitudes.

Moreover the generous supper was not without its decided influence; and with it he had drunk a cup of good coffee, that nectar of the gods, whose subtile, delicate influence is felt in body and brain, in every fibre of the nature not deadened and blunted by stronger and coarser stimulants. He who leaves out physical causes in accounting for mental and moral states, will usually come wide of the mark. But while giving the influences above referred to their due force, so far from ignoring, we would acknowledge with emphasis, the chief cause of man's ability to receive and appreciate all the highest phases of truth and good, namely, God's help asked for and given. Prayer was a habit with Dennis. He asked God with childlike faith for the bestowment of every Christian grace, and those who knew him best saw that he had no reason to complain that his prayers were unanswered.

But now, at a time when he would most appreciate it, God was about to reveal to him a truth that would be a rich source of help and comfort through life, and a sudden burst of sunshine upon his dark way at the present hour. He was to be shown how he might look to heaven for help and guidance in respect to his present and earthly interests, as truly as in his spiritual life.

As he opened his Bible his eyes caught the words of our Lord, — "Launch out into the deep and let down your nets for a draught."

Then Peter's answer, — "Master, we have toiled all the night and have taken nothing: nevertheless, at Thy word I will let down the net."

The result, — "They enclosed a great multitude of fishes."

With these words light broke in upon his mind. "If our Lord," he mused, "helped His first disciples catch fish, why should He not help me find a good place?" Then unbelief suggested, "It was not for the sake of the fish; they were only means to a higher end."

But Dennis, who had plenty of good common-sense, at once answered this objection: "Neither do I want position and money for low, selfish purposes. My ends are the best and purest, for I am seeking my own honest living and the support of my mother and sisters, — the very imperative duties that God is now imposing on me. Would God reveal a duty and no way of performing it?"

Then came the thought: "Have I asked Him to help me? Have I not been seeking in my own wisdom, and trusting in my own strength? and this too when my ignorance of business, the dull season of the year, and everything was against me, when I specially needed help. Little wonder that I have fared as I have."

Turning the leaves of his Bible rapidly, he began searching for instances of God's interference in behalf of the temporal interests of His servants, — for passages where earthly prosperity was promised or given. After an hour he closed the Bible with a long breath of wonder, and said to himself: "Why, God seems to care as much for the well-being and happiness of his children here as He will when He has us all about Him in the home above. I've been blind for twenty-one years to one of the grandest truths of this Book."

Then, as the thought grew upon him, he exclaimed, joyously, "Take heart, Dennis Fleet: God is on your side in the struggle for an honest success in this life as truly as in your fight against sin and the devil."

It was long before he slept that night, but a truth had been revealed that rested and strengthened him more than the heavy slumbers after the weary days that had preceded.

The dawn of the winter morning was cold and faint when Dennis appeared in the bar-room the next day. The jolly-faced Teuton was making the fire, stopping often to blow his cold fingers, and wasting enough good breath to have kindled a furnace. His rubicund visage, surrounded by shaggy hair and beard of yellow, here appeared in the dust and smoke he was making like the sun rising in a fog.

"Hillo!" he said, on seeing Dennis; "vat you oop dis early for? Don't vant anoder dinner yet, I hope?"

"I will take that in good time," said Dennis; "and shall want a bigger one than that which so astonished you at first."

"O my eyes!" said the German; "den I go and tell de cook to pegin to get him right avay."

Laughing good-naturedly, Dennis went to the door and looked out. On sidewalk and street the snow lay six or eight inches deep, untrodden, white and spotless, even in the heart of the great city. "How different this snow will look by night," thought he; "how soiled and black! Perhaps very many come to this city in the morning of life like this snow, pure and unstained; but after being here awhile they become like this snow when it has been tossed about and trodden under every careless foot. God grant that, however poor and unsuccessful I may remain, such pollution may never be my fate."

But feeling that he had no time for moralizing if he would secure bread for the coming day of rest, he turned and said to the factotum of the bar-room, "How much will you give to have the snow cleared off the sidewalk in front of your house?"

"Zwei shillen."

"Then I will earn my breakfast before I eat it, if you will lend me a shovel."

"I dought you vas a shentlemans," said the German, staring at him.

"So I am; just the shentlemans that will clean off your sidewalk for zwei shillen, if you will let him."

"You vant to do him for exercise?"

"No; for zwei shillings."

"I dought you vas a shentlemans," said the man, still staring in stolid wonder at Dennis.

"Didn't you ever know of a gentleman who came from Germany to this country and was glad to do anything for an honest living?"

"Often and often I haf. You see von here," said the man, with a grin.

"Well, I am just that kind of a gentleman. Now if you will lend me a shovel I will clean off your sidewalk for two shillings, and be a great deal more thankful than if you had given me the money for nothing."

"Little fear of dot," said the man, with another grin. "Vel, you are der queerest Yankee in Chicago, you are; I dink you are 'bout haf Sherman. I tells you vat, — here, vat's your name? — if you glean off dot sidewalk goot, you shall haf preakfast and dinner, much as you eat, vidout von shent to pay. I don't care if der cook is cooking all day. I like your — vat you call him? — shpunk."

"It's a bargain," said Dennis; "and if I can make a few more like it to-day, I shall be rich."

"You may vel say dot. I vill go into der market and see if dere's enough for me to keep my bart of der bargain goot."

For half an hour Dennis worked away lustily, and then called his task-master and said, "Will you accept the job?"

Surveying with surprise the large space cleared, and looking in vain for reason to find fault, he said: "I say nothin' agin him. I hope you vill eat your dinner as quick. Now come in to your preakfast."

He pretended to be perfectly aghast at Dennis's onslaught on the buckwheat cakes, and rolled up his eyes despairingly as each new plate was emptied.

Having finished, Dennis gave him a nod, and said, "Wait till dinner-time."

"Ah! dere vill be von famine," said the German, in a tone of anguish, wringing his hands.

Having procured the needful implement, Dennis started out, and, though there was considerable competition, found plenty to do, and shovelled away with little cessation till one o'clock. Then, counting his gains, he found that he had paid for his shovel, secured breakfast and dinner, and had a balance on hand of two dollars and fifty cents, and he had nearly half a day yet before him. He felt rich, — nay, more than that, he felt like a man who, sinking in a shoreless ocean, suddenly catches a plank that bears him up until land appears in the distance.

"This is what comes of asking God to help a fellow," said he to himself. "Strange, too, that He should answer my prayer in part before I asked, by causing that queer jumble of good and evil, Bill Cronk, to suggest to me this way of turning an honest penny. I wish Bill was as good a friend to himself as he is to others. I fear that he will go to the dogs. Bless me! the gnawings of hunger are bad enough, but what must be those of conscience? I think I can astonish my German friend to-day as never before;" and, shouldering his shovel, he walked back to dinner, feeling like a prince bearing aloft the insignia of his power.

When he entered the bar and lunch room, he saw that something was wrong. The landlord met him, instead of his jolly, satirical friend.

Now the owner of the place was a wizen-faced, dried-up old anatomy, who seemed utterly exhaling away in tobacco smoke, while his assistant was becoming spherical under the expansive power of lager. It was his custom to sit up and smoke most of the night, and therefore he was down late in the morning. When he appeared his assistant told him of the bargain he had made with Dennis as a good joke. But old Hans hadn't any faculty for jokes. Dollars and cents and his big meerschaum made up the two elements of his life. The thought of losing zwei shillings or zwei cents by Dennis, or any one else, caused him anguish, and instead of laughing, his fun-loving assistant was aghast at seeing him fall into a passion.

"You be von big fule. Vat for we keep mens here who haf no money? You should gleared him off, instead of making pargains for him to eat us out of der house."

"We haf his trunk," said Jacob, for that was his name.

"Nothin' in it," growled Hans, yet somewhat mollified by this fact.

When Dennis appeared, he put the case without any circumlocution: "I makes my livin' by keepin' dis house. I can no make my livin' unless efrypodies bays me. I haf reason to dink dot you haf no moneys. Vat ish de druf? 'Gause if you haf none, you can no longer stay here."

"Have I not paid for everything I have had so far?" said Dennis.

"Dot is not der question. Haf you got any moneys?"

"What is your bill in advance up to Monday morning?"

"Zwei dollar and a quarter, if you dake preakfast."

"Deduct breakfast and dinner to-day for clearing off the sidewalk."

"Dot ish too much; you did it in half-hour."

"Well, it would have taken you three. But a bargain is a bargain, the world over. Did not you promise it?" — to Jacob.

"Yah! und you shall haf him, too, if I be der loser. Yahcob Bunk ish not der man to go pack on his vort."

"Vel, den," said old Hans, "von dollar sheventy-five to Monday morning."

"There's the money; now let me have my dinner, for I am in a hurry."

At the sight of money Hans at once became the most obsequious of hosts, and so would remain while it lasted. But Dennis saw that the moment it was gone his purchased courtesy would change, and he trembled at his narrow escape from being thrust out into the wintry streets, friendless, penniless, to beg or starve, — equally hard alternatives to his mind.

"Come, Yahcob, thou snail, give der shentlemans his dinner," said Hans.

Jacob, who had been looking on with heavy, stolid face,

now brightened up on seeing that all was right, and gave Dennis a double portion of the steaming pot-pie, and a huge mug of coffee. When Dennis had finished these and crowned his repast with a big dumpling, Jacob came to him with a face as long and serious as his harvest moon of a visage could be made, and said: "Dere ish nodding more in Chicago; you haf gleaned it out. Ve must vait dill der evenin' drain gomes pefore ve haf supper."

"That will be time enough for me," said Dennis, laughing, — for he could laugh to-day at little things, — and started off again with his shovel.

CHAPTER IX.

LAND AT LAST.

DURING the latter part of a busy afternoon, Dennis came to a spacious, elegant store before which the snow lay untouched save as trodden by passers-by. Over the high arched door-way was the legend in gilt letters, "Art Building;" and as far as a mere warehouse for beautiful things could deserve the title, this place did, for it was crowded with engravings, paintings, bronzes, statuary, and every variety of ornament. With delighted eyes and lingering steps he had passed slowly through this store a few days previous in his search, but had received the usual cool negative. He had gone reluctantly out into the cold street again as Adam went out of Paradise.

A large florid-looking man with a light curling mustache now stood in the door-way. His appearance was unmistakably that of a German of the highest and most cultivated type. And yet, when he spoke, his English was so good that you detected only a foreign accent. Strong vexation was stamped upon his face as he looked at the snowy, untidy sidewalk.

"Mr. Schwartz," he asked of one of his clerks, "was Pat here this morning?"

"Yes, sir."

"Was he perfectly straight?"

"I cannot say that he was, sir."

"He is off on a spree again. Send him to me the moment he returns."

"Shall I clear your sidewalk?" said Dennis, stepping up and touching his hat respectfully.

"Yes," said the gentleman, scarcely looking at him; "and when you have finished come to the office for your money;" and then he walked back into the store with a frowning brow.

Though Dennis was now pretty thoroughly fatigued with the hard day's work, he entered on this task with a good will as the closing labor of the day, hoping, from the wide space to be cleared, to receive proportionate recompense. And yet his despatch was not so great as usual, for in spite of himself his eyes were continually wandering to the large show-windows, from which smiled down upon him summer landscapes, and lovely faces that seemed all the more beautiful in contrast with the bleak and darkening street.

He was rudely startled from one of his stolen glances at a sweet, girlish face that seemed peering archly at him from a corner. His ears were assailed by the loud tones and strong brogue of "Pat," returning thus late to his neglected duties.

"Bad luck to yez! what yez doin' here?"

"Clearing the sidewalk," said Dennis, laconically.

"Give me that shovel, or I'll knock bloody blazes out of yez."

Dennis at once stood on the defensive, and raised his tool threateningly. At the same time seeing a policeman, he called out, "Will you please cause this drunken fellow to move on?"

The officer was about to comply, when the Irishman, with a snort like that of a mad bull, rushed to the door of the art building, wrenched it open, and, leaving it so, tore down the long store, crying, "Misther Ludolph! Misther Ludolph! here's a bloody spalpane a-doin' my work."

He had scarcely got half-way to the office before there was a crash followed by a general commotion.

Pat, in his blind rage, and with steps uncertain from the effects of whiskey, had struck a valuable marble, and it lay broken on the floor. This catastrophe sobered him, and he stood looking in dismay at the destruction he had wrought. His employer, the gentleman whom Dennis had seen at the door, now appeared upon the scene in a towering passion, and scrupled not to heap maledictions upon the head of the unfortunate Hibernian.

"What do you mean by rushing through the store in this mad style?" he demanded.

"There's an impudent fellow outside a-doin' my work," said Pat.

"Why didn't you do it yourself, instead of going off to the gin-mills this morning? Didn't I warn you? Didn't I tell you your last spree should be the last in my employ? Now begone, you drunken idiot! and if you ever show your face on these premises again I'll have you arrested and compel payment for this marble, and it will take every cent you have in the world, and more too."

"Ah! Misther Ludolph, if ye'll only give me one more—"

"I tell you be off! or I will call the policeman at once."

"But Bridget and the childer will starve."

"What are Bridget and the children to me? If you won't take care of them, you can't expect other people to. Begone!" said his employer, advancing threateningly and stamping his foot.

Pat looked around in vain for help: the clerks were but fainter echoes of their master.

Seeing his case to be hopeless, he turned about and hurried away, his big red face distorted by many contending emotions. Nor did he stop until he reached one of the fatal "gin-mills," where he soon drowned memory and trouble in huge potations of the fiery element that was destroying him and bringing wretchedness to "Bridget and the childer."

Again Dennis had a lesson on drinking for the effects.

He rapidly completed his work and entered the store. A clerk handed him fifty cents.

"May I see Mr. Ludolph a moment?" he asked.

"Yes," replied the clerk, "he is in the inner office there; but I guess you won't find him very smooth this evening," looking at the same time suggestively toward the broken marble.

But Mr. Ludolph was not in as bad a humor as was imagined. This thrifty Teuton had not lost much by the mishap of the afternoon, for a month or two of wages was due Pat, and this kept back would pay in the main for the injury he had done. His whole soul being bent on the acquirement of money, for reasons that will be explained further on, his momentary passion soon passed away when he found he had sustained no material injury. To Dennis's knock he responded in his usual tone, "Come in!" and Dennis stood in a warm, lighted, cosey office, where the object of his quest sat writing rapidly with his back to the door. Dennis waited respectfully till the facile pen glided through the sentence, and then Mr. Ludolph looked up. Dennis's bearing and appearance were so unmistakably those of a gentleman that Mr. Ludolph, not recognizing him as the person who had cleared his sidewalk, rose courteously and said, "Did you wish to see me?"

"Yes, sir," replied Dennis; "I understand that you dismissed a person in your employ this afternoon. I would respectfully apply for his place, if it is not promised."

The gentleman smiled and said: "You are mistaken, I think. I discharged a drunken Irishman, who had been porter and man-of-all-work about the store, this afternoon; but I have no place vacant, young sir, that you would care to fill."

"If you think me competent to fill the position of porter

and your man-of-all-work, I would be very glad to obtain it; that is, if it will support me and those dependent on me."

The merchant muttered to himself, "I thought he was a gentleman."

Then, as this was a business matter of some importance, he caused Dennis to stand full in the light, while he withdrew somewhat in the shadow, and gave it his attention with characteristic shrewdness and caution.

"You seem rather above the situation you ask for," he said.

"I am not above it in circumstances," said Dennis, "and it certainly is better than shovelling snow all day."

"Are you the man that just cleaned my sidewalk?"

"I am, sir."

"You must be aware that your general appearance is very different from that of the man discharged to-day, and from those seeking the menial place in question. Can you explain this fact satisfactorily?"

"I can readily explain it, and I hope satisfactorily. At any rate I shall be perfectly open;" and Dennis told him briefly, but plainly, just how he was situated.

As the keen man of the world watched with the closest scrutiny the honest young face, he believed every word. Accustomed to deal with all classes of men from childhood, he had learned to read them as the open page of a book.

He asked coolly, however, "Have you no recommendations?"

Dennis produced the ministerial letter, which Mr. Ludolph glanced at with good-natured contempt.

"This is all right," he said; "superstition is an excellent thing for some minds. I managed Pat a year through his priest, and then he got beyond the priest and me too."

This undisguised contempt of all that he held sacred, and

the classing of true faith with gross superstition, pained Dennis; and his face showed it, though he said nothing.

"There," said the gentleman, "I did not mean to hurt your feelings, but to the educated in our land these things seem very childish."

"I should serve you none the worse," said Dennis, with quiet dignity, "if I believed that the duty I owed to you I owed also to God."

Mr. Ludolph looked as if a new idea had struck him, smiled, and said: "Most people's religion, as far as my experience has gone, is not of this practical kind. But I believe that I can trust you, and your face and story are worth much more to me than this letter. A scamp might possess that as well as an honest youth like you. Now, as to terms: I will give you forty dollars a month for the first two months, and then, if you develop and take well to the work, I will give you sixty."

Dennis thought that this, with close economy, would enable him to live and support his mother and sisters, and he accepted the terms.

"Moreover, to show the advantage of telling a straightforward story, you may sleep in the store: the building will be safer for having some one in it. I will pay you at the end of every week as long as you suit, so that you can commence sending something to your mother immediately. You see that I take an interest in you," said the shrewd man, "and expect you to take an interest in my business, and work for me as for yourself."

Simple, honest Dennis could not see that Mr. Ludolph cared infinitely more for himself than for all the world combined, and made it his life-study to get the most out of it with the least cost to himself. Under the words that seemed so kind and considerate, the young man's heart swelled with the strong and grateful purpose to spare himself in no way in the service of such an employer. The wily man saw this, and smiled to himself over the credulity of mankind.

"Have you enough to last till next Saturday night?" he asked.

"I will make it last," said Dennis, sturdily.

"That is right," said Mr. Ludolph. "Stand on your own feet if you can. I never give any more help than will barely enable a man to help himself," — a maxim which had the advantage not only of being sound, but of according exactly with his disposition.

After a moment's thought, Mr. Ludolph spoke in a tone so sharp, and a manner so stern, that Dennis was startled.

"Mark me, young man, I wish a plain understanding in one respect: you take Pat's place, and I expect you to do Pat's work. I wish no trouble to arise from your being above your business."

"You will have none," said Dennis, quietly and firmly.

"All right, then. Mr. Schwartz will show you about closing up the store. Be here early Monday morning, and remember that all depends upon yourself."

In the depths of his grateful heart Dennis felt how much the success of that day and every day of life depended on God.

Mr. Ludolph put on his coat and gloves and went out with Dennis into the store.

"Gentlemen," said he to his clerks, "this young man, Dennis Fleet by name, will take the place of Pat Murphy, discharged to-day. Mr. Schwartz, will you show him what it is necessary to do to-night? He will be here on Monday morning at the usual time for opening the store, and after that will sleep in the building."

The clerks looked at him for a moment, as they might at a new piece of furniture, or a labor-saving machine, and then coolly finished their duties, and followed their employer.

Mr. Schwartz showed him about closing the store, taking care of the furnace, etc., and Dennis saw that his place was no sinecure. Still it was not work, but its lack, that he dreaded, and his movements were so eager and earnest that a faint expression of surprise and curiosity tinged the broad, stolid face of Mr. Schwartz; but he only buttoned his coat to the chin and muttered, "New broom," and went his way homeward, leaving Dennis to go his.

CHAPTER X.

THE NEW BROOM.

THE following Sabbath was a bright winter day without, but bright summer in Dennis's heart. He inquired his way to a neighboring church, and every word of prayer, praise, and truth fell on a glad, grateful spirit. Returning, he wrote a long letter to his mother, telling her all he had passed through, especially dwelling on the truth he had discovered of God's wish to make this life happy and successful, as well as the life beyond.

In closing, he wrote: "Here am I, Dennis Fleet, who a few days since thought the world scarcely large enough for what I meant to do, standing contentedly and gratefully in Pat Murphy's shoes. I will not conceal from you, speaking figuratively (the fates forbid that it should be literally true), that I hope to outgrow them, and arrive at something better before many months pass. In them ean time I am indeed thankful for the means of winning honest bread for us all. It is quite a come-down from the classics and law to the position of porter and man-of-all-work in a picture and music store, but if God means me to rise He can lead me upward from my lowly standpoint as well as from the most favored that I could have chosen for myself. I have learned that if I will *trust Him* and do present duty thoroughly, He will not forget me."

On Monday morning, half an hour before the specified time, Dennis stood at the store. Impatiently he walked up and down before what would become the scene of joys and sorrows such as he had never before experienced. But we will not anticipate.

In due time Mr. Schwartz appeared. He gave Dennis a cool nod, and said, "Glad to see you so prompt," then muttered again to himself, "New broom."

In Mr. Schwartz's slow, plodding soul the fire of enthusiasm had never burned. He was eminently conservative, and looked with wary suspicion on anything that appeared like earnestness. In the midst of a driving, bustling Western city, he stuck in the mud of his German phlegm, like a snag in the swift current of the Mississippi. Yet Mr. Ludolph found him a most valuable assistant. He kept things straight. Under his minute supervision everything had to be right on Saturday night as well as on Monday morning, on the 31st of December as well as on the 1st of January. He was one who through life would be satisfied with a subordinate position, conscious of the lack of enterprise needful to push his own way in the world. His painstaking, methodical spirit was just the kind to pervade a large warehouse like that he had in charge, and prevent loss and confusion in the multiplicity of objects it contained. Pat's careless Irish ways had vexed his soul beyond words, and now Dennis's eager manner suggested a hare-brained Yankee youth who would raise a dust for a week and then be off at something else. He was therefore cool and curt, seeking by frostiness of manner to nip the budding enthusiasm that annoyed him.

Dennis heeded him not, but bent every faculty to the mastery of the duties required of him. He was to mop out the store with damp cloths, so as to raise no dust, to look after the furnace and graduate the heat throughout the building, to receive boxes, to assist in packing and unpacking pianos and other musical instruments that occupied part of the upper floors, and to make himself generally useful. So far from being an easy position, it was one that required great strength and despatch, and these had been Pat's qualities save when drink got the better of him. For one of his age, Dennis was very strong, and his experience in helping his mother in household duties had made him quick and dexterous, where most young men would have been awkward and slow. After a day or two Mr. Schwartz relaxed his grimness somewhat, for if Dennis worked eagerly he also worked well for a beginner. Still it would require several years of well-doing to satisfy old Schwartz that all was right. But Mr. Ludolph, with his quick insight into character, watched this "new broom" a few days, and then congratulated himself on gaining another decided help toward the object nearest his heart.

The other clerks were of German descent, and under Mr. Schwartz's rigid system each one filled his appropriate niche, and performed carefully the duties assigned.

Even to Dennis's uncultivated eye there was an inartistic formality about the whole establishment. His sense of this was at first but a feeling,—a vague impression that grew upon him without his quite knowing why. He soon discovered, however, that everything was arranged squarely, according to system, order, and not with a view of placing in the best lights and shadows the beautiful things to be sold. He saw that Mr. Ludolph was annoyed by the same defect. One bright day, when everything stood out with glaring distinctness, he seemed provoked beyond measure by this inartistic rigidity, and stormed through the store at a great rate.

"This art building and everybody and everything in it look as if they had swallowed a ramrod," snarled he. "Mr. Schwartz, can't you teach the young men to throw a little ease and grace into the arrangement of the articles under their charge?"

Mr. Schwartz looked at him with a blank, impassive face, and his employer felt that he might as well ask an elephant to teach dancing.

Turning suddenly on a stolid youth, he exclaimed, "By the gods! if you have not arranged all the statuettes on your counter in straight lines, and half of them with their backs toward the door at which our customers enter! Here, gather round me while I give you some ideas of arrangement."

The clerks gathered around him, while with hands of skill and taste he placed everything artistically. The effect of a little transposition was marvellous, and Mr. Schwartz acknowledged that the groups looked doubly pretty and inviting. Dennis stood at a respectful distance, but was a close observer. He was the only one who gained much benefit from the lesson, because the only one capable of receiving it. With quick, appreciative eye he saw the grouping needful to produce the desired effect.

As Mr. Ludolph looked up he caught Dennis's intelligent gaze.

"That is right, Fleet," he said; "you learn, too, if you can, and when you are dusting around see if you cannot combine a little order and grace."

From that day forward the hand and taste of Dennis Fleet gradually, and almost imperceptibly at first, gave a new aspect and created a new atmosphere in the "Art Building." But at first he was kept busy enough at his humble routine duties. Every one felt and expressed a little surprise at his getting into harness so quickly, but Mr. Schwartz's influence was not conducive to conversation or emotions, however faint. All went forward quietly and orderly, like well-oiled machinery. Customers received every attention, and though many no doubt had the undefined feeling that something was wrong in the arrangement of the store, each found an abundance of beautiful things suited to his taste and purse, and so trade was good, even though the holiday season was over.

As for Dennis, he was to a certain extent in Paradise. Nature had given him a deep, earnest love of the beautiful, and a keen perception of it.

Though his days were busy indeed, he found time gradually to study every pretty thing in the store. Though much was mystery to him as yet, he felt that he had crossed the threshold of a beautiful world, — the world of art. When a boy in New England he had taken drawing-lessons, and had shown remarkable aptness. While at college, also, he had given some attention to drawing and coloring, but circumstances had prevented him from following the bent of his taste. Now the passion awoke with tenfold force, and he had not been in his place a week before he began to make sketches of little things that pleased him. Some of the pictures and bronzes became almost dear because of the pleasure and inspiration that they occasioned, and at their sale his feeling was akin to regret. Early in the morning, when refreshed and brightened by the night's rest, he would walk through the store as through fairy-land, and, forgetting that he was a humble servitor, would feel as if all were his. But in fact was not his possession truer than that of many whose palace walls glow with every rich gem of art, and yet whose eyes are blind and their hearts dull to the beauty they have paid for?

A few days after his arrival a little incident occurred that was hard and practical enough, and might justly cause him to feel that he occupied a humble place, not only in the world of art, but in the world in general. There had been a day of rain, slush, and mud. One of the younger clerks had been sent out on an errand, and came in well splashed. Drawing off his boots, he threw them to Dennis, saying:

"Here you, Fleet! black my boots as quick as you can. I must go out again."

Dennis reddened, and for a moment drew himself up as if he had been struck. The young man saw it and said, in a loud, coarse tone that could be heard by several customers: "Vat! you above your biz? I thought it vould be so."

Dennis acted with decision. He meant to have the matter settled at once. Picking up the muddy boots, he marched straight into Mr. Ludolph's office. That gentleman looked up, impatient at interruption, and saw his man-of-all-work standing before him with the splashed boots dangling in his hands.

"Well, what is it?" asked he, sharply.

"Mr. Berder threw me those boots and told me to black them. Is this a part of my duty here?" said Dennis, in a firm, quiet tone.

"Curse it all!" said Mr. Ludolph, with much irritation; "I thought there would be trouble with your uppishness."

"There shall be no trouble whatever," said Dennis; "but I prefer to take my orders from you, and not from Mr. Berder. If you say this is expected, the disagreeable task shall be done as well as I can do it."

Mr. Ludolph looked sharply at the young man for a moment and hesitated. In his heart he felt that he was speaking to a gentleman, and that it was not the thing to ask of him such menial work. But his irritation and desire to crush out anything like insubordination prevailed. Still, rather than directly order it, he appealed to the custom of the past, and stepping to the door of the office he called: "Mr. Schwartz, come here! Did Pat black the shoes of the *gentlemen* of this store?"

"Yes, sir."

"You took Pat Murphy's place, did you not?"

"Yes, sir," said Dennis.

"It seems to me, then, that this settles the question," said Mr. Ludolph, coolly, turning to his writing; but he furtively and carefully watched Dennis's course.

Determined to show that he was not above his business, that he accepted the bitter with the sweet, Dennis went up-stairs to his room, got blacking and brush, and taking his station in a corner where Mr. Ludolph could plainly see him through the glass doors of his office, he polished away as vigorously as if that were his only calling. Mr. Ludolph looked and smiled. His was a nature that could be pleased with a small triumph like this. But the other clerks, seeing Mr. Berder's success, and determining to do their part, also, in taking Dennis "down a peg," as they expressed it, brought their boots, too, and Mr. Berder came with his again in the afternoon. Dennis cleaned and polished away in full view of Mr. Ludolph, who began to realize with vexation that his man-of-all-work would have little time for the duties of the store if he were installed general bootblack of the establishment. But, after this, cold and snow kept the streets dry and clean for some time, and the matter passed on without further notice. Boots were seldom brought to him, and when they were, they were cleaned without a word. In the mean time, his ability and faithfulness in the discharge of his regular duties, and in some slight degree his taste and judgment, began to be recognized, and Mr. Ludolph congratulated himself that in giving Dennis Pat Murphy's place he had made a decided change for the better.

CHAPTER XI.

TOO MUCH ALIKE.

ONE of the duties that Dennis enjoyed most was the opening of new goods. With the curiosity and pleasure of a child he would unpack the treasures of art consigned to his employer, and when a number of boxes were left at the front door he was eager to see their contents. During his first three weeks at the store, there had not been many such arrivals of goods and pictures. But now new things were coming in; and, above all, Mr. Ludolph was daily expecting pictures imported directly from Europe.

One afternoon early in February a large flat box was brought to the store. Mr. Ludolph examined its marks, smiled, and told Dennis to open it with great care, cutting every nail with a chisel. There was little need of cautioning him, for he would have bruised his right hand rather than mar one line of beauty.

The "Art Building" contained two or three small show-rooms, where the more valuable pictures could be exhibited in a good light. Into one of these the large box was carried, and most carefully opened. The two clerks who were helping Dennis laughed at his eager interest, and called him under their breath a "green 'un." Mr. Schwartz looked upon him as a mild sort of lunatic. But Mr. Ludolph, who stood near, to see if the picture was safe and right, watched him with some curiosity. His manner was certainly very different from Pat Murphy's at such a time, and his interest both amused and pleased his employer.

When at last the picture was lifted from the box and placed on a large easel, all exclaimed at its beauty save Dennis. On looking at him, they saw that his eyes had filled with tears, and his lips were quivering so that he could not have spoken.

"Is she a relation of yours?" asked Mr. Schwartz, in a matter-of-fact tone.

A loud laugh followed this sally from such an unusual source. Dennis turned on his heel, left the room, and busied himself with duties in a distant part of the store the rest of the day. It seemed to him that they were like savages bartering away gold and pearls, whose value they could not understand; much less could they realize his possession of a nature of exquisite sensibility to beauty.

When all were gone he returned to the room, and sat down before the picture in rapt attention. It was indeed a fine work of art, finished in that painstaking manner characteristic of the Germans.

The painting was a winter scene in Germany. In the far background rose wooded and snow-clad hills. Nearer in the perspective was a bold bluff, surmounted by a half-ruined castle. At the base of the bluff flowed a river, now a smooth glare of ice, and in the distance figures were wheeling about upon skates. In the immediate foreground were two persons. One was a lovely young girl, dressed in black velvet trimmed with ermine. The basque fitted closely to her person, revealing its graceful outlines, and was evidently adapted to the active sport in which she was engaged. While the rich warm blood mantled her cheeks, the snow was not whiter than her temples and brow. Down her shoulders flowed a profusion of wavy hair, scattered threads of which glistened like gold in the slanting rays of the sun. Her eyes, of a deep violet, were turned, in sympathy with the scorn of the full, smiling mouth, upon the figure of a young man kneeling before her, making awkward attempts to fasten her skate to the trim little foot. It was evident that the favor was too much for him, and that his fluttering heart made his hands trembling and unskilful. But the expression of the maiden's face clearly indicated that her heart was as cold toward him as the ice on which he knelt.

The extreme beauty of the picture and its exquisite finish fascinated Dennis, while the girl's face jarred upon his feelings like a musical discord. After gazing fixedly for a long time, he said, "What possessed the man to paint such a lovely face and make its expression only that of scorn, pride, and heartless merriment?"

All the long night the face haunted and troubled him. He saw it in his dreams. It had for him a strong interest that he could not understand, — that strange fascination which a very beautiful thing that has been marred and wronged has for some natures. So powerful was this impression upon his sensitive nature that he caught himself saying, as of a living being, "O that I could give to that face the expression God meant it to have!"

And then he laughed at his own folly.

His wakefulness caused him to oversleep the next morning, and he was later than usual in getting through the routine duties of the store. At length, about nine o'clock, dusty and begrimed from mopping, feeding the furnace, etc., he stood with duster and brush in hand before the painting that had so disturbed his rest. He was in his shirt-sleeves, and in careful economy had a large coarse apron of ticking girded about his person. His black dishevelled locks looked like an inverted crow's nest, and altogether he was unpresentable, appearing more like the presiding divinity of a dust-heap than of an "Art Building."

After gazing a few moments on the scornful, beautiful face

that might have obtained its haughty patrician lineaments from the old barons of the ruined castle just above, he seemed to grow conscious of this himself, and shrunk behind the picture half ashamed, as if the fair girl could see him.

While engaged in cleaning off some stains and marks upon the frame, he did not hear a light footstep in the room. Finishing his task, he stepped out from behind the picture with the purpose of leaving the apartment, when a vision met his gaze which startled him to that degree that he dropped his brush and duster upon the floor, and stood transfixed. There before him, in flesh and blood it seemed, stood the lady of the picture, — the same dress, the same beautiful blond face, and, above all, the same expression. He was made conscious of his absurd position by a suppressed titter from the clerks at the door, and a broad laugh from Mr. Ludolph. The beautiful face turned toward him for a moment, and he felt himself looked over from head to foot. At first there was an expression of vexation at the interruption, and then, as if from the ludicrousness of his appearance, the old laughing, scornful look returned. Casting a quick, furtive glance at the picture, which seemed to satisfy him, Dennis, with hot cheeks, gathered up his tools and beat a hasty retreat. As he passed out, Mr. Ludolph asked, good-naturedly, "Why, Fleet, what is the matter?"

"Indeed, sir, I hardly know," answered the bewildered youth, "but it seems to me that I have lost my wits since that picture came. For a moment I thought that the lady on the canvas had stepped out upon the floor."

"Now that you speak of it," exclaimed Mr. Ludolph, advancing into the room, "there is a striking resemblance."

"Nonsense! father," Dennis heard the young lady say; "you are too old to flatter. As for that hare-brained youth of the dust-brush, he looked as if he might have the failing of poor Pat, and not always be able to see straight."

At this Dennis's cheeks grew hotter still, while a low laugh from one or two of the clerks near showed that they were enjoying his embarrassment.

Dennis hastened away to his room, and it was well that he did not hear the conversation that followed.

"Oh, no!" responded Mr. Ludolph, "that is not Dennis's failing. He is a member of a church in 'good and regular standing.' He will be one of the 'pillars' by and by."

"You are always having a fling at superstition and the superstitious," said his daughter, laughingly. "Is that the reason you installed him in Pat's place?"

"Can you doubt it, my dear?" replied her father, in mock solemnity.

"Well," said she, "I think your new factotum fails decidedly in good manners, if nothing else. He stared most impudently at me when he came out from behind the picture. I should have reprimanded him myself if I had not been so full of laughter at his ridiculous appearance."

"That's the joke of it. It was as good as a play to see him. I never saw a man more startled and confused. He evidently thought for a moment, as he said, that the girl in the painting had stepped out upon the floor, and that you were she."

"How absurd!" exclaimed his daughter.

"Yes; and now that I think of it, he glanced from you to the picture, to satisfy himself that his senses were not deceiving him, before he started to come away."

"I cannot see any special resemblance," she replied, at the same time inwardly pleased that she should be thought like the beautiful creature on the canvas.

"But there is a strong resemblance," persisted her father, "especially in general effect. I will prove it to you. There is old Schwartz; he is not troubled with imagination, but sees things just as they are. He would look at you, my dainty daughter, as if you were a bale of wool, and judge as composedly and accurately."

"I fear, my father," replied she, smilingly, "that you have conspired with him to pull the entire bale over my eyes. But let him come."

By this time Dennis had returned, and commenced dusting some pictures near the entrance, where he could see and hear. He felt impelled by a curiosity that he could not resist. Moreover he had a little natural vanity in wishing to show that he was not such a guy, after all. It was hard for him to remember that he stood in Pat Murphy's position. What difference did it make to the lady whether such as he was a fright or not?

Mr. Schwartz entered, and at Mr. Ludolph's bidding looked at the living and the painted girl. In his slow, sententious tones, one could not help feeling that he was telling just how things appeared to him. The young lady stood beside the painting and unconsciously assumed the expression of her fair shadow. Indeed it seemed an expression but too habitual to her face.

"Yes," he said, "there is a decided resemblance — close in dress — close in complexion — color of hair much the same — eyes much alike — Miss Ludolph not quite so tall," etc. Then with an awkward attempt at a compliment, like an elephant trying to execute a quickstep, he continued, —

"If I may be permitted to be so bold as to speak — express an opinion — I should beg leave to say that Miss Ludolph favors herself — more favored — is better-looking," he blurted out at last, backing out of the door at the same time, with his brow bathed in perspiration from the throes of this great and unwonted effort at gallantry.

"Bah!" said Dennis to himself, "the old mole left out the very chief thing in tracing the likeness, — the expression! See her now as she listens to his awkward attempt at compliment. She is looking at him with the same scornful, laughing face that the girl in the picture wears toward the bungling admirer at her feet. He is right in one thing though, she is better-looking."

But the moment Mr. Schwartz's bulky figure vanished from the door-way, Miss Ludolph caught the critical, intelligent gaze of Dennis Fleet, and the expression of her face changed instantly to a frown. But, to do her justice, it was more in vexation with herself than with him. Her innate delicacy of feeling showed her that it looked like small vanity to be standing there while comparisons like the above were instituted. Her manner at once became cold, observant, and thoroughly self-possessed. She stepped out into the store, and by a few keen, critical glances seemed to take in its whole effect. Again disapprobation clouded her fair brow, and she pronounced audibly but one word, — "Stiff."

Then she passed into her father's private office.

CHAPTER XII.

BLUE BLOOD.

DENNIS'S mind was a chaos of conflicting feelings. The picture had deeply interested him, and so did the beautiful girl that it by strange coincidence so strongly resembled. It could not be otherwise with one of his beauty-loving nature. And yet the impression made by the face in the painting — of something wrong, discordant — was felt more decidedly in respect to the living face.

But before he had time to realize what had just passed the lady and her father appeared at the door of the office, and he heard the latter say: "I know you are right, my dear. It's all wrong. The arrangement of the store is as stiff and methodical as if we were engaged in selling mathematical instruments. But I have not time to attend to the matter, and there is not one in the store that has the least idea of artistic combination, unless it is Fleet. I have noticed some encouraging symptoms in him."

"What! he of the duster and mop? I fear our case is desperate, then, if he is our best hope."

Dennis's cheeks were burning again; but, turning his back, he rubbed away harder than ever at a Greek god that he was polishing. But they gave him no thought. Speaking with sudden animation the young lady said, "Father, I have a great mind to try it myself, — that is, if you are willing."

"But, my daughter, I could not permit you to be engaged in any such employment before our customers."

"Certainly not! I would come early in the morning, before art-customers are stirring. I really should enjoy the task greatly, if I had any one to help me who could in some faint degree comprehend the effects I wished to produce. The long spring mornings soon to come would be just the time for it. To what better use could I put my taste and knowledge of art than in helping you and furthering our plan for life?"

Mr. Ludolph hesitated between his pride and his strong desire to gain the advantages which the acceptance of this offer would secure. Finally he said: "We will think about it. I am expecting a great many new and beautiful things early in the spring, and no doubt it would be well then to re-arrange the store completely, and break up the rigid system into which we have fallen. In the mean time I appreciate your offer, and thank you warmly."

Dennis's heart leaped within him at the thought of instruction from such a teacher, and he longed to offer his services. But he rightly judged that the proposal would be regarded as an impertinence at that time. The successor of Pat Murphy was not expected to know anything of art, or have any appreciation of it. So he bent his head lower, but gave Jupiter Olympus such a rubbing down as the god had deserved long ago. In a moment more Miss Ludolph passed him on her way out of the store, noticing him no more than she did his dust-brush.

Mr. Ludolph was the younger son of a noble but impoverished German family, and was intensely proud of his patrician blood. His parents, knowing that he would have to make his own way in the world, had sent him, while a mere boy, to this country, and placed him in charge of a distant relative, who was engaged in the picture-trade in New York. He had here learned to speak English in his youth with the fluency and accuracy of a native, but had never become Americanized, so much family pride had he inherited, and so strongly did he cling to the traditions of his own land.

He showed great business ability in his chosen calling, especially displaying remarkable judgment in the selection of works of art. So unusual was his skill in this direction, that when twenty-one years old he was sent abroad to purchase pictures. For several years he travelled through Europe. He became quite cosmopolitan in character, and for a time enjoyed life abundantly. His very business brought him in contact with artists and men of culture, while his taste and love of beauty were daily gratified. He had abundant means, and money could open many doors of pleasure to one who, like him, was in vigorous health and untroubled by a conscience. Moreover, he was able to spend much time in his beloved Germany, and while there the great ambition of his life entered his heart. His elder brother, who was living in exclusive pride and narrow economy on the ancient but diminished ancestral estate, ever received him graciously. This brother had married, but had not been blessed or cursed with children, for the German baron, with his limited finances, could never decide in what light to regard them. Too poor to mingle with his equals, too proud to stoop to those whom he regarded as inferiors, he had lived much alone, and grown narrower and more bigoted in his family pride day by day. Indeed, that he was Baron Ludolph, was the one great fact of his life. He spent hours in conning over yellow, musty records of the ancient grandeur of his house, and would gloat over heroic deeds of ancestors he never thought of imitating. In brief, he was like a small barnacle on an old and water-logged ship, that once had made many a gallant and prosperous voyage richly freighted, but now had drifted into shallow water and was falling to decay. He made a suggestion, however, to his younger brother, that wakened the ambition of the latter's stronger nature, and set him about what became his controlling purpose, his life-work.

"Make a fortune in America," said his brother, "and come back and restore the ancient wealth and glory of your family."

The seed fell into receptive soil, and from that day the art and pleasure loving citizen of the world became an earnest man with a purpose. But as he chose his purpose mainly from selfish motives it did not become an ennobling one. He now gave double attention to business and practical economy. He at once formed the project of starting in business for himself, and of putting the large profits resulting from his judicious selection of pictures into his own pocket. He made the most careful arrangements, and secured agencies that he could trust in the purchase of pictures after he should return to the United States.

During his stay in Paris, on his way back, an event occurred that had a most untoward influence on his plans and hopes. He fell desperately in love with a beautiful French woman. Like himself, she was poor, but of patrician blood, and was very fascinating. She attracted him by her extreme beauty and brilliancy. She was very shrewd, and could seem anything she chose, being a perfect actress in the false, hollow life of the world. In accordance with Parisian ideas, she wanted a husband to pay her bills, to be a sort of protector and base of general operations. Here was a man who promised well, fine-looking, and, if not rich, capable of making large sums of money.

She insinuated herself into his confidence, and appeared to share his enthusiasm for the darling project of his life. He felt that, with such a beautiful and sympathetic woman to spur him on and share his success, earth would be a Paradise indeed; and she assured him, in many delicate and bewitching ways, that it would. In brief, he married her; and then learned, in bitterness, anger, and disgust, that she had totally deceived him. To his passionate love she returned indifference; to his desire for economy, unbounded extravagance, contracting debts which he must pay to avoid disgrace. She showed an utter unwillingness to leave the gayety of Paris, laughing in his face at his plan of life, and assuring him that she would never live in so stupid a place as Germany. His love died hard. He made every appeal to her that affection prompted. He tried entreaty, tenderness, coldness, anger, but all in vain. Selfish to the core, loving him not, utterly unscrupulous, she trod upon his quivering heart as recklessly as upon the stones of the street. Soon he saw that, in spite of his vigilance, he was in danger of being betrayed in all respects. Then he grew hard and fierce. The whole of his strong German nature was aroused. In a tone and manner that startled and frightened her, he said: "*We* sail for New York in three days. Be ready. If you prove unfaithful to me,—if you seek to desert me, I will *kill* you. I swear it,—not by God, for I don't believe in Him. If He existed, such creatures as you would not. But I swear it by my family pride and name, which are dearer to me than life, if you leave a stain upon them you shall *die*. You need not seek to escape me. I would follow you through the world. I would kill you on the crowded street,—anywhere, even though I died myself the next moment. And now look well to your steps."

The glitter of his eye was as cold and remorseless as the sheen of steel. She saw that he meant and would do just what he said.

The woman had one good point,—at least, it turned out to be such in this case. She was a coward naturally, and her bad life made her dread nothing so much as death. Her former flippant indifference to his remonstrances now changed into abject fear. He saw her weak side, learned his power, and from that time forward kept her within bounds by a judicious system of terrorism.

He took her to New York and commanded her to appear the charming woman she could if she chose. She obeyed, and rather enjoyed the excitement and deceit. His friends were delighted with her, but he received their congratulations with a grim, quiet smile. At times, though, when she was entertaining them with all grace, beauty, and sweetness, the thought of what she was seemed only a horrid dream. But he had merely to catch her eye, with its gleam of fear and hate, to know the truth.

He felt that he could not trust to the continuance of her good behavior, and was anxious to get away among strangers as soon as possible. He therefore closed his business relations in New York. Though she had crippled him greatly by her extravagance, he had been able to bring out a fair stock of good pictures, and a large number of articles of virtu, selected with his usual taste. The old firm, finding that they could not keep him, offered all the goods he wanted on commission. So in a few weeks he started for Chicago, the most promising city of the West, as he believed, and established himself there in a modest way. Still the chances were even against him, for he had involved himself heavily, and drawn to the utmost on his credit in starting. If he could not sell largely the first year, he was a broken man. For months the balance wavered, and he lived with financial ruin on one side, and domestic ruin on the other. But, with a heart of ice and nerves of steel, he kept his hand on the helm.

His beautiful collection, though in an unpretentious store, at last attracted attention, and after some little time it became *the* thing in the fashionable world to go there, and from that time forward his fortune was made.

When his wife became a mother, there was a faint hope in Mr. Ludolph's heart that this event might awaken the woman within her, if aught of the true woman existed. He tried to treat her with more kindness, but found it would not answer. She mistook it for weakness on his part. From first to last she acted in the most heartless manner, and treated the child with shameless neglect. This banished from her husband even the shadow of regard, and he cursed her to her face. Thenceforth will and ambition controlled his life and hers, and with an iron hand he held her in check. She saw that she was in the power of a desperate man, who would sacrifice her in a moment if she thwarted him.

Through cowardly fear she remained his reluctant but abject slave, pricking him with the pins and needles of petty annoyances, when she would have pierced him to the heart had she dared. This monstrous state of affairs could not last forever, and, had not death terminated the unnatural relation, some terrible catastrophe would no doubt have occurred. Having contracted a western fever, she soon became delirious, and passed away in this unconscious state, to the intense joy and relief of her husband.

But the child lived, thrived, and developed into the graceful girl whose beauty surpassed, as we have seen, even the painter's ideal. Her father at first cared little for the infant, but secured it every attention. As it developed into a pretty girl, however, with winning ways, and rich promise, he gradually associated her with his hopes and plans, till at last she became an essential part of his ambition.

His plan now was briefly this: He would entangle himself with no alliances or intimate associations in America, nor would he permit his daughter to do so. His only object in staying here was the accumulation of a large fortune, and to this for a few years he would bend every energy of mind and body. As soon as he felt that he had sufficient means to live in such style as befitted the ancient and honorable name of his family, he would return to Germany, buy all he could of the ancestral estate that from time to time had been parted with, and restore his house to its former grandeur. He himself would then seek a marriage connection that would strengthen his social position, while his daughter also should make a brilliant alliance with some member of the nobility. Mr. Ludolph was a handsome, well-preserved man; he had been most successful in business, and was now more rapidly than ever accumulating that which is truly a power with Europeans of blue blood, as with democratic Americans. Moreover, his daughter's beauty promised to be such that, when enhanced by every worldly advantage, it might well command attention in the highest circles. He sought with scrupulous care to give her just the education that would enable her to shine as a star among the high-born. Art, music, and knowledge of literature, especially the German, were the main things to which her attention was directed, and in her father, with his richly stored mind, faultless taste, and cultured voice, she had an instructor such as rarely falls to the lot of the most favored.

When Christine Ludolph was about sixteen years of age, events occurred which might have greatly marred her father's plans. She secretly formed a most unfortunate attachment, which came near resulting in a clandestine marriage. Although the world would have judged her harshly, and the marriage could only have been exceedingly disastrous to her future life, the motherless girl was not very much to blame. Even among the mature there is a proverbial blindness in these matters. She was immature, misled by her imagination, and the victim of uncurbed romantic fancies. But, after all, the chief incentive to her folly was a natural craving for the love and sympathy which she had never found in her own home. To her chilled young heart these gifts were so sweet and satisfying that she was in no mood to criticise the donor, even had her knowledge of the world enabled her to do so. Thus far, in his care of Christine, Mr. Ludolph had conformed to the foreign ideas of seclusion and repression, and the poor girl, unguided, unguarded by kind womanly counsel, was utterly unsophisticated, and she might have easily become the prey of the unscrupulous man whose chief incentive had been her father's wealth. Mr. Ludolph fortunately discovered the state of affairs in time to prevent gossip. Under his remorseless logic, bitter satire, and ridicule her young dream was torn to shreds. The man whom she had surrounded with a halo of romance was shown to be worthless and commonplace. Her idol had chiefly been a creature of the imagination, and when the bald, repulsive truth concerning him had been proved to her in such a way that she could not escape conviction, she was equally disgusted with him and herself.

For some weeks Mr. Ludolph treated his daughter with cold distrust. "She will be like her mother, I suppose," he thought. "Already she has begun to deceive me and to imperil everything by her folly;" and his heart was full of bitterness toward his child. Thus the poor girl dwelt in a chilled and blighting atmosphere at a time when she most sorely needed kindness and wise guidance.

She was very unhappy, for she saw that her father had lost all confidence in her. She fairly turned sick when she thought of the past. She had lived in the world of romance and mystery; she had loved with all her girlish power; and, however wrongly and unjustly, by the inevitable laws of association she connected the words "love" and "romance" with one whom she now detested and loathed. Within a week after her miserable experience she became as utter a sceptic in regard to human love, and happiness flowing from it, as her father had taught her to be respecting God and the joy of believing. Though seemingly a fair young girl, her father had made her worse than a pagan. She believed in nothing save art and her father's wisdom. He seemed to embody the culture and worldly philosophy that now became, in her judgment, the only things worth living for. To gain his confidence became her great desire. But this had received a severe shock. Mr. Ludolph had lost all faith in everything save money and his own will. Religion was to him a gross superstition, and woman's virtue and truth, poetic fictions.

He watched Christine narrowly, and said just enough to draw out the workings of her mind. He then decided to tell his plan for life, and give her strong additional motives for doing his will. The picture he portrayed of the future dazzled her proud, ambitious spirit, and opened to her fancy what then seemed the only path to happiness. She entered into his projects with honest enthusiasm, and bound herself by the most solemn promises to aid in carrying them out. But in bitterness he remembered one who had promised with seeming enthusiasm before, and he distrusted his daughter, watching her with lynx-eyed vigilance.

But gradually he began to believe in her somewhat, as he saw her looking forward with increasing eagerness to the heaven of German fashionable life, wherein she, rich, admired, allied by marriage to some powerful noble family, should shine a queen in the world of art.

"I have joined her aspirations to mine," he said, in self-gratulation. "I have blended our ambitions and sources of hope and enjoyment, and that is better than all her promises."

When Dennis saw first the face that was so beautiful and yet so marred by pride and selfishness, Christine was about nineteen years old, and yet as mature in some respects as a woman of thirty. She had the perfect self-possession that familiarity with the best society gives. Mr. Ludolph was now too shrewd to seek safety in seclusion. He went with his daughter into the highest circles of the city, and Christine had crowds of admirers and many offers. All this she enjoyed, but took it coolly as her right, with the air of a Greek goddess accepting the incense that rose in her temple. She was too proud and refined to flirt in the ordinary sense of the word, and no one could complain that she gave much encouragement. But this state of things was all the more stimulating, and each one believed, with confidence in his peculiar attractions, that he might succeed where all others had failed. Miss Ludolph's admirers were unaware that they had a rival in some as yet unknown German nobleman. At last it passed into a proverb that the beautiful and brilliant girl who was so free and courtly in society was as cold and unsusceptible as one of her father's statues.

Thus it would seem that when circumstances brought the threads of these two lives near each other, Dennis's and Christine's, the most impassable barriers rose between them, and that the threads could never be woven together, or the lives blended. She was the daughter of the wealthy, aristocratic Mr. Ludolph; he was her father's porter.

Next to the love of art, pride and worldly ambition were her strongest characteristics. She was an unbeliever in God and religion, not from conviction, but from training. She knew very little about either, and what light she had came to her through false mediums. She did not even believe in that which in many young hearts is religion's shadow, love and romance, nor did her father take a more worldly and practical view of life than she.

In marked contrast we have seen the character of Dennis Fleet, drawing its inspiration from such different sources.

Could two human beings be more widely separated,—separated in that which divides more surely than continents and seas?

Could Dennis have seen her warped, deformed moral nature, as clearly as her beautiful face and form, he would have shrunk from her; but while recognizing defects, he shared the common delusion, that the lovely outward form and face must enshrine much that is noble and ready to blossom into good, if the right motives can be presented.

As for Christine, she had one chance for life, one chance for heaven. She was *young*. Her nature had not so hardened and crystallized in evil as to be beyond new and happier influences.

CHAPTER XIII.

VERY COLD.

WHEN Dennis entered Mr. Ludolph's store Christine was absent on a visit to New York. On her return she resumed her old routine. At this time she and her father were occupying a suite of rooms at a fashionable hotel. Her school-days were over, Mr. Ludolph preferring to complete her education himself in accordance with his peculiar views and tastes. She was just passing into her twentieth year, and looked out upon the world from the vantage points of health, beauty, wealth, accomplishments of the highest order, and the best social standing. Assurance of a long and brilliant career possessed her mind, while pride and beauty were like a coronet upon her brow. She was the world's ideal of a queen.

And yet she was not truly happy. There was ever a vague sense of unrest and dissatisfaction at heart. She saw that her father was proud and ambitious in regard to her, but she instinctively felt that he neither loved nor trusted her to any great extent. She seemed to be living in a palace of ice, and at times felt that she was turning into ice herself; but her very humanity and womanhood, deadened and warped though they were, cried out against the *cold* of a life without God or love. In the depths of her soul she felt that something was wrong, but what, she could not understand. It seemed that she had everything that heart could wish, and that she ought to be satisfied.

She had at last concluded that her restlessness was the prompting of a lofty ambition, and that if she chose she could win world-wide celebrity as an artist. This, with the whole force of her strong nature, she had determined to do, and for over two years had worked with an energy akin to enthusiasm. She had resolved that painting should be the solid structure of her success, and music its ornament.

Nor were her dreams altogether chimerical, for she had remarkable talent in her chosen field of effort, and had been taught to use the brush and pencil from childhood. She could imitate with skill and taste, and express with great accuracy the musical thought of the composer; but she could not create new effects, and this had already begun to trouble her. She worked hard and patiently, determined to succeed. So great had been her application that her father saw the need of rest and change, and therefore her visit to New York. She had now returned strengthened, and eager for her former studies, and resumed them with tenfold zest.

The plan of re-arranging the store on artistic principles daily grew in favor with her. It was just the exercise of taste she delighted in, and she hoped some day to indulge it on palace walls that would be her own. Her father's pride caused him to hesitate for some time, but she said: "Why, Chicago is not our home; we shall soon be thousands of miles away. You know how little we really care for the opinions of people here: it is only our own pride and opinion that we need consult. I see nothing lowering or unfeminine in the work. I shall scarcely touch a thing myself, merely direct; for surely among all in your employ there must be one or two pairs of hands not so utterly awkward but that they can follow plain instructions. My taste shall do it all. We are both early risers, and the whole change can be made before the store is opened. Moreover," she added (with an expression indicating that she would have little difficulty in ruling her future German castle, and its lord also), "this is an affair of our own. Those you employ ought to understand by this time that it is neither wise nor safe to talk of our business outside."

After a moment's thought she concluded: "I really think that the proper arrangement of everything in the store as to light, display, and effect, so that people of taste will be pleased when they enter, would add thousands of dollars to your sales; and this rigid system of old Schwartz's, which annoys us both beyond endurance, will be broken up."

Won over by arguments that accorded with his inclinations, Mr. Ludolph gave his daughter permission to carry out the plan in her own way.

She usually accompanied her father to the store in the morning. He, after a brief glance around, would go to his private office and attend to correspondence. She would do whatever her mood prompted. Sometimes she would sit down for a half-hour before one picture; again she would examine most critically a statue or a statuette. Whenever new music was received, she looked it over and carried off such pieces as pleased her fancy.

She evidently was a privileged character, and no one save her father exercised the slightest control over her movements. She treated all the clerks, save old Schwartz, as if they were animated machines; and by a quiet order, as if she had touched a spring, would set them in motion to do her bidding. The young men in the store were of German descent, and rather heavy and undemonstrative. Mr. Schwartz's system of order and repression had pretty thoroughly quenched them. They were educated to the niches they filled, and seemed to have no thought beyond; therefore they were all unruffled at Miss Ludolph's air of absolute sovereignty. Mr. Schwartz was as obsequious as the rest, but, as second to her father in power, was permitted some slight familiarity. In fact this heavy, stolid prime-minister both amused and annoyed her, and she treated him with the caprice of a child toward an elephant, — at times giving him the sugar-plum of a compliment, and oftener pricking him with the pin of some caustic remark. To him she was the perfection of womankind, — her reserved, dispassionate manner, her steady, unwearied prosecution of a purpose, being just the qualities that he most honored; and he worshipped her reverently at a distance, like an old astrologer adoring some particularly bright fixed star. No whisking comets or changing satellites for old Schwartz.

As for Dennis, she treated him as she probably had treated Pat Murphy, and for several days had no occasion to notice him at all. In fact he kept out of her way, choosing at first to observe rather than be observed. She became an artistic study to him, for her every movement was grace itself, except that there was no softness or gentleness in her manner. Her face fascinated him by its beauty, though its expression troubled him, — it was so unlike his mother's, so unlike what he felt a woman's ought to be. But her eager interest in that which was becoming so dear to him — art — would have covered a multitude of sins in his eyes, and with a heart abounding in faith and hope, not yet diminished by hard experience, he believed that the undeveloped angel existed within her. But he remembered her frown when she had first noticed his observation of her. The shrewd Yankee youth saw that her pride would not brook even a curious glance. But while he kept at a most respectful distance he felt that there was no such wide gulf between them as she imagined. By birth and education he was as truly entitled to her acquaintance as the young men who sometimes came into the store with her and whom she met in society. Position and wealth were alone wanting, and in spite of his hard experience and lowly work he felt that there must be some way for him, as for others, to win these.

He longed for the society of ladies, as every right-feeling young man does, and to one of his nature the grace and beauty of woman were peculiarly attractive. If, before she came, the lovely faces of the pictures had filled the place with a sort of witchery, and created about him an atmosphere in which his artist-soul was awakening into life and growth, how much more would it be true of this living vision of beauty that glided in and out every day!

"She does not notice me," he at first said to himself, "any more than do these lovely shadows upon the canvas. But why need I care? I can study both them and her, and thus educate my eye, and I hope my hand, to imitate and perhaps surpass their perfections in time."

But this cool, philosophic mood did not last long. It might answer very well in regard to the pictures on the walls, but there was a magnetism about this living, breathing woman that soon caused him to long for the privilege of being near her and speaking to her of that subject that interested them both so deeply. Though he had never seen any of her paintings to know them, he soon saw that she was no novice in such matters and that she looked at works of art with the eye of a connoisseur. In revery he had many a spirited conversation with her, and he trusted that some day his dreams would become real. He had the romantic hope that if she should discover his taste and strong love of art she might at first bestow upon him a patronizing interest which would gradually grow into respect and acknowledged equality.

CHAPTER XIV.

SHE SPEAKS TO HIM.

AFTER the plan for the re-arrangement of the store had been determined upon, Miss Ludolph began to study its topography. She went regularly through the building, examining closely every part and space, sometimes sketching a few outlines in a little gilt book. Apparently she was seeking by her taste to make the show-rooms pictures in themselves, wherein all the parts should blend harmoniously, and create one beautiful effect. Dennis saw what was coming. The carrying-out of the plan he had heard discussed, and he wished with intense longing that he might be her assistant. But she would as soon have thought of sending for Pat Murphy. She intended to select one of the older clerks to aid her. Still Dennis hoped that by some strange and happy turn of fortune part of this work might fall to him.

Every spare moment of early morning and evening he spent in sketching and studying, but he sadly felt the need of instruction, and of money to buy materials. He was merely groping his way as best he might; and he felt that Miss Ludolph could teach him so much, if she would only condescend to the task! He was willing to be a very humble learner at first. If in some way he could only make known his readiness to pick up the crumbs of knowledge that she might be willing out of kindness to scatter in his path, he might expect something from ordinary good nature.

But a week or two passed without his receiving so much as a glance from those cold blue eyes that rested so critically on all before them; and on an unlucky day in March all hope of help from her vanished.

Under the influence of spring the streets were again becoming muddy, and his duties as boot-black increased daily. He had arranged to perform this menial task in a remote corner of the store, as much out of sight as possible. The duty had become still more disagreeable since the young lady haunted the place, for he feared she would learn to associate him with only the dust-brush and blacking-brush.

Just behind where he usually stood, a good picture had been hung, under Mr. Schwartz's system, simply because it accurately fitted the space. It was in a wretched light, and could never be seen or appreciated there. Miss Ludolph in her investigations and plannings discovered this at a time most unfortunate for poor Dennis. While polishing away one morning, he suddenly became conscious that she was approaching. It seemed that she was looking directly at him, and was about to speak. His heart thumped like a trip-hammer, his cheeks burned, and a blur came over his eyes, for he was diffident in ladies' presence. Therefore he stood before her the picture of confusion, with a big boot poised in one hand, and the polishing-brush in the other. With the instincts of a gentleman, however, he made an awkward bow, feeling, though, that under the circumstances his politeness could only appear ridiculous. And he was right. It was evident from the young lady's face that her keen perception of the ridiculous was thoroughly aroused. But for the sake of her own dignity (she cared not a jot for him), she bit her lip to control her desire to laugh in his face, and said, rather sharply, "Will you stand out of my way?"

She had spoken to him.

He was so mortified and confused that in his effort to obey he partially fell over a bronze sheep, designed to ornament some pastoral scene, and the heel of Mr. Schwartz's heavy boot came down with a thump that made everything ring. There was a titter from some of the clerks. Mr. Ludolph, who was following his daughter, exclaimed, "What's the matter, Fleet? You seem rather unsteady, this morning, for a church member."

For a moment he had the general appearance usually ascribed to the sheep, his unlucky stumbling-block. But by a strong effort he recovered himself. Deigning no reply, he set his teeth, compressed his lips, picked up the boot, and polished away as before, trying to look and feel regardless of all the world. In fact there was as much pride in his face as there had ever been in hers. But, not noticing him, she said to her father: "Here is a specimen. Look where this picture is hung. In boot-black corner I should term it. It would not sell here in a thousand years, for what little light there is would be obscured much of the time by somebody's big boots and the artist in charge. It has evidently been placed here in view of one principle alone, — dimensions; its length and breadth according with the space in the corner. You will see what a change I will bring about in a month or two, after my plans are matured;" and then she strolled to another part of the store. But, before leaving, Miss Ludolph happened to glance at Dennis's face, and was much struck by its expression. Surely Pat Murphy never would or could look like that. For the first time the thought entered her mind that Dennis might be of a different clay and character from Pat. But the next moment his expression of pride and offended dignity, in such close juxtaposition to the big boot he was twirling almost savagely around, again appealed to her sense of the ludicrous, and she turned away with a broad smile. Dennis, looking up, saw the smile and guessed the cause; and when, a moment after, Mr. Schwartz appeared, asking in his loud, blunt way, "My boots ready?" he felt like flinging both at his head, and leaving the store forever. Handing them to him without a word, he hastened upstairs, for he felt that he must be alone.

At first his impulse was strong to rebel, — to assert that by birth and education he was a gentleman, and must be treated as such, or he would go elsewhere. But, as the tumult in his mind calmed, the case became as clear to him as a sum in addition. He had voluntarily taken Pat Murphy's place, and why should he complain at Pat's treatment? He had pledged his word that there should be no trouble from his being above his business, and he resolved to keep his word till Providence gave him better work to do. He bathed his hot face in cool water, breathed a brief prayer for strength and patience and went back to his tasks strong and calm

CHAPTER XV.

PROMOTED.

LATE in the afternoon of the same day (which was Saturday), as Mr. Ludolph was passing out of the store on his way home, he noticed the table that he had arranged artistically some little time before, as a lesson to his clerks. Gradually it had fallen back into its old straight lines and rigid appearance. He seemed greatly annoyed.

"What is the use of re-arranging the store?" he muttered. "They will have it all back again on the general principle of a ramrod in a little while. But we have put our hands to this work, and it shall be carried through, even if I discharge half of these wooden-heads."

Then calling the clerk in charge, he said, "Look here, Mr. Berder, I grouped the articles on this counter for you once, did I not?"

"Yes, sir."

"Let me find them Monday morning just as I arranged them on that occasion."

The young man looked as blank and dismayed as if he had been ordered to swallow them all before Monday morning.

He went to work and jumbled them up as if that was grouping them, and then asked one or two of the other clerks what they thought of it. They shook their heads, and said it looked worse than before.

"I vill study over him all day to-morrow, and den vill

come early Monday and fix him;" and the perplexed youth took himself off.

Dennis felt almost sure that he could arrange it as Mr. Ludolph had done, or with something of the same effect, but did not like to offer his services, not knowing how they would be received, for Mr. Berder had taken a special delight in snubbing him.

After the duties of the store were over, Dennis wrote to his mother a warm, bright, filial letter, portraying the scene of the day in its comic light, making all manner of fun of himself, that he might hide the fact that he had suffered. But he did not hide it, as a return letter proved, for it was full of sympathy and indignation that *her* son should be so treated, but also full of praise for his Christian manliness and patience.

"And now, my son," she wrote, "let me tell you of at least two results of your steady, faithful performance of your present humble duties. The money you send so regularly is more than sufficient for our simple wants. We have every comfort, and I am laying something by for sickness and trouble, for both are pretty sure to come before long in this world. In the second place, you have given me that which is far better than money, — comfort and strength. I feel more and more that we can lean upon you as our earthly support, and not find you a 'broken reed.' While so many sons are breaking their mothers' hearts, you are filling mine with hope and joy. I am no prophetess, my son, but from the sure word of God I predict for you much happiness and prosperity for thus cheering and providing for your widowed mother. Mark my words. God has tried you and not found you wanting. He will soon give you better work to do, — work more in keeping with your character and ability."

This prediction was fulfilled before Dennis received the letter containing it, and it happened on this wise.

Early on Monday morning Mr. Berder appeared and attempted the hopeless task of grouping the articles on his table in accordance with Mr. Ludolph's orders. After an hour's work he exclaimed in despair, "I cannot do him to save my life."

Dennis at a distance, with a half-amused, half-pitying face, had watched Mr. Berder's wonderful combinations, and when Rip Van Winkle was placed between two togated Roman senators, and Ichabod Crane arranged as if making love to a Greek goddess, he came near laughing outright. But when Mr. Berder spoke he approached and said, kindly and respectfully, "Will you let me try to help you?"

"Yes," said Mr. Berder; "you cannot make dings vorse."

Acting upon this ungracious permission, Dennis folded his arms and studied the table for five minutes.

"Come," said Mr. Berder, "standing dere and looking so vise as an owl von't help matters. Mr. Ludolph vill be here soon."

"I am not losing time," said Dennis; and a moment proved he was not, for, having formed a general plan of arrangement, he went rapidly to work, and in a quarter of an hour could challenge Mr. Ludolph or any other critic to find serious fault.

"There! I could do better if I had more time, but I must go to my sweeping and dusting, or Mr. Schwartz will be down on me, and he is pretty heavy, you know. I never saw such a man, — he can see a grain of dust half across the store."

Mr. Berder had looked at Dennis's quick, skilful motions in blank amazement, and then broke out into unwonted panegyric for him: "I say, Vlete, dot's capital! Where you learn him?" Then in a paroxysm of generosity he added, "Dere's a quarter for you."

"No, I thank you," said Dennis; "I did not do it for money."

"Vat did der fool do it for, den, I'd like to know?" muttered Mr. Berder, the philosophy of his life resuming its former control. "Saved a quarter, anyhow, and, vat's more, know vere to go next dime der old man comes down on me."

A little after nine Mr. and Miss Ludolph came in, and paused at the table. Dennis, unnoticed, stood behind Benjamin Franklin and Joan of Arc, placed lovingly together on another counter, face to face, as if in mutual admiration, and from his hiding-place watched the scene before him with intense anxiety. One thought only filled his mind, — Would they approve or condemn his taste? for he had arranged the table on a plan of his own. His heart gave a glad bound when Mr. Ludolph said: "Why, Berder, this is excellent. To be sure you have taken your own method, and followed your own taste, but I find no fault with that, when you produce an effect like this."

"I declare, father," chimed in Miss Ludolph, "this table pleases me greatly. It is a little oasis in this great desert of a store. Mr. Berder, I compliment you on your taste. You shall help me re-arrange, artistically, everything in the building."

Dennis, in his agitation, came near precipitating Benjamin Franklin into the arms of Joan of Arc, a position scarcely in keeping with either character.

"Yes, Christine, that is true," continued Mr. Ludolph. "Mr. Berder will be just the one to help you, and I am glad you have found one competent. By all the furies! just compare this table with the one next to it, where the Past, Present, and Future have not the slightest regard for each other, and satyrs and angels, philosophers and bandits, are mixed up about as closely as in real life. Here, Berder, try your hand at this counter also; and you, young men, gather round and see the difference when *art*, instead of mathematics, rules the world of art. If this thing goes on, we shall have the golden age back again in the store."

Mr. Berder, though somewhat confused, had received all his compliments with bows and smiles. But Dennis, after his thrill of joy at having pleased Mr. and Miss Ludolph's fastidious taste, felt himself reddening with honest indignation that Mr. Berder should carry off all his laurels before his face. But he resolved to say nothing, knowing that time would right him. When Mr. Ludolph asked the young men to step forward, he came with the others.

"That's right, Fleet," said Mr. Ludolph, again, "you can get a useful hint, too, like enough."

"Nonsense, father," said Miss Ludolph, in a tone not so low but that Dennis heard it; "why spoil a good sweeper and duster by putting uppish notions in his head? He keeps the store cleaner than any man you ever had, and I don't soil my dresses as I used to."

Dennis's color heightened a little, and his lips closed more firmly, but he gave no other sign that he heard this limitation of his hope and ambition. But it cut him rather deep. The best he could ever do, then, in her view, was to keep her dresses from being soiled.

In the mean time Mr. Berder had shown great embarrassment at Mr. Ludolph's unexpected request. After a few moments of awkward hesitation he stammered out that he could do it better alone. The suspicion of keen Mr. Ludolph was at once aroused and he persisted: "Oh, come, Mr. Berder, we don't expect you to do your best in a moment, but a person of your taste can certainly make a great change for the better in the table before you."

In sheer desperation the entrapped youth attempted the task, but he had not bungled five minutes before Mr. Ludolph said, sharply, "Mr. Berder, you did not arrange this table."

"Vell," whined Mr. Berder, "I didn't say dot I did."

"You caused me to believe that you did," said Mr. Ludolph, his brow growing dark. "Now, one question, and I wish the truth: Who did arrange this table?"

"Vleet, dere, helped me," gasped Mr. Berder.

"*Helped* you? Mr. Fleet, step forward, if you please, for I intend to have the truth of this matter. How much help did Mr. Berder give you in arranging this table?"

"None, sir," said Dennis, looking straight into Mr. Ludolph's eyes.

All looked with great surprise at Dennis, especially Miss Ludolph, who regarded him most curiously. "How different he appears from Pat Murphy!" she again thought.

"Some one has told a lie, now," said Mr. Ludolph, sternly. "Mr. Fleet, I shall put you to the same test that Berder failed in. Arrange that counter sufficiently well to prove that it was your hands that arranged this."

Dennis stepped forward promptly, but with a pale face and compressed lips. Feeling that both honor and success were at stake, he grouped and combined everything as before, as far as the articles would permit, having no time to originate a new plan. As he worked, the clerks gazed in open astonishment, Mr. Ludolph looked significantly at his daughter, while she watched him with something of the same wonder which we have when one of the lower animals shows human sagacity and skill.

Mr. Ludolph was Napoleonic in other respects than his ambition and selfishness. He was shrewd enough to "promote on the field for meritorious services." Therefore, as Dennis's task approached completion, he said: "That will do, Mr. Fleet, you can finish the work at your leisure. Mr. Berder, you are discharged from this day for deception. I would have borne with your incompetency if you had been truthful. But I never trust any one who has deceived me once," he said, so sternly that even Christine's cheek paled. "Mr. Schwartz will settle with you, and let me never see or hear from you again. Mr. Fleet, I promote you to Mr. Berder's counter and pay."

Thus this man of the world, without a thought of pity, mercy, or kindly feeling in either case, gave one of his clerks a new impetus toward the devil, and another an important lift toward better things, and then went his way, congratulating himself that all things had worked together for his good, that morning, though where he would find another Dennis Fleet to fill Pat's place, again vacant, he did not know.

But Miss Ludolph looked at Dennis somewhat kindly, and with a little honest admiration in her face. He was very different from what she had as a matter of course supposed him to be, and had just done in a quiet, manly way a thing most pleasing to her, so she said with a smile that seemed perfectly heavenly to him, "*You* are above blacking boots, sir."

CHAPTER XVI.

JUST IN TIME.

AT the close of the day on which Dennis received his promotion, and his horizon was widened so unexpectedly, Mr. Ludolph, in passing out, noticed him engaged as usual on one of Pat Murphy's old tasks. He stopped and spoke kindly, "Well, Fleet, where am I going to find a man to fill your place made vacant to-day?"

"Would you be willing to listen to a suggestion from me?"

"Certainly."

"If a young boy was employed to black boots, run errands, and attend to minor matters, I think that by industry I might for a while fill both positions. In a short time the furnace will require no further attention. I am a very early riser, and think that by a little good management I can keep the store in order and still be on hand to attend to my counter when customers are about."

Mr. Ludolph was much pleased with the proposition, and said, promptly, "You may try it, Fleet, and I will pay you accordingly. Do you know of a boy who will answer?"

"I think I do, sir. There is a German lad in my mission class who has interested me very much. His father is really a superior artist, but is throwing himself away with drink, and his mother is engaged in an almost hopeless effort to support the family. They have seen much better days, and their life seems very hard in contrast with the past."

"Can we trust such a boy? Their very necessities may lead to theft."

"They are not of the thieving sort, sir. I am satisfied that they would all starve rather than touch a penny that did not belong to them."

"Very well, then, let him come and see me; but I will hold you responsible for him."

Mr. Ludolph, being in a good humor, was disposed to banter Dennis, so he added: "Do you find time to be a missionary, also? Are you not in danger of becoming a 'Jack at all trades'?"

"I am not entitled to the first character, and hope to shun the latter. I merely teach a dozen boys in a mission school on Sundays."

"When you ought to be taking a good long nap, or a row on the lake for fresh air and recreation."

"I should be dishonest if I spent my Sabbaths in that way."

"How so?"

"I should give the lie to my profession and belief. I must drop the name of Christian when I live for myself."

"And if you should drop it, do you think you would be much the loser?"

"Yes, sir," said Dennis, with quiet emphasis.

"You are expecting great reward, in some sort of Paradise, for your mission work, etc.?"

"Nothing done for God is forgotten or unrewarded."

"Believing that, it seems to me that you are looking after self-interest as much as the rest of us," said his employer, with a shrewd smile.

Looking straight into Mr. Ludolph's eyes, Dennis said, earnestly: "Without boasting, I think that I can say that I try to serve you faithfully. If you could see my heart, I am sure you would find that gratitude for your kindness is a part of my motive, as well as my wages. In the same manner, while I do not lose sight of the rich rewards God promises and daily gives for the little I can do for Him, I am certain that I can do much out of simple gratitude and love, and ask no reward."

"Ignorance is certainly bliss in your case, young man. Stick to your harmless superstition as long as you can."

And he walked away, muttering: "Delusion, delusion! I have not said a word or done a thing for him in which I had not in view my interests only, and yet the poor young fool sees in the main disinterested kindness. Little trouble have the wily priests in imposing on such victims, and so they get their hard-earned wages and set them propagating the delusion in mission schools, when mind and body need change and rest. Suppose there is a Supreme Being in the universe, what a monstrous absurdity to imagine that He would trouble Himself to reward this Yankee youth for teaching a dozen ragamuffins in a tenement-house mission school!"

Thus Mr. Ludolph's soliloquy proved that his own pride and selfishness had destroyed the faculty by which he could see God. The blind are not more oblivious to color than he was to those divine qualities which are designed to win and enchain the heart. A man may sadly mutilate his own soul.

At a dainty dinner-table Mr. Ludolph and his daughter discussed the events of the day.

"I am glad," said the latter, "that he is willing to fill Pat's place, for he keeps everything so clean. A dusty, slovenly store is my abomination. Then it shows that he has no silly, uppish notions so common to these Americans." (Though born here, Miss Ludolph never thought herself other than a German lady of rank.) "But I do not wish to see him blacking boots again. Yet he is an odd genius,

How comical he looked bowing to me with one of Mr. Schwartz's big boots describing a graceful curve on a level with his head. Let old Schwartz black his own boots. He ought to as a punishment for carrying around so much leather. This Fleet must have seen better days. He is like all Yankees, however, sharp after the dollar, though he seems more willing to work for it than most of them."

"I'll wager you a pair of gloves," said her father, "that they get a good percentage of it down at the mission school. He is just the subject for a cunning priest, because he sincerely believes in their foolery. He belongs to a tribe now nearly extinct, I imagine, — the martyrs, who in old-fashioned times died for all sorts of delusions."

"How time mellows and changes everything! There is something heroic and worthy of art in the ancient martyrdoms, while nothing is more repulsive than modern fanaticism. It is a shame, though, that this young man, with mother and sisters to support, should be robbed of his hard earnings as was Pat Murphy by his priest, and I will try to open his eyes some day."

"I predict for you no success."

"Why so? — he seems intelligent."

"I have not studied character all my life in vain. He would regard you, my fair daughter, as the devil in the form of an angel of light tempting him."

"He had better not be so plain-spoken as yourself."

"Oh, no need of Fleet's speaking; his face is like the page of an open book."

"Indeed! a face like a sign-board is a most unfortunate one, I should think."

"Most fortunate for us. I wish I could read every one as I can Fleet."

"You trust no one, I believe, father."

"I believe what I see and know."

"I wish I had your power of seeing and knowing. But how did he get his artistic knowledge and taste?"

"That I have not inquired into fully, as yet. I think he has an unusual native aptness for these things, and gains hints and instruction where others would see nothing. And, as you say, in the better days past he may have had some advantages."

"Well," said she, caressing the greyhound beside her, "if Wolf here should go to the piano and execute an opera, I should not have been more astonished than I was this morning."

And then their conversation glided off on other topics.

After dessert, Mr. Ludolph lighted a cigar and sat down to the evening paper, while his daughter evoked from the piano true after-dinner music, — light, brilliant, mirth-inspiring. Then both adjourned to their private billiard-room.

The scene of our story now changes from Mr. Ludolph's luxurious apartments in one of the most fashionable hotels in the city to a forlorn attic in De Koven Street. It is the scene of a struggle as desperate, as heroic, against as tremendous odds, as was ever carried on in the days of the Crusades. But as the foremost figure in this long, weary conflict was not an armed and panoplied knight, but merely a poor German woman, only God and the angels took much interest in it. Still upon this evening she was almost vanquished. She seemed to have but one vantage-point left on earth. For a wonder, her husband was comparatively sober, and sat brooding with his head in his hands over the stove where a fire was slowly dying out. The last coal they had was fast turning to ashes. From a cradle came a low, wailing cry. It was that of hunger. On an old chest in a dusky corner sat a boy about thirteen. Though all else was in shadow, his large eyes shone with unnatural brightness, and followed his mother's feeble efforts at the wash-tub with that expression of premature sadness so pathetic in childhood. Under a rickety deal table three other and smaller children were devouring some crusts of bread in a ravenous way, like half-famished young animals. In a few moments they came out and clamored for more, addressing — not their father; no intuitive turning to him for support — but the poor, over-tasked mother. The boy came out of his corner and tried to draw them off and interest them in something else, but they were like a pack of hungry little wolves. The boy's face was almost as sharp and famine-pinched as his mother's, but he seemed to have lost all thought of himself in his sorrowful regard for her. As the younger children clamored and dragged upon her, the point of endurance was passed, and the poor woman gave way. With a despairing cry she sunk upon a chair and covered her face with her apron.

"O mine Gott, O mine Gott," she cried, "I can do not von more stroke if ve all die."

In a moment her son had his arms around her neck, and said: "O moder, don't cry, don't cry. Mr. Fleet said God would surely help us in time of trouble if we would only ask Him."

"I've ask Him, and ask Him, but der help don't come. I can do no more;" and a tempest of despairing sobs shook her gaunt frame.

The boy seemed to have got past tears, and just fixed his large eyes, full of reproach and sorrow, on his father.

The man rose and turned his bloodshot eyes slowly around the room. The whole scene, with its meaning, seemed to dawn upon him. His mind was not so clouded by the fumes of liquor but that he could comprehend the supreme misery of the situation. He heard his children crying, — fairly howling for bread. He saw the wife he had sworn to love and honor, where she had fallen in her unequal conflict, brave, but overpowered. He remembered the wealthy burgher's blooming, courted daughter, whom he had lured away to marry him, a poor artist. He remembered how, in spite of her father's commands and her mother's tears, she had left home and luxury to follow him throughout the world because of her faith in him and love for him, — how under her inspiration he had risen to great promise as an artist, till fame and fortune became almost a certainty, and then, under the debasing influence of his terrible appetite, he had dragged her down and down, till now he saw her — prematurely old, broken in health, broken in heart — fall helplessly before the hard drudgery that she no longer had strength to perform. With a sickening horror he remembered that he had taken even the pittance she had wrung from that wash-tub, to feed, not his children, but his accursed appetite for drink. Even his purple, bloated face grew livid as all the past rushed upon him, and despair laid an icy hand upon his heart.

A desperate purpose formed itself within his mind.

Turning to the wall where hung a noble picture, a lovely landscape, whose rich coloring, warm sunlight, and rural peace formed a sharp, strange contrast with the meagre, famine-stricken apartment, he was about to take it down from its fastening when his hand was arrested by a word, — "Father!"

He turned, and saw his son looking at him with his great eyes full of horror and alarm, as if he were committing a murder.

"I tell you I must, and I vill," said he, savagely.

His wife looked up, sprung to his side, and with her hands upon his arm, said, "No, Berthold, you must not, you shall not sell dot picture."

He silently pointed to his children crying for bread.

"Take der dress off my back to sell, but not dot picture.

Ve may as vell die before him goes, for ve certainly vill after. Dot is de only ding left of der happy past. Dot, in Gott's hands, is my only hope for der future. Dot picture dells you vat you vas, vat you might be still if you vould only let drink alone. Many's der veary day, many's der long night, I've prayed dot dot picture vould vin you back to your former self, ven tears and sufferings vere in vain. Leave him, and some day he vill tell you so plain vat you are, and vot you can be, dot you break der horrid spell dot chains you, and your artist-soul come again. Leave him, our only hope, and sole bar against despair and death. I vill go and beg a dousand times before dot picture's sold; for if he goes, your artist-soul no more come back, and you're lost, and ve all are lost."

The man hesitated. His good angel was pleading with him, but in vain.

Stamping his foot with rage and despair, he shouted, hoarsely, "It is too late; I am lost now."

And he tore the picture from its fastening. His wife sunk back against the wall with a groan as if her very soul were departing.

But before his rash steps could leave the desolation he had made, he was confronted by the tall form of Dennis Fleet.

The man stared at him for a moment as if he had been an apparition, and then said, in a hard tone, "Let me pass!"

Dennis had knocked for some time, but such was the excitement within no one had regarded the sound. He had, therefore, heard the wife's appeal and its answer, and from what he knew of the family from his mission scholar, the boy Ernst, comprehended the situation in the main. When, therefore, matters reached the crisis, he opened the door and met the infatuated man as he was about to throw away the last relic of his former self and happier life. With great fact he appeared as if he knew nothing, and quietly taking a chair he sat down with his back against the door, thus barring egress. In a pleasant, affable tone, he said: "Mr. Bruder, I came to see you on a little business to-night. As I was in something of a hurry, and no one appeared to hear my knock, I took the liberty of coming in."

The hungry little ones looked at him with their round eyes of childish curiosity, and for a time ceased their clamors. The wife sunk into a chair and bowed her head in her hands with the indifference of despair. Hope had gone. A gleam of joy lighted up Ernst's pale face at the sight of his beloved teacher, and he stepped over to his mother and commenced whispering in her ear, but she heeded him not. The man's face wore a sullen, dangerous, yet irresolute expression. It was evident that he half believed that Dennis was knowingly trying to thwart him, and such was his mad frenzy that he was ready for any d deed.

CHAPTER XVII.

RESCUED.

IN a tone of suppressed excitement, which he tried in vain to render steady, Mr. Bruder said: "You haf der advantage of me, sir. I know not your name. Vat is more, I am not fit for bissiness dis night. Indeed, I haf important bissiness elsewhere. You must excuse me," he added, sternly, advancing toward the door with the picture.

"Pardon me, Mr. Bruder," said Dennis, politely. "I throw myself entirely on your courtesy, and must ask as a very great favor that you will not take away that picture till I see it, for that, in part, is what I came for. I am in the picture trade myself, and think I am a tolerably fair judge of paintings. I heard accidentally you had a fine one, and from the glimpse I catch of it, I think I have not been misinformed. If it is for sale, perhaps I can do as well by you as any one else. I am employed in Mr. Ludolph's great store, the 'Art Building.' You probably know all about the place."

"Yes, I know him," said the man, calming down somewhat.

"And now, sir," said Dennis, with a gentle, winning courtesy impossible to resist, "will you do me the favor of showing me your picture?"

He treated poor Bruder as a gentleman, and he, having really been one, was naturally inclined to return like courtesy. Therefore he said, "Oh, certainly, since you vish to see him. I suppose I might as vell sell him to you as any von else."

Mr. Bruder was a man of violent impulses, and his mad excitement was fast leaving him under Dennis's cool, business-like manner. To gain time was now the great desideratum.

The picture having been replaced upon the wall, Mr. Bruder held the lamp so as to throw upon it as good a light as possible.

Dennis folded his arms calmly and commenced its study. He had meant to act a part, — to pretend deep interest and desire for long critical study, — that he might secure more time, but in a few moments he became honestly absorbed in the beautiful and exquisitely finished landscape.

The poor man watched him keenly. Old associations and feelings, seemingly long dead, awoke. As he saw Dennis manifest every mark of true and growing appreciation, he perceived that his picture was being studied by a discriminating person. Then his artist-nature began to quicken into life again. His eyes glowed, and glanced rapidly from Dennis to the painting, back and forth, following up the judgment on each and every part which he saw written in the young man's face. As he watched, something like hope and exultation began to light up his sullen, heavy features; thought and feeling began to spiritualize and ennoble what but a little before had been so coarse and repulsive.

Ernst was looking at Dennis in rapt awe, as at a messenger from heaven.

The poor wife, who had listened in a dull apathy to the conversation, raised her head in sudden and intelligent interest when the picture was replaced upon the wall. It seemed that her every hope was bound up in that. As she saw Dennis and her husband standing before it, — as she saw the face of the latter begin to assume something of its former look, — her whole soul came into her great blue eyes, and she watched as if more than life were at stake.

If that meagre apartment, with its inmates, their contrasts of character, their expressive faces, could have then been portrayed, it would have made a picture with power to move the coldest heart.

At last Dennis drew a long breath, turned and gave his hand to the man, saying with hearty emphasis, "Mr. Bruder, you are an artist."

The poor man lifted his face to heaven with the same expression of joy and gratitude that had rested on it long, long years ago, when his first real work of merit had received similar praise.

His wife saw and remembered it, and, with an ecstatic cry that thrilled Dennis's soul, exclaimed, "Ah! mine Gott be praised! mine Gott be praised! his artist-soul come back!" and she threw herself on her husband's neck, and clung to him with hysteric energy. The man melted completely, and bowed his head upon his wife's shoulder, while his whole frame shook with sobs.

"I will be back in half an hour," said Dennis, hastily, brushing tears from his own eyes. "Come with me, Ernst."

At the foot of the stairs Dennis said: "Take this money, Ernst, and buy bread, butter, tea, milk, and coal, also a nice large steak, for I am going to take supper with you to-night. I will stay here and watch, for your father must not be permitted to go out."

"Oh, Gott bless you! Gott bless you!" said the boy, and he hurried away to do his errand.

Dennis walked up and down before the door on guard. Ernst soon returned, and carried the welcome food upstairs. After a little time he stole down again and said: "Father's quiet and queer like. Mother has given the children a good supper and put them to bed. Better come now."

"In a few moments more; you go back and sit down quietly and say nothing."

After a little Dennis went up and knocked at the door. Mrs. Bruder opened it, and held out her hand. Her quivering lips refused to speak, but her eyes filled with grateful tears. The children were tucked away in bed. Ernst crouched by the fire, eating some bread and butter, for he was cold and half-famished. Mr. Bruder sat in the dusky corner with his head in his hands, the picture of dejection. But, as Dennis entered, he rose and came forward. He tried to speak, but for a moment could not. At last he said, hoarsely: "Mr. Vleet, you haf done me and mine a great kindness. No matter vat the result is, I dank you as I never danked any living being. I believe Gott sent you, but I fear too late. You see before you a miserable wreck. For months and years I haf been a brute, a devil. Dot picture dere show you vat I vas, vat I might haf been. You see vat I am," he added, with an expression of intense loathing. "I see him all to-night as if written in letters of fire, and if dere is a vorse hell dan der von I feel vithin my soul, Gott only knows how I am to endure him."

"Mr. Bruder, you say I have done you a favor."

"Gott knows you haf."

"I want you to do me one in return. I want you to let me be your friend," said Dennis, holding out his hand.

The man trembled, hesitated; at last he said, brokenly, "I am not fit — to touch — your hand."

"Mr. Bruder," said Dennis, gently, "I hope that I am a Christian."

"Still more, den, I am unfit efer to be in your presence."

"What! am I greater than my Master? Did not Christ take the hand of every poor, struggling man on earth that would let Him? Come, Mr. Bruder, if you have any real gratitude for the little I have done to show my interest in you and yours, grant me my request."

"Do you really mean him?" he gasped. "Do you really vant to be drunken old Berthold Bruder's friend?"

"God is my witness, I do," said Dennis, still holding out his hand.

The poor fellow drew a few short, heavy breaths, and then grasped Dennis's hand, and clung to it with the force of a drowning man.

"Oh!" said he, after a few moments of deep emotion, "I feel dot I haf a plank under me now."

"God grant that you may soon feel that you are on the Rock Christ Jesus," said Dennis, solemnly.

Fearing the reaction of too great and prolonged emotion, Dennis now did everything in his power to calm and quiet his new-found friends. He told them that he boarded at a restaurant, and he asked if he might take supper with them.

"Him is yours already," said Mr. Bruder.

"No, it isn't," said Dennis, — "not after I have given it to you. But I want to talk to you about several matters, for I think you can be of great service to me;" and he told them of his experience during the day; that he had been promoted, and that he wanted Ernst to come and aid him in his duties. Then he touched on the matter nearest his heart, — his own wish to be an artist, his need of instruction, — and told how by his increase of pay he had now the means of taking lessons, while still able to support his mother and sisters.

"And now, Mr. Bruder, I feel that I have been very fortunate in making your acquaintance. You have the touch and tone that I should be overjoyed to acquire. Will you give me lessons?"

"Yes, morning, noon, and night, vithout von shent of pay."

"That will not do. I'll not take one on those terms."

"I vill do vatever you vant me to," said the man, simply. "I vish I could be led and vatched over as a little child."

Dennis saw his pathetic self-distrust, and it touched him deeply.

"As your friend," he said, with emphasis, "I will not advise you to do anything that I would not do myself."

So they arranged that Ernst should go to the store in the morning, and that Dennis should come three nights in the week for lessons.

All made a hearty supper save Mr. Bruder. He had reached that desperate stage when his diseased stomach craved drink only. But a strong cup of tea, and some bread that he washed down with it, heartened him a little, and it was evident that he felt better. The light of a faint hope was dawning in his face.

Dennis knew something of the physical as well as moral struggle before the poor man, and knew that after all it was exceedingly problematical whether he could be saved. Before he went away he told Mrs. Bruder to make her husband some very strong coffee in the morning, and to let him drink it through the day. As for Bruder, he had resolved to die rather than touch another drop of liquor.

But how many poor victims of appetite have been haunted to the grave by such resolves, — shattered and gone almost as soon as made!

After a long, earnest talk, in which much of the past was revealed on both sides, Dennis drew a small Testament from his pocket and said: "Mr. Bruder, I wish to direct your thoughts to a better Friend than I am or can be. Will you let me read you something about Him?"

"Yes, and dank you. But choose someding strong, — suited to me."

Dennis read something strong, — the story of the Demoniac of Gadara, and left him "sitting at the feet of Jesus, clothed and in his right mind."

"Mr. Bruder, permit me as your *friend* to say that I think

that is the only safe place for you. Your better self, your true manhood, has been overpowered by the demon of intemperance. I do not undervalue human will and purpose, but I think you need a divine, all-powerful Deliverer."

"I know you are right," said Mr. Bruder. "I haf resolved ofer and ofer again, only to do vorse, and sink deeper at der next temptation, till at last I gave up trying. Unless I am sustained by some strength greater dan mine, I haf no hope. I feel dot your human sympathy and kindness vill be a great help to me, and somehow I dake him as an earnest dot Gott vill be kind to me too."

"O Mr. Fleet!" he continued, as Dennis rose to go, "how much I owe to you! I vas in hell on earth ven you came. I vould haf been in hell beneath before morning. I proposed, from the proceeds of dot picture, to indulge in von more delirium, and den seek to quench all in der vaters of der lake."

Dennis shuddered, but said: "And I believe that God purposes that you should have a good life here, and a happy life in heaven. Co-work with Him."

"If He vill help me, I'll try," said the man, humbly. "Good-night, and Gott bless you;" and he almost crushed Dennis's hand.

As the young man turned to Mrs. Bruder, he was much struck by her appearance: she was very pale, and a wonderful light shone from her eyes. She took his hand in both of hers, and looked at him for a moment with an expression he could never forget, and then slowly pointed heavenward without a word.

Dennis hastened away, much overcome by his own feelings. But the silent, deserted streets seemed luminous, such was the joy of his heart.

CHAPTER XVIII.

MISS LUDOLPH MAKES A DISCOVERY.

SEVERAL hours were measured off by the clock of a neighboring steeple before Dennis's excited mind was sufficiently calm to permit sleep, and even then he often started up from some fantastic dream in which the Bruders and Mr. and Miss Ludolph acted strange parts. At last he seemed to hear exquisite music. As the song rose and fell, it thrilled him with delight. Suddenly it appeared to break into a thousand pieces, and fall scattering on the ground, like a broken string of pearls, and this musical crash, as it were, awoke him. The sun was shining brightly into the room, and all the air seemed vibrating with sweet sounds. He started up and realized that he had greatly overslept. Much vexed, he began to dress in haste, when he was startled by a brilliant prelude on the piano, and a voice of wonderful power and sweetness struck into an air that he had never heard before. Soon the whole building was resonant with music, and Dennis stood spell-bound till the strange, rich sounds died away, as before, in a few instrumental notes that had seemed in his dream like the song breaking into glittering fragments.

"It must be Miss Ludolph," thought Dennis. "And can she sing like that? What an angel true faith would make of her! Oh, how could I oversleep so!" And he dressed in breathless haste. In going down to the second floor, he found a piano open and new music upon it, which Miss

Ludolph had evidently been trying; but she was not there. Yet a peculiar delicate perfume which the young lady always used pervaded the place, even as her song had seemed to pulsate through the air after it had ceased. She could not be far off. Stepping to a picture show-room over the front door, Dennis found her sitting quietly before a large painting, sketching one of the figures in it.

"I learned from my father that you were a very early riser," she said, looking up for a moment, and then resuming her work. "I fear there is some mistake about it. If we are ever to get through re-arranging the store you will have to curtail your morning naps."

"I most sincerely beg your pardon. I never overslept so before. But I was out late last night, and passed through a most painful scene, that so disturbed me that I could not sleep till nearly morning, and I find to my great vexation that I have overslept. I promise you it shall not happen again."

"I am not sure of that, if you are out late in Chicago, and passing through painful scenes. I should say that this city was a peculiarly bad place for a young man to be out late in."

"It was an experience wholly unexpected to me, and I hope it may never occur again. It was a scene of trouble that I had no hand in making, but which even humanity would not permit me to leave at once."

"Not a scene of measles or small-pox, I hope. I am told that your mission people are indulging in these things most of the time. You have not been exposed to any contagious disease?"

"I assure you I have not."

"Very well; be ready to assist me to-morrow morning, for we have no slight task before us, and I wish to complete it as soon as possible. I shall be here at half-past six, and do not promise to sing you awake every morning. Were you not a little startled to hear such unwonted sounds echoing through the prosaic old store?"

"I was indeed. At first I could not believe that it was a human voice."

"That is rather an equivocal compliment."

"I did not mean to speak in compliment at all, but to say in all sincerity that I have seldom heard such heavenly music."

"Perhaps you have never heard very much of any kind, or else your imagination overshadows your other faculties. In fact I think it does, for did you not at first regard me as a painted lady who had stepped from the canvas to the floor?"

"I confess that I was greatly confused and startled."

"In what respect did you see such a close resemblance?"

Dennis hesitated.

"Are you not able to tell?" asked she.

"Yes," said Dennis, with heightened color, "but I do not like to say."

"But I wish you to say," said she, with a slightly imperious tone.

"Well, then, since you wish me to speak frankly, it was your expression. As you stood by the picture you unconsciously assumed the look and manner of the painted girl. And all the evening and morning I had been troubling over the picture and wondering how an artist could paint so lovely a face, and make it express only scorn and pride. It seemed to me that such a face ought to have been put to nobler uses."

Miss Ludolph bit her lip and looked a little annoyed, but turning to Dennis she said, with some curiosity: "You are not a bit like the man who preceded you. How did you come to take his place?"

"I am poor, and will gratefully do any honest work rather than beg or starve."

"I wish all the poor were of the same mind, but, from the way they drag on us who have something to give, I think the rule is usually the other way. Very well, that will answer; since you have asked papa to let you continue to do Pat's duties, you had better be about them, though it is not so late as you think;" and she turned to her sketching in such a way as to quietly dismiss him.

She evidently regarded him with some interest and curiosity, as a unique specimen of the genus homo, and, looking upon him as a humble dependant, was inclined to speak to him freely and draw him out for her amusement.

On going downstairs he saw that Mr. Ludolph was writing in his office. He was an early riser, and sometimes, entering the side door by a pass key before the store was opened, would secure an extra hour for business. He shook his head at Dennis, but said nothing.

By movements wonderfully quick and dexterous Dennis went through his wonted tasks, and at eight o'clock, the usual hour, the store was ready for opening.

Mr. Ludolph often caught glimpses of him as he darted to and fro, his cheeks glowing, and every act suggesting superabundant life.

He sighed and said: "After all, that young fellow is to be envied. He is getting more out of existence than most of us. He enjoys everything, and does even hard work with a zest that makes it play. There will be no keeping him down, for he seems possessed by the concentrated vim of this driving Yankee nation. Then he has a world of delusions besides that seem grand realities. Well, it is a sad thing to grow old and wise."

Indeed it is, in Mr. Ludolph's style.

When Dennis opened the front door, there was Ernst

cowering in the March winds, and fairly trembling in the flutter of his hopes and fears. Dennis gave him a hearty grasp of the hand and drew him in, saying, "Don't be afraid; I'll take care of you."

The boy's heart clung to him as the vine tendril clasps the oak, and, upheld by Dennis's strength, he entered what was to him wonder-land indeed.

Mr. Ludolph looked him over as he and his daughter passed out on their return to breakfast, and said, "He will answer if he is strong enough."

He saw nothing in that child's face to fear.

Dennis assured him with a significant glance, which Mr. Ludolph understood as referring to better fare, that "he would grow strong fast now."

Miss Ludolph was at once interested in the boy's pale face and large, spiritual eyes; and she resolved to sketch them before good living had destroyed the artistic effect.

Under kindly instruction, the boy took readily to his duties, and promised soon to become very helpful. At noon Dennis took him out to lunch, and the poor, half-starved lad feasted as he had not for many a long day.

The afternoon mail brought Dennis his mother's letter, and he wondered that her prediction should be fulfilled even before it reached him, and thus again his faith was strengthened. He smiled and said to himself, "Mother lives so near the heavenly land that she seems to get the news thence before any one else."

During the day a lady who was talking to Mr. Ludolph turned and said to Dennis: "How prettily you have arranged this table! Let me see; I think I will take that little group of bronzes. They make a very nice effect together."

Dennis, with his heart swelling that he had arrived at the dignity of salesman, with much politeness, which evidently pleased the lady, assured her that they would be sent promptly to her address.

Mr. Ludolph looked on as if all was a matter of course while she was present, but afterward said: "You are on the right track, Fleet. You now see the practical result of a little thought and grace in arrangement. In matters of art, people will pay almost as much for these as for the things themselves. The lady would not have bought those bronzes under Berder's system. When things are grouped rightly, people see just what they want, and buy the *effect* as well as the articles;" and with this judicious praise Mr. Ludolph passed on, better pleased with himself even than with Dennis.

But, as old Bill Cronk had intimated, such a peck of oats was almost too much for Dennis, and he felt that he was in danger of becoming too highly elated.

After closing the store, he wrote a brief but graphic letter to his mother, describing his promotion, and expressing much sympathy for poor Berder. Regarding himself as on the crest of prosperity's wave, he felt a strong commiseration for every degree and condition of troubled humanity, and even could sigh over unlucky Berder's deserved tribulations.

About eight o'clock he started to see his new friends in De Koven Street, and take his lesson in drawing. They welcomed him warmly, for they evidently looked upon him as the one who might save them from the ingulfing waves of misfortune and evil.

The children were very different from the clamorous little wolves of the night before. No longer hungry, they were happy in the corner, with some rude playthings, talking and cooing together like a flock of young birds. Ernst was washing the tea-things, while his mother cared for the baby, recalling to Dennis, with a rush of tender memories, his mother and his boyhood tasks. Mr. Bruder still sat in the dusky corner. The day had been a hard one for him.

Having nothing to do in the present, he had lived the miserable past over and over again. At times his strength almost gave way, but his wife would say, "Be patient! your friend Mr. Fleet will be in soon."

From a few hints of what had passed, Dennis saw the trouble at once. Mr. Bruder must have occupation. After a few kindly generalities, they two got together, as congenial spirits, before the rescued picture; and soon both were absorbed in the mysteries of the divine art.

As the wife looked at the kindling, interested face of her husband, she murmured to herself over and over again, like the sweet refrain of a song, "His artist-soul haf come back; it truly haf."

The lesson that night could be no more than a talk on general principles and rules. But Mr. Bruder soon found that he had an apt scholar, and Dennis's enthusiasm kindled his own flagging zeal, and the artist-soul awakening within him, as his wife believed, longed to express itself as of old in glowing colors.

Moreover, his ambition was renewed in this promising pupil. Naturally generous, and understanding his noble profession, he felt his poor benumbed heart stir and glow at the thought of aiding this eager aspirant to become what he had hoped to be. He might live again in the richer and better-guided genius of his scholar.

"I will send you by Ernst in the morning some sketching paper, materials, and canvas, and you can prepare some studies for me. I will let him bring some drawings and colorings that I have made of late in odd moments, and you can see about how advanced I am, and what faults I have fallen into while groping my own way. And I am going to send you some canvas, also, for I am quite sure that if you paint a picture Mr. Ludolph will buy it."

The man's face brightened visibly at this.

"Will you let your friend make a suggestion?" continued Dennis.

"You can command me," said Mr. Bruder, with emphasis.

"No; friends never do that; but I would like to suggest that at first you take some simple subject, that you can soon finish, and leave efforts that require more time for the future. That picture there shows what you can do, and you need to work now more from the commercial standpoint than the artist's."

After a moment's thought, the man said, "You are right. As I look around dis room, and see our needs, I see dat you are right. Do' I meant to attempt someding difficult, to show Mr. Ludolph vat I could do."

"That will all come in good time; and now, my friend, good-night."

The next day was far more tolerable for poor Bruder, because he was occupied, and he found it much easier to resist the clamors of appetite.

Dennis's sketches interested him greatly, for, though they showed the natural defects of one who had received little instruction, both power and originality were manifest in their execution.

"He, too, can be an artist, if he vill," was his emphatic comment, after looking them over.

He prepared one study, to be continued under his own eye, and another for Dennis to work at alone. Afterward he sat down to something for himself. He thought a few moments, and then outlined rapidly as his subject the figure of a man dashing a wineglass to the ground.

As he worked, his wife smiled encouragement to him as of old, and often looked upward in thankfulness to heaven.

CHAPTER XIX.

WHAT IS THE MATTER WITH HIM?

THE sun was just tingeing the eastern horizon with light when Dennis sprung from his bed on the following morning. He vowed that Miss Ludolph should never have cause to complain of him again; for, great as was the luxury of being awakened by such exquisite music, it was one that he could not afford.

It must be confessed that he gave a little more care than usual that morning to his toilet; but his resources were very limited. Still, as nature had done so much for him, he could not complain. By half-past six his duties in the store were accomplished, and brushed and furbished up as far as possible, he stood outside the door awaiting his fair task-mistress. Sometimes he wondered at the strange fascination she exercised over him, but generally ended by ascribing it to her beauty and love of art.

A little after the time appointed she appeared with her father, and seemed pleased at Dennis's readiness for work.

"I shall not have to sing you awake this morning," she said, "and I am glad, for I am in a mood for business."

She was attired in a close-fitting walking-dress that set off her graceful person finely. It was evident that her energetic nature would permit no statuesque repose while Dennis worked, but that she had come prepared for active measures.

She had inherited a good constitution, which under her father's direction had been strengthened and confirmed by due regard to hygienic rules. Therefore she had reached the stage of early womanhood abounding in vitality and capable of great endurance. Active, graceful motion was as natural to her as it is for a swallow to be on the wing. The moment she dropped her book, palette, or pencil, she was on her feet, her healthful nature seeming like a mountain brook, that, checked for a time in its flow, soon overleaps its bounds and speeds on more swiftly than ever. But the strange part of this superabundant activity was, that she never seemed to do anything in an abrupt way, as from mere impulse. Every act glided into another smoothly and gracefully. Her lithe, willowy figure, neither slight nor stout, was peculiarly adapted to her style of movement. She delighted in the game of billiards, for the quick movements and varied attitudes permitted, and the precision required, were all suited to her taste; and she had gained such marvellous skill that even her father, with his practised hand, was scarcely her match.

As she tripped lightly up the long winding stairs to the show-room over the front door where their labors were to begin, she appeared to Dennis the very embodiment of grace and beauty. And yet she seemed so cold and self-centred, so devoid of warm human interest in the great world of love, joy, and suffering, that she repelled while she fascinated.

"If the blood should come into the cheeks of one of her father's statues, and the white marble eyes turn to violet blue, and the snowy hair to wavy gold, and it should spring from its pedestal into just such life, it would be more like her than any woman I ever saw," thought Dennis, as he stood for a moment or two waiting to do her bidding.

Her plans had been thoroughly matured, and she acted with decision. Pointing to the side opposite the door,— the side which would naturally strike the eye of the visitor first, — she said, "I wish all the pictures taken down from that wall and placed around the room so that I can see them."

She began as an absolute dictator, intending to give no hint of her plans and purposes except as conveyed by clear, terse orders. But these had so intelligent and appreciative an interpreter in Dennis, that gradually her attention was drawn to him as well as to his work.

He had his step-ladder ready, and with a celerity decidedly pleasing, soon placed the pictures safely on the floor, so that she could still see them and judge of their character. Though his dexterous manner and careful handling of the pictures were gratifying, it must be confessed that his supple form, the graceful and varied attitudes he unconsciously assumed in his work, pleased her more, and she secretly began to study him as an artistic subject, as he had studied her.

In her complacency she said: "So far, very well, Mr. Fleet. I congratulate myself that I have you to assist me, instead of that awkward fraud, Mr. Berder."

"And I assure you, Miss Ludolph, that I have longed intensely for this privilege ever since I knew your purpose."

"You may have cause to repent, like many another whose wishes have been gratified; for your privilege will involve a great deal of hard work."

"The more the better," said Dennis, warmly.

"How so? I should think you had more to do now than you would care about."

"Work is no burden to one of my years and strength, provided it is suited to one's tastes. Moreover, I confess that I hope to derive great advantages from this labor."

"In what way?" she asked, with a slight frown, imagining that he thought of extra pay.

"Because unconsciously you will give me instruction, and I hope that you are not unwilling that I should gain such hints and suggestions as I can from the display of your taste that I must witness."

"Not at all," said she, laughing. "I see that you are ambitious to learn your business and rise in the store."

"I am ambitious to gain a knowledge of one of the noblest callings."

"What is that?"

"Art."

"What!" said she, with a half-scornful smile; "are you a disciple of art?"

"Yes; why not?"

"Well, I do not wish to hurt your feelings, but, to tell you the honest truth, it seems but the other day that you were Pat Murphy."

"But am I a Pat Murphy?" he asked, with gentle dignity.

"No, Mr. Fleet; I will do you the justice to say that I think you very much above your station."

"I am sufficiently a democrat, Miss Ludolph, to believe that a man can be a man in any honest work."

"And I, Mr. Fleet, am not in the least degree a democrat."

Which fact she proceeded to prove by ordering him about for the next hour like the most absolute little despot that ever queened it over a servile province in the dark ages. But it was rather difficult to keep up this style of dictatorship with Dennis. He seemed so intelligent and polite that she often had it on her tongue to ask his opinion on certain points. Toward the last she did so, and the opinion he gave, she admitted to herself, was judicious; but for a purpose of her own she disregarded it, and took a different way.

Dennis at once saw through her plan of arrangement. In the centre of that side of the room which he had cleared, she caused him to hang one of the largest and finest pictures, which, under Mr. Schwartz's management, had been placed in a corner. Around the central painting all the others were to be grouped, according to color, subject, and merit. At the same time each wall was to have a character of its own. Such a task as this would require no little thought, study, and comparison; and Miss Ludolph was one to see delicate points of difference which most observers would not notice. It was her purpose to make the room bloom out naturally like a great flower. This careful selection of pictures was necessarily slow, and Dennis rejoiced that their united work would not soon be over.

To her surprise she often saw his eyes instinctively turning to the same picture that she was about to select, and perceived that he had divined her plan without a word of explanation, and that his taste was constantly according with hers in producing the desired effects. Though all this filled her with astonishment, she revealed no sign of it to him. At eight she said: "That will do for to-day. We have made a good beginning, — better indeed than I had hoped. But how is it, Mr. Fleet, since you are such an uncompromising democrat, that you permit a young lady to order you about in this style?"

Dennis smiled and said: "It seems perfectly natural for you to speak in this way, and it does not appear offensive as it might in another. Moreover, I have voluntarily taken this position and am in honor bound to accept all it involves."

"But which was the controlling motive of your mind?"

"Well, a few seem born to command, and it is a pleasure to obey," said Dennis, paying a strong but honest compliment to the natural little autocrat.

"Indeed, Mr. Fleet, do church members flatter?" said she, secretly much pleased.

"I did not mean to flatter," said he, flushing. "They who have power should use it like the All-powerful, — gently, considerately."

It was her turn to flush now, and she said, "Oh, I perceive, the compliment was the sugar-coating of the little homily to follow."

"I have no such diplomacy as you credit me with," said Dennis, looking straight into her eyes with honest frankness. "I merely spoke my passing thought."

"But he has fine eyes," said she to herself, and then she said to him: "Very well, I certainly will give you credit for being superior to your position. Be ready again to-morrow at the same hour;" and with a smile somewhat kindly she vanished.

Somehow she seemed to take the light out of the room with her. The pictures suddenly looked tame and ordinary, and everything commonplace. Here was an effect not exactly artistic, which he could not understand. He sighed, he scarcely knew why.

But the day's duties came with a rush, and soon he was utterly absorbed in them.

That evening Dennis was much cheered by Mr. Bruder's comments on his sketches.

"Considering de advantages you haf had, and de little time you can give, dey are very goot. You haf fallen into de natural faults of dose who work alone, but ve can soon cure dese. Now here is some vork dat I vant you to do under my eye, and dat study on outlining you can take home. Moreover, I can give you some lessons in outlining from my own picture;" and Mr. Bruder showed him what he had done.

Dennis saw in the clear, vigorous profile the artist's thought, and congratulated himself that his teacher was a master in his profession.

For two hours they worked and talked, and Dennis felt that every such lesson would be a long step forward.

Poor Bruder looked more and more like himself every day, but God only knew how he had to struggle.

"I don't know how him vill end," he said. "I pray nearly every minute, but sometimes I feel dat I must drink even do' I die dat moment."

It was disease as well as appetite that he was fighting, for appetite indulged beyond a certain point becomes disease.

His wife's face was different also, — the sharp look of misery fading out of it. Dennis noticed the changes, and thought to himself, while walking home: "After all, the highest art is to bring out on the living face all we can of God's lost image. How beautiful the changes in these two poor people's faces! and the best part of it is, that they are the reflex of changes going on in the soul, the imperishable part."

Then, in quick and natural transition, his mind reverted to Christine Ludolph; and the thought of her face, which God had fashioned so fair, but which was already sadly marred by sin, becoming fixed and rigid in pride and selfishness, was as painful as if, according to an old legend, her lithe, active form should gradually turn to stone. But if the reverse could ever be true, — if the beautifying Christian graces could dwell within her soul and light up her face, — as lamps illumining some rare and quaint transparency, the resulting loveliness would realize the artist's fondest ideal.

Musing thus, what wonder that he vowed then and there, under the starlight, to pray and work for her till the new life should illumine her heart. Little dreamed Christine, as she slept that night, that the first link of a chain which might bind her to heaven had been forged.

The dawn was late and lowering on the following morning. Great masses of clouds swept across the sky, and soon the rain was falling in gusty torrents. Dennis rose and hastened through his duties as before, and was ready at the hour appointed, but had little hope of seeing Miss Ludolph. Still he opened the door and looked up the street. To his surprise he saw her coming, attended by her father's valet. Only part of her glowing face was visible, for she was incased from head to foot in a light and delicate suit of rubber.

Dennis opened the door, and she stepped quickly in, scattering spray on every side like a sea-nymph. The young man looked at her with open-eyed admiration and surprise, which both amused and pleased her.

"True enough," she thought, "his face is like a signboard."

She seemed to him, as she threw off her wet coverings, like an exquisite flower, that, lifted by the breeze after a storm, scatters the burdensome rain-drops on every side and stands up more beautiful and blooming than ever.

"You were not expecting me, I imagine," she said.

"Well, I must admit I scarcely did, and yet I could not help looking for you."

"Isn't that a distinction without a difference?" she asked, with a pleasant smile, for she was gratified at not finding the store closed and dark.

"I am very glad you have come," he replied, flushing slightly with pleasure, "for it would have been a long, dreary morning if you had not."

Dennis thought he referred to the lack of occupation. He did not know, nor did she notice, that he meant the lack of herself.

"Well," said she, "I am glad you like the work, for you are destined to have enough of it."

CHAPTER XX.

IS HE A GENTLEMAN?

THE days and weeks that followed were to Dennis such as only come once in a lifetime, and not in every lifetime either. A true, pure love was growing up within his heart, — growing as the little child develops in strength and pleasurable life, and yet unconsciously to itself. It seemed as if some strong magician's wand had touched the world or him. Everything was transfigured, and no wonder-land was more full of interest than that in which he existed. His life was a waking dream, in which nothing was distinct or definite, but all things abounded in hope and happy suggestion. He compared it afterward to a tropical island of the Pacific, a blissful fragment of life by itself, utterly distinct from the hard, struggling years that preceded, and the painful awakening that followed.

Even the place of his daily toil was pervaded by a beautiful presence. For many days he and Christine worked together, and at last her eyes had rested on, or her fingers had touched, nearly everything in the store, and therefore all was associated with her. Throughout their labors his quick sympathy and appreciation made him almost hands and feet to her, and she regarded him as a miracle of helpfulness, — one of those humble, useful creatures who are born to wait upon and interpret the wishes of the rich and great. His admiring glances disturbed her not and raised no suspicion in her mind. She had been accustomed to such for years, and took them as a matter of course.

She treated the young men whom she met in society with a courtly ease and freedom, but her smiles and repartee ever seemed like brilliant moonlight that had no warmth; and, while no restraint appeared, she still kept all at a distance. There was a marked difference in her intercourse with Dennis. Regarding him as too humble ever to presume upon her frankness, she daily spoke more freely, and more truly acted out herself before him. She was happy and in her element among the beautiful works of art they were arranging, and in this atmosphere her womanly nature, chilled and dwarfed though it was, would often manifest itself in ways sweet and unexpected. Under no other circumstances could she have appeared so well. She as often spoke to herself in racy comment on what was before her as to Dennis, and ever and anon would make some pleasant remark to him, as she might throw a dainty morsel to her greyhound Wolf, looking wistfully at her while she dined. At the same time it must be confessed that she had a growing respect for him, as she daily saw some new proof of his intelligence and taste; but both education and disposition inclined her instinctively to the old feudal idea that even genius, if poor, must wait a humble servitor on wealth and rank, and where a New-England girl would have been saying to herself, "This gifted, educated man is my equal, and, whether I want to or not, I ought to treat him as such," she was not troubled at all. To her, he was her father's clerk and man-of-all-work, a most useful, trusted, and agreeable servant, and she was kind to him as such. Indeed the little autocrat was kind to every one that pleased her. She was a benign queen to obedient subjects, but woe to those who were otherwise.

To Dennis, however, though he realized it not, she was becoming as the very apple of his eye. He was learning to regard her with a deeper interest because of the very defects that he plainly recognized. While on the one hand he had the enthusiastic love caused by his admiration for her, on the other he felt the tenderer and greater love which was the result of pity. He tried to account for his feelings toward her by the usual sophistries of unconscious lovers. It was friendship; it was artistic interest in her beauty; it was the absorbing, unselfish regard of a Christian for one providentially commended to him to be led out of darkness into light. How could he help thinking of one for whom he prayed night and morning and every hour in the day? It was all this, but he was soon to learn that it was a great deal more. And so the days of occupation and companion ship passed; the spell worked on with increasing and bewildering power, and the crisis could not be delayed much longer.

One morning in the latter part of April she seemed more gracious than usual. Their labors were drawing to a close, and, as he had proved so tasteful and efficient in the store, she concluded that he might be equally useful in other ways and places. She could command him at the store, but not in respect to a task that she had in view; so she adopted a little feminine artifice as old as the time when Eve handed Adam the apple, and she looked at him in such a way that he could not refuse.

Blind, honest Dennis, it is needless to say, saw nothing of this little strategy of which he was destined to be the happy, willing victim, and his love expanded and bloomed under the genial light of her presence and kindness, like the flowers of the convolvulus in a bright dawn of June. She brought her general graciousness to a definite and blissful climax by saying, when about to go home, "Well, Mr. Fleet, you have done better than usual to-day, and I certainly must give you credit for possessing more taste than any young man of my acquaintance."

Dennis's heart gave as great a bound as if the laurel crown of all the Olympic games had been placed upon his brow.

"I am now going to ask a favor," she continued.

"You may command me, Miss Ludolph," interrupted Dennis.

"No, not in this case," she replied. "Whatever you do will be regarded as a personal favor to me. At the same time it will afford you scope for such display of your taste as will secure many compliments."

"If I am able to satisfy *you* I shall be more than compensated," said Dennis, with a bow.

She smiled and thought to herself, "That isn't bad for a porter and man-of-all-work," and explained as follows: —

"Some young ladies and gentlemen have decided upon giving an entertainment, consisting of music, tableaux, and statuary. Now, in regard to the two latter parts, we need above all things some person of taste like yourself, whose critical eye and dexterous hand will insure everything to be just right. You will be a sort of general stage manager and superintendent, you know. I feel sure you will be all the more willing to enter upon this work when you know that the proceeds are to go toward the Church of the Holy Virgin. This is going to be a very select affair, and the tickets are five dollars each."

"Is it a Protestant church?" asked Dennis, in some trepidation.

"Oh, certainly," she answered, with a peculiar smile, "an Episcopal church."

"It seems a strange name for a Protestant church," said Dennis. "It is enough for me that you wish it; at the same time it certainly is a pleasure to contribute what little I can to aid any Christian organization."

"Come, Mr. Fleet, you are narrow" she said, with a

controversial twinkle in her eye. "Why not toward a Catholic church?"

"I fear that all people with decided religious opinions are sometimes regarded as narrow," he answered, with a smile.

"That is an inadequate answer to my question," she said; "but I will not find fault since you have so good-naturedly acceded to my request. Come to No. — Wabash Avenue at three this afternoon. Papa gives you leave of absence."

She vanished, and figuratively the sun went down to Dennis, and he was in twilight till he should see her again. He looked forward to the afternoon with almost feverish eagerness, for several reasons. It would be his first introduction to "good society," for as such the unsophisticated youth regarded the prospect. He had the natural longing of a young, healthful nature for the companionship of those of his own age and culture, and his life in the great city had often been very lonely. He expected, as a matter of course, to be treated as an equal at the artistic entertainment in which he was to participate. In his business relations at the store he had taken a subordinate position and made up his mind to the logical consequences. But now that he was invited to a private house, and would appear there possessing all the qualities of a gentleman, he surely would be treated as one. "Is not this Chicago, whose citizens were nearly all poor a few years ago?" he thought; "and surely, if what Miss Ludolph says is true, I have advantages in my taste over most poor young men." Moreover, it was his ideal of an entertainment, where art and music should take the place of the coarser pleasures of eating, drinking, and dancing. Chief of all, Christine would be there, and even he in his blindness became a little uneasy and self-conscious as he realized how this thought towered above the others.

She had given him a list of the things he was to bring with him in the afternoon, and he occupied every spare moment in getting them ready. At a quarter past two he summoned the carman of the store, and they loaded up the miscellaneous cargo needed for the coming mysteries, and by three all were before the large elegant mansion to which he had been directed. Dennis rang the bell and was shown by a servant into the front parlor, where he found Miss Ludolph, Miss Brown, a tall, haughty brunette, and the young lady of the house, Miss Winthrop, a bright, sunny-faced blonde, and two or three other young ladies of no special coloring or character, being indebted mainly to their toilets for their attractions. Dennis bowed to Miss Ludolph, and then turned toward the other ladies, expecting as a matter of course to be introduced. No introduction came, but his expectant manner was so obvious that Miss Ludolph colored and looked annoyed, and the other young ladies tittered outright.

Advancing a step or two she said, coldly, "Mr. Fleet, you may help Mapes carry the things into the back parlor, and then we will direct you as to the arrangement."

Dennis crimsoned painfully. At first he was too confused to think, and merely obeyed mechanically. Then came the impulse to say boldly that this kind of thing might answer at the store, but not here, and he nearly carried it out; but soon followed the sober second thought, that such action would bring a blight over all his prospects, and involve the loss of his position at the store. Such giving way to passion would injure only himself. They would laugh, and merely suffer a momentary annoyance; to him and his the result would be most disastrous. Why should he let those who cared not a jot for him cause such sad injury?

By the time he had carried his first armful into the back parlor, he had resolved for his mother and sisters' sakes that he would go through the following scenes as well as he could, and then turn his back on society till he could enter it a recognized gentleman; and with compressed lips and flashing eye he mentally vowed that that day should soon come.

As he was unpacking his materials he could not help hearing the conversation in the front parlor.

"Did you ever see such presumption?" exclaimed Miss Brown. "He evidently expected to be introduced, and that we should rise and courtesy all around."

"He must have seen better days, for he certainly appeared like a gentleman," said Miss Winthrop.

"I should hardly give that title to a man who swept a store out every morning," replied Miss Brown.

"No indeed!" chorused the three colorless young ladies.

"I know nothing about this young man," said Miss Winthrop, ruffling her plumage somewhat for an argument, of which she was fond; "but, as a case in hand, suppose a highly educated and refined man for some reason swept a store out every morning, what would you call him?" and she looked around as if she had given a poser.

The colorless young ladies looked blank, — their natural expression.

"Nonsense!" said the positive Miss Brown; "such men don't sweep stores. He may have passed current in some country village, but that is not our set."

"But the case is certainly supposable," retorted Miss Winthrop, more intent upon her argument than upon Dennis. "Come, what does the Countess say?" she asked, turning to Christine; for that was the familiar name by which she went among her young companions.

"The case is not supposable, but actual," she answered, so distinctly that it seemed that she meant Dennis to hear. "As far as I have any means of judging, he is a refined, educated man, and I have learned from papa that his motive in sweeping the store is the support of his mother and sisters, — certainly a very worthy one. To your question, Susie, I answer unhesitatingly that in accordance with your American principles and professions he is a gentleman, and you ought to treat him as such. But you Americans are sometimes wonderfully inconsistent, and there is often a marvellously wide margin between your boasted equality and the reality. Now in Europe these questions have been settled for ages, and birth and rank define a person's position accurately."

"I do not believe in equality," said Miss Brown, with a toss of her head. (Her father was a mighty brewer, but he and his were in character and antecedents something like the froth on their own beer.)

Miss Winthrop was a little embarrassed at finding her supposed case a real one, for it might involve some practical action on her part. Many an ardent advocate of the people in theory gives them practically the cold shoulder, and is content to stay on the summit of Mt. Olympus. She was a girl of good impulses and strong convictions of abstract right, but rarely had either the courage or the opportunity to carry them out. She was of the old Boston family of Winthrops, and therefore could meet Miss Ludolph on her own ground in the way of pedigree.

But, however Dennis fared, she felt that she must look after her argument, and, having conquered theoretically as far as America was concerned, determined to carry war into Europe, so she said: "Are you not mistaken in saying that birth and rank only settle position abroad? Some of the most honored names there are or were untitled."

"Oh, certainly, but they were persons of great genius, and *genius* is the highest patent of nobility. But I leave you republicans to settle this question to suit yourselves. I am going to look after the preparations for this evening, as I have set my heart on a success that shall ring through the city."

But they all flocked after her into the back parlor, now doubly interesting as it contained an object of curiosity in Dennis Fleet, — a veritable gentleman who swept a store.

CHAPTER XXI.

CHRISTINE'S IDEA OF CHRISTIANS.

THE large apartment where the amateur performers expected to win their laurels was now filled with all the paraphernalia needed to produce musical, artistic, and scenic effects. Much had been gathered before Dennis's arrival, and his cart-load added all that was necessary. Everything seemed in inextricable confusion.

"The idea of having anything here to-night!" exclaimed Miss Winthrop. "It will take us a week to get things arranged."

"The thing is hopeless," said the blank young ladies.

Even Christine looked somewhat dismayed, but she said, "Remember we have till half-past eight."

"I will call two or three of the servants," said Miss Brown.

"I beg of you do not, at least not yet," exclaimed Christine. "What will their clumsy hands do in work like this, but mar everything? I have great faith in Mr. Fleet's abilities," she continued, turning toward Dennis, with an enchanting smile, and resuming the tactics of the morning. Though the smile went to Dennis's heart like a fiery arrow, his pride, thoroughly aroused, made him cold and self-possessed. He naturally assumed the manner possible only to the true gentleman who, though wronged, chooses not to show his feelings save by a grave, quiet dignity. In view of their action and manner, he consciously felt himself their superior; and this impression, like an atmosphere, was felt by them also. As they looked upon his tall, erect form, manly bearing, and large dark eyes, in which still lurked the fire of an honest indignation, they felt the impossibility of ordering him about like Mapes the carman. They regarded him for a moment in awkward silence, not knowing what to do or say. Even haughty Christine was embarrassed, for the stronger spirit was present and thoroughly aroused, and it overpowered the weaker natures. Christine had never seen Dennis look like that, and did not know that he could. He was so different from the eager, humble servitor that heretofore had interpreted her very wishes, even before they were spoken! Moreover, the success of their entertainment now depended upon him, and she felt that he was in a mood requiring delicate treatment, and that she could not order him around in the *rôle* to which she had assigned him. And yet if she had known him, she might, for he had made up his mind to go through even the most menial service with proud humility, and then be careful not to be so caught again; and, when Dennis had resolved upon a thing, that settled the question so far as he was concerned. Seeing Christine's hesitation and embarrassment, he stepped forward and said: "Miss Ludolph, if you will indicate *your* wishes I will carry them out as rapidly as possible. I can soon bring order out of this confusion; and you must have some plan of arrangement."

She gave him a quick, grateful glance, that thawed more of his ice than he cared to have melt so quickly.

"Of course we have," said she. "This is but the nervous hesitation before the shock of a battle that has all been planned on paper. Here is our programme."

"All battles do not go forward in the field as planned on paper, if my feeble memory serves me," said Miss Winthrop, maliciously.

"I grant you that," said Christine, quietly, "and you need not tax your memory so greatly to prove it."

She was now very kind and gracious to Dennis, believing that to be the best policy. It usually is, but she received no special proof of it from him: he listened alike to request, suggestion, and compliment. There was nothing sullen or morose in his appearance, nothing resentful or rude. With the utmost respect he heard all she said, and carried out her wishes with that deft, graceful promptness in which he had few equals. At the same time his manner was that of one who thoroughly respected himself, — that of a refined and cultivated person, who, having become committed to a disagreeable part, performed it with only the protest of dignified silence.

As his first step, he cleared a space for action, and arranged everything to be in view when needed. The rapidity with which order emerged from confusion was marvellous to the young ladies.

Then he took their programme, studied it a few moments, and compared it with the pictures of the scenes they wished to imitate. He then arranged for these one after another, placing everything needed within reach, and where it could readily be seen, making the combinations beforehand as far as possible. As he worked so intelligently and skilfully, requiring so few explanations, the young ladies exchanged significant glances, and strolled into the front parlor. They must express an opinion.

"I declare, Christine," said Miss Winthrop, "it is a shame that you did not introduce him, for he is a gentleman. He works like a captive prince."

"How romantic!" gushed the colorless young ladies.

"Nonsense!" said Miss Brown; "I hate to see any one in his position putting on such airs."

As soon as she had seen Dennis fairly at work just like

her mother's servants, or her father's men, she felt that he ought to be treated as such, — riches being Miss Brown's patent of nobility; and she resolved if possible to lower his ridiculous pride, as she regarded it. Miss Brown was a very handsome, stylish girl of a certain type, but she no more understood Dennis's feelings than she did Sanskrit.

Christine said nothing, but admitted to herself, with a secret wonder, that Dennis awakened in her a respect, a sort of fear, that no other man had inspired, save her father. There was something in his manner, though altogether respectful, that made her feel that he was not to be trifled with. This impression was decidedly heightened when, a few moments later, Miss Brown, pursuant of her resolution to lower Dennis's pride, ordered him in an offensive manner to do something for her that had no connection with the entertainment. At first he acted as if he had not heard her, but his rising color showed that he had. In spite of warning glances from Christine and Miss Winthrop, she repeated her request in a loud, imperious tone.

Dennis drew himself up to his full height, and, turning his dark eyes full upon her, said, firmly, "I am ever ready to *offer* any service that a gentleman can to a lady, but surely I am not your footman."

"Your pride is ridiculous, sir. You are here to help, and will be paid for it. This is my house, and I expect persons of your position, while in it, to do as they are bidden."

"Since such are the rules and principles of your house, permit me at once to leave you in full possession;" and he was about to retire with a manner as cold as Mr. Ludolph himself could have assumed, and as haughty, when a light hand fell upon his arm. Looking down he met the deep blue eyes of Christine Ludolph lifted pleadingly to his.

"Mr. Fleet, you need not do what is asked. It is not right to require it. In fact we all owe you an apology."

Then, in a low, quick tone, she added, "Will you not stay as a favor to me?"

She felt his arm tremble under her hand, there was a moment's hesitation, then he replied, in the same manner, "Miss Ludolph, *you* can command me on *this* occasion" (there was no promise for the future); and then he turned to his work as if resolved to see and know nothing else till the ordeal ended.

In spite of herself Christine blushed, but taking Miss Brown by the arm she led her aside and gave her a vigorous lecture.

"Are you sane?" she said. "Do you not remember that nearly a thousand dollars' worth of tickets are sold, and that the people will be here by half-past eight, and at nine we must appear? Even after what he has done, if you should drive him away the thing would be a failure, and we should be the ridiculous town-talk for a year."

"But I hate—"

"No matter what you hate. Treat him as you please to-morrow. We need him now;" and so the petted, wilful girl, spoiled by money and flattery, was kept under restraint.

A great deal of preparation was required for the last two pieces on the programme, and the young ladies grouped themselves not far off while Dennis worked. Christine explained from time to time as the natural leader of the party. Still an awkward silence followed the scene above described. This restraint could not long endure, and one of the colorless young ladies asked a question that led to more than she intended, and, indeed, more than she understood.

"Christine, what do you do with yourself Sundays? Your pew is not occupied once in an age."

"I usually paint most of the day, and ride out with papa in the afternoon when it is pleasant."

"Why, you are a perfect little heathen!" they all exclaimed in chorus.

"Yes, I suppose I am worse than a pagan," she said, "for I not only do not believe in your superstitions, but have none of my own."

"What do you believe in, then?" asked Miss Winthrop.

"Art, music, fame, power."

She announced her creed so coolly and decidedly that Dennis lifted a startled face to hers. She saw his grieved, astonished expression, and it amused her very much. Henceforth she spoke as much for his benefit as for theirs.

"If you would be equally honest," she continued, "you would find that your creeds also are very different from the one in the prayer-book."

"And what would mine be, pray," asked one of the colorless young ladies.

"I will sum it up in one sentence, Miss Jones,—'Keep in the fashion.'"

"I think that you are very unjust. I'm sure I go to church regularly, and attend a great many services in Lent and on Saints' days. I've been confirmed, and all that."

"Yes, it is the thing to do in your set. Now, here is Miss Winthrop, a Presbyterian, who manifests quite another religious phase."

"Pray what is mine?" asked that lady, laughing.

"Oh, you want hair-splitting in regard to the high doctrines,—clear, brilliant arguments, cutting like sharp, merciless steel into the beliefs of other denominations. Then, after your ism has been glorified for an hour on Sunday morning, and all other isms pierced and lashed, you descend from your intellectual heights, eat a good dinner, take a nap, and live like the rest of us till the next Sabbath, when (if it is a fine day) you climb some other theological peak, far beyond the limits of perpetual snow, and there take anether bird's-eye view of something that might be found very different if you were nearer to it."

"And what is my phase?" asked Miss Brown.

"Oh, you are an out-and-out sinner, and do just what you please, in spite of priest or prayer-book," said Christine, with a laugh in which all the ladies joined.

"Well," said Miss Brown, "I do not think that I am worse than the rest of you."

"Not in the least," replied Christine. "We all have some form of religion, or none at all, as it accords with our peculiar tastes."

"And you mean to say that having a religion or not is a mere matter of taste?" asked Miss Winthrop.

"Yes, I should say it was, and practically that it *is*. You ladies, and nearly all that I have met, seem to choose a style of religion suited to your tastes; and the tastes of many incline them to have no religion at all."

"Why, Miss Ludolph!" exclaimed Miss Winthrop, her cheeks glowing with honest dissent and zeal for the truth; "our religion is taken from the Bible. Do you not believe in the Bible?"

"No! not in the sense in which you ask the question; nor you either, my charming Miss Winthrop."

"Indeed I do, every word of it," said the orthodox young lady, hotly.

"Let me test you. Miss Brown, have you such a book in the house? Oh, yes, here is an elegantly bound copy, but looking as if never opened. And now, Miss Winthrop, this city is full of all sorts of horrid people, living in alleys and tenement houses. They are poor, half-naked, hungry, and sometimes starving. Many are in prison, and more ought to be; many are strangers, more utterly alone and lonely in our crowded streets than on a desert island. They are suffering from varieties of disgusting disease, and having a hard time generally. How many hungry people have you fed? How many strangers (I do not mean distinguished ones from abroad) have you taken in and comforted? How many of the naked have you clothed? And how long is your list of the sick and imprisoned that you have visited, my luxurious little lady?"

A real pallor overspread Miss Winthrop's sunny face, for she saw what was coming, but she answered, honestly, "I have done practically nothing of all this." Then she added: "Papa and mamma are not willing that I should visit such places and people. I have asked that I might, but they always discourage me, and tell of the awful experiences of those who do."

"Then they don't believe the Bible, either," said Christine; "for if they did they would insist on your doing it; and if you believed you would do all this in spite of them; for see what is written here; the very Being that you worship and dedicate your churches to will say, because of your not doing this, 'Depart from me, ye cursed, into everlasting fire, prepared for the devil and his angels.' And this is but one of many similar passages. Now all this is a monstrous fable to me. The idea of any such experiences awaiting my light-hearted little Sybarite here!"

Miss Winthrop had buried her face in her hands, and was trembling from head to foot. The words of God never seemed so real and true before as now when uttered by an unbeliever.

"I don't believe there is any such place or things," said Miss Brown, bluntly.

"There spake my mature and thoughtful friend who is not to be imposed upon," said Christine, with a touch of irony in her tone.

Dennis had listened in sad wonder. Such words of cynical unbelief were in dark, terrible contrast with the fair young face. He saw the mind and training of her father in all she said, but he bitterly condemned the worldly, inconsistent life of multitudes in the church who do more to confirm unbelievers than all their sophistries. But as she went on, seemingly having the argument all her own way, his whole soul burned to meet and refute her fatal views. For her own sake and the others' as well as for the dishonored name of his Lord, he must in some way turn the tide. Though regarded as a humble servitor, having no right to take part in the conversation, he determined that his hands must lift up the standard of truth if no others would or could. To his joy he found that the programme would soon give him the coveted opportunity.

Christine went on with a voice as smooth and musical as the flow of a stream over a glacier.

"I have read the Bible several times, and that is more than all of you can say, I think. It is a wonderful book, and has been the inspiration of some of our best art. There are parts that I enjoy reading very much for their sublimity and peculiarity. But who pretends to live as this old and partially obsolete book teaches? Take my father for instance All the gentlemen in the church that I know of can do, and are accustomed to do, just what he does, and some I think do much worse; and yet he is an infidel, as you would term him. And as to the ladies, not the Bible, but fashion rules them with a rod of iron. I have cut free from it all, and art shall be my religion and the inspiration of my life."

As Christine talked on, the twilight deepened, and Dennis worked with increasing eagerness.

"After all," she continued, "it is only history repeating itself. The educated mind to-day stands in the same attitude toward Christianity as that of the cultured mind of Greece and Rome toward the older mythology in the second century. Then as now the form of religion was kept up, but belief in its truth was fast dying out. The cities abounded in gorgeous temples, and were thronged with worshippers, but they sacrificed at the dictates of fashion, custom, and law, not of faith. So our cities are adorned with splendid churches, and fashion and the tastes of the congregation decide as to the form of service. The sects differ widely with each other, and all differ with the Bible. The ancients gave no more respect to what was regarded as the will of their imaginary deities than do modern Christians to the precepts of the Bible. People went to the ceremonies, got through with them, and then did what they pleased; and so they do now.

"Take for instance one of your commonest doctrines, that of prayer: the majority have no practical belief in it. My father has taken me, and out of curiosity I have attended several prayer meetings. The merest fraction of the congregation are present at the best of times, and if the night is stormy the number out is ridiculously small. Yet all profess to believe that the Lord of heaven and earth will be present, and that it is His will that they should be. Your Bible teaches that the Being who controls completely the destiny of every person will be in the midst of those gathered in His name, to hear and answer their petitions. If this is true, then no earthly ruler was ever so neglected and insulted, so generally ignored, as this very Deity to whom you ascribe unlimited power, and from whom you say you receive life and everything. An eastern despot would take off the heads of those who treated him in such a style; and a republican politician would scoff at the idea of giving office to such lukewarm followers. Why, here in Christian Chicago the will of God is no more heeded by the majority than that of the Emperor of China, and the Bible might as well be the Koran. Looking at these facts from my impartial standpoint, I am driven to one of two alternatives: either you regard your God as so kind and good, so merciful, that you can trespass on His forbearance to any extent, and treat Him with a neglect and an indifference that none would manifest toward the pettiest earthly potentate, and still all will be well; or else you have no real practical belief in your religion. Though not very charitably inclined, I cannot think quite so meanly of human nature as to take the former view, so I am driven to the latter. For surely no man who wished to live and prosper, no woman who loved her husband and children, could so coolly and continually disregard the Deity in whom they profess to believe, with the old Greek poet, that they 'live, move, and have their being.'"

The twilight deepened, and Christine continued, her words, portraying the decline of faith, according ominously with the increasing gloom.

"Why, in order to see the truth of what I am saying, look at the emblem of your faith, — the Cross. All its historical associations are those of self-denial, and suffering for others. The Founder of your faith endured death upon it. He was a great, good man like Socrates, though no doubt a mistaken enthusiast. But what He meant He said plainly and clearly, as, for instance, 'Whosoever doth not bear his cross and come after Me cannot be My disciple.' I admit that in the past He had a wonderful following. In the ages of martyrdom multitudes left all, and endured all that He did, for His sake. But so there have been other great leaders with equally devoted followers. But in this practical age religious enthusiasm has but little chance. What crosses do the members of the Church of the Holy Virgin take up? and what are borne by your great rich church, Miss Winthrop? The shrewd people of this day manage better, and put their crosses on top of the church. I suppose they reason that the stone tower can carry it for the whole congregation, on the principle of a labor-saving machine. But honestly, your modern disciples are no more like their Master than one of the pale, slim, white-kidded gentlemen who will be here to-night is like Richard Cœur de Lion as he led a charge against the Moslems. Your cross is dwindling to a mere pretty ornament, — an emblem of a past that is fast fading from men's memories. It will never have the power to inspire the heart again, as when the Crusaders — "

At that moment their eyes were blinded by a sudden, dazzling light. There was a general and startled exclamation, and then, awe-struck and silent, they gazed as if spell-bound upon a luminous cross blazing before them.

CHAPTER XXII.

EQUAL TO AN EMERGENCY.

THE fiery cross that so awed Christine and her little group of auditors was to be the closing scene of the evening entertainment. It was of metal, and by a skilful adjustment of jets was made to appear as if all aflame. While the others were intent on Christine's words, and she in the interest of her theme had quite forgotten him, Dennis made all his arrangements, and at the critical point narrated in the preceding chapter he turned on the gas with the most startling effect. It seemed a living, vivid refutation of Christine's words, and even she turned pale. After a moment, for the emblem to make its full impression, Dennis stepped out before them all, his face lighted up by the luminous cross. They admitted that no crusader could look more earnest and brave than he.

"Miss Ludolph," he said, in a firm, yet respectful tone, "I should evermore be unworthy of your respect and confidence, — what is more, I should be false to myself, false to my faith, — should I remain silent in view of what I have been compelled to hear. That sacred emblem has not spent its meaning, or its power. Millions to-day would die for the sake of Him who suffered on it. Many even of those weak, inconsistent ones that you have so justly condemned would part with life rather than with the faint hope that centres there," pointing to the radiant symbol.

"You are rude, sir," said Christine, her face pale, but her eyes flashing in turn.

"No, he is right! he is right!" exclaimed Miss Winthrop, springing up with tears in her eyes. "Undeserving as I am of the name of Christian, I would die, I know I would die, before I would give up my poor little hope, — though I confess you make me fear that it is a false one. But it's the best I have, and I mean it shall be better. I think a good touch of persecution, that would bring people out, would do the church more good than anything else."

"Pardon me, Miss Ludolph," continued Dennis; "but I appeal to your sense of justice. Could I be a true man and be silent, believing what I do? Could I hear the name of my Best Friend thus spoken of, and say not one word in His behalf?"

"But I spoke most highly of the Christ of the Bible."

"You spoke of Him as a great, good, but mistaken *man*, an enthusiast. To me He is the mighty God, my Divine Saviour, to whom I owe infinitely more than life. You know that I mean no disrespect to you," he added, with gentle but manly courtesy. "I regret more deeply than words can express that you honestly think as you do. But if I as honestly believe the Bible, am I not acting as you said a true follower ought? For I assure you it is a heavier cross than you can ever know to speak thus unbidden where I am regarded only as a serving-man. But should I not be false and cowardly if I held my peace? And if you afterward should know that I claimed the name of Christian, would you not despise me as you remembered this scene?"

Christine bit her lip and hesitated, but her sense of justice prevailed, and she said, "I not only pardon you, but commend your course in view of your evident sincerity."

Dennis replied by a low bow.

At this moment there was a loud ring at the door.

"There come the gentlemen," exclaimed Miss Brown. "I am so glad! O dear! what a long, uncomfortable preachment we have had! Now for some fun!"

The colorless young ladies had stared first at Christine, and then at the cross, in blank amazement.

At the word "gentlemen" they were all on the alert and ready for *real* life; but Miss Winthrop left the room for a short time.

A handsome, lively youth entered, scattering bows and compliments on every side with the off-hand ease of an accomplished society man. He paid no heed to Dennis, evidently regarding him as the showman.

"Well, ladies, you have done your part," he said; "your arrangements seem complete."

"Yes, Mr. Mellen; but where is our tenor?" asked Christine. "We have only three-quarters of an hour for music rehearsal, before we must retire to dress for our parts."

"Bad news for you, Miss Ludolph," said Mr. Mellen, coming to her side; "Archer is sick and can't come."

"Can't come?" they all exclaimed in dismayed chorus.

"What is the matter?" asked Miss Winthrop, anxiously, coming in at that moment.

"Matter enough," said Miss Brown, poutingly; "that horrid Archer has gone and got sick. I do believe he did it on purpose. He did not know his parts near as well as he ought, and he has taken this way to get out of it."

"But he promised me he would study them all the morning," said Christine. "Oh, I am so sorry! What shall we do? Our entertainment seems fated to be a failure;" and she spoke in a tone of deep disappointment.

"I assure you I feel the deepest sympathy for you," said Mr. Mellen, looking tenderly at Christine, "but I did my best. I tried to drag Archer here out of his sick-bed, and then I ran around among some other good singers that I know, but none would venture. They said the music was difficult, and would require much practice, and that now is impossible."

"Oh, isn't it too bad?" mourned Miss Winthrop. "The programme is all printed, and the people will be so disappointed! We can't have that splendid duet that you and Mr. Archer were to sing, Christine. I have a score of friends who were coming to hear that alone."

"Oh, as for that matter, half our music is spoiled," said Christine, dejectedly. "Well, this is the last time I attempt anything of the kind. How in the world we are going to get out of this scrape I do not know. The tickets are so high, and so much has been said, that the people are expecting a great deal, and there is every prospect of a most lame and impotent conclusion."

A general gloom settled upon the faces of all. At this moment Dennis stepped forward hesitatingly and said to Christine, "Have you the music that Mr. Archer was to sing?"

"Certainly! do you suppose it was of the kind that he would extemporize?" said Miss Brown, pertly.

"Will you let me see it? If you are willing, perhaps I can assist you in this matter."

All turned toward him with a look of great surprise.

"What do you think of that from the man who sweeps Mr. Ludolph's store?" asked Miss Brown, in a loud whisper.

"I think the fellow is as presuming as he is ignorant," said Mr. Mellen, so plainly that all heard him.

"It is not presuming, sir, to offer a kindness where it is needed," said Dennis, with dignity, "and my ignorance is not yet proved. The presumption is all on your part."

Mr. Mellen flushed and was about to answer angrily when Miss Winthrop said hastily, but in a kindly tone, "But really, Mr. Fleet, much of our music is new and very difficult."

"But it is written, is it not?" asked Dennis, with a smile.

Christine looked at him in silent wonder. What would

he not do next? But she was sorry that he had spoken, for she foresaw only mortification for him.

"Oh, give him the music by all means," said Miss Brown, expecting to enjoy his blundering attempts to sing what was far beyond him. "There, I will play the accompaniment. It's not the tune of Old Hundred that you are to sing now, young man, remember."

Dennis glanced over the music, and she began to play a loud, difficult piece.

He turned to Miss Ludolph, and said: "I fear you have given me the wrong music. Miss Brown is playing something not written here."

They exchanged significant glances, and Miss Winthrop said, "Play the right music, Miss Brown."

She struck into the music that Dennis held, but played it so out of time that no one could sing it. Dennis laid down his sheets on the piano and said quietly, though with flushed face: "I did not mean to be obtrusive. You all seemed greatly disappointed at Mr. Archer's absence and the results, and I thought that in view of the emergency it would not be presumption to offer my services. But it seems that I am mistaken."

"No, it is not presumption," said Miss Winthrop. "It was true kindness and courtesy, which has been ill requited. But you see, to be frank, Mr. Fleet, we all fear that you do not realize what you are undertaking."

"Must I of necessity be an ignoramus because, as Miss Brown says, I sweep a store?"

"Let me play the accompaniment," said Christine, with the decided manner that few resisted, and she went correctly through the difficult and brilliant passage. Dennis followed his part with both eye and ear, and then said, "Perhaps I had better sing my part alone first, and then you can correct any mistakes."

There was a flutter of expectation, a wink from Mr. Mellen, and an audible titter from Miss Brown.

"Certainly," said Miss Ludolph, who thought to herself, "If he will make a fool of himself, he may;" and she played the brief prelude.

Then prompt at the proper moment, true to time and note, Dennis's rich, powerful tenor voice startled and then entranced them all. He sung the entire passage through with only such mistakes as resulted from his nervousness and embarrassment.

At the close, all exclaimed in admiration save Miss Brown, who bit her lip in ill-concealed vexation, and said, with a half-sneer, "Really, Mr. What-is-your-name, you are almost equal to Blind Tom."

"You do Blind Tom great injustice," said Dennis. "I read my music."

"But how did you learn to read music in that style?" asked Christine.

"Of course it took me years to do so. But no one could join our musical club at college who could not read anything placed before him."

"It must have been small and select, then."

"It was."

"How often had you sung that piece before?" asked Miss Brown.

"I never saw it before," answered Dennis.

"Why, it is just out," said Christine.

"Well, ladies and gentlemen, our troubles are over at last," said Miss Winthrop. "Mr. Fleet seems a good genius, — equal to any emergency. If he can sing that difficult passage, he can sing anything else we have. We had better run over our parts, and then to our toilets."

One of the colorless young ladies played the accompaniments, her music making a sort of neutral tint, against which their rich and varied voices came out with better effect. They sung rapidly through the programme, Dennis sustaining his parts correctly and with taste He could read like the page of an open book any music placed before him, and years of practice enabled him to sing true and with confidence. As he sung one thing after another with perfect ease, their wonder grew; and when, in the final duet with Christine, they both came out strongly, their splendid, thoroughly-trained voices blending in perfect harmony, they were rewarded with a spontaneous burst of applause, in which even Miss Brown was compelled to join

Christine said nothing, but gave Dennis a quick, grateful glance, which amply repaid him for the martyrdom she had led him into that afternoon.

He acknowledged the plaudits of the others with a slight, cool bow, but her thanks with a warm flush of pleasure, and then turned to complete his arrangements as if nothing had happened. There was not the slightest show of exultation, or of a purpose to demand equality, in view of what had taken place. His old manner returned, and he acted as if they were all strangers to him. They exchanged significant, wondering glances, and after a brief consultation retired to the dining-room, where coffee and sandwiches were waiting. Miss Winthrop and Christine sincerely hoped that Miss Brown would invite Dennis out, but she did not, and since it was her house, as she had said, they could not interfere. Dennis heard the clatter of knives and forks, and saw that he was again slighted; but he did not care now. Indeed, in the light of the sacred emblem before which he had stood, he had learned patience. He remembered how the rich and great of the world had treated his Master. Then too Christine's kind, grateful glance seemed to fall upon him like a warm ray of sunlight.

When they had finished and were about to dress for their

parts, Miss Brown put her head within the door and said, "You will find some lunch in the dining-room."

Dennis paid no heed to her, but he heard Miss Winthrop say: "Really, Miss Brown, that is too bad after what he has done and shown himself to be. I wonder that he does not leave the house."

"He will not do that until he is no longer needed," said Christine.

"Then he may as soon as he chooses," said Miss Brown. She was a girl of violent prejudices, and from her very nature would instinctively dislike such a person as Dennis Fleet.

"Well," said Miss Winthrop, "he is a gentleman, and he gave the strongest proof of it when he quietly and modestly withdrew after achieving a success that would have turned any one's head, and that ought to have secured him full recognition."

"I told you he was a gentleman," said Christine, briefly, "and I consider myself a judge;" and then their voices passed out of hearing.

Dennis, having arranged everything so that he could place his hands readily upon it, found that he had half an hour to spare. He said to himself: "Miss Ludolph is wrong. I shall leave the house for a short time. I am a most unromantic individual; for, no matter what or how I feel, I do get hungry. But I am sure Miss Brown's coffee and sandwiches would choke me. I have already swallowed too much from her to care for any more, so here's for a restaurant."

Miss Winthrop hastened through her toilet in order that she might come down and speak to Dennis while he was alone. She wished to thank him for his course and his vindication of the truth, and to assure him that she both respected him and would treat him as a true gentleman. She went into the back parlor, but he was not there; then she passed to the dining-room, but found only servants clearing away and preparing for the grand supper of the evening.

In quick alarm she asked, "Where is Mr. Fleet?"

"Is it the man in the back parlor, mum? He's just after goin' out."

"O girls!" exclaimed Miss Winthrop, rushing upstairs, "Mr. Fleet has gone."

And there was general consternation.

CHAPTER XXIII.

THE REVELATION.

THE toilets of the young ladies were nearly completed, but, without waiting to add another touch, all hastened to the place where they had left Dennis. One of the colorless young ladies appeared upon the scene with a shawl around her bare shoulders, and a great deal of color on one cheek, and none on the other as yet; but this slight discrepancy was unnoted in the dire calamity they feared.

Many were the exclamations and lamentations.

"Why, the people will be here in fifteen minutes," said Miss Winthrop, in a nervous tremor.

"Did he leave no word?" asked Miss Brown of the servants.

"No word, mum," was the dismal echo.

"What shall we do?" they said, looking at one another with blank faces; but none could answer.

"I do hate such proud, freakish people. There is no managing or depending on them," said Miss Brown, spitefully.

Miss Winthrop bit her lips to keep from saying to her hostess what would be more true than polite. There was a flash of anger in Christine's dark blue eyes, and she said, coldly: "I imagine that you have finished the business this time, Miss Brown. But I confess that I am greatly surprised, for he said I could depend upon him for to-night."

"So you can," said Dennis, coming in behind them. "I

am sorry you have had this needless alarm. But the fact is, I am a plain, ordinary mortal, and live in a very material way."

"There was plenty of lunch in the dining-room," said Miss Brown, tartly. "You need not have gone out and made all this trouble."

"Pardon me for slighting your hospitality," said Dennis, with slight emphasis on the word.

Again significant glances were exchanged. Miss Brown darted a black look at Dennis, and left the room.

"I can assure you, ladies," added he, "that all is ready. I can lay my hand in a moment on whatever is needed. Therefore you need give yourselves no further anxiety."

There was a general stampede for the dressing-rooms, but Miss Winthrop lingered. When Dennis was alone she went up to him and frankly gave her hand, saying: "Mr. Fleet, I wish to thank you for your course to-day. Between Miss Ludolph's unwitting sermon and your brave and unexpected vindication of our faith, I hope to become more deserving of the name of Christian. You *are* a gentleman, sir, in the truest and best sense of the word, and as such it will ever be a pleasure to welcome you at my father's house;" and she gave him her card.

A flush of grateful surprise and pleasure mantled Dennis's face, but before he could speak she was gone.

The audience were soon thronging in. By half-past eight the performers were all in the back parlor, and there was a brilliant army of actors and actresses in varied and fanciful costume, many coming to the house dressed for their parts. There were gods and goddesses, shepherds and shepherdesses, angels, crusaders, who would take leave of languishing ladies, living statuary, and tableaux of all sorts. Dennis was much shocked at the manner in which ladies exposed themselves in the name of art and for the sake of effect. Christine seemed perfectly Greek and pagan in this respect, yet there was that in her manner that forbade a wanton glance. But, as he observed the carriage of the men around him, he was more than satisfied that no plea of art could justify the "style," and felt assured that every pure-minded woman would take the same view if she realized the truth. Under the names of fashion and art much is done in society that would be simply monstrous on ordinary occasions.

The music, as far as possible, was in character with the scenes. The entertainment went forward with great applause. Every one was radiant; and the subtile, exhilarating spirit of assured success glowed in every eye, and gave a richer tone and coloring to everything.

Christine appeared in several and varied characters, and Dennis had eyes only for her. The others he glanced over critically as the artist in charge, and then dismissed them from his thoughts; but on Christine his eyes rested in a spell-bound admiration that both amused and pleased her. She loved power of every kind, and when she read approval in the trained and critical eye of Dennis Fleet she knew that all the audience were applauding.

But Dennis had little time for musing, so great was the strain upon him to prevent confusion. His voice excited great surprise and applause, many inquiring vainly who he was. When he and Christine sung together the audience were perfectly carried away, and stormed and applauded without stint. Indeed, it seemed that they could not be satisfied. The call was so urgent that several asked Christine to sing again, and she did so alone. For ten minutes she held the audience perfectly entranced, and no one more so than Dennis. Usually she was too cold in all that she did, but now in her excitement she far surpassed herself, and he acknowledged that he had never heard such music before.

The very soul of song seemed breathed into her, and

every nook and corner of the house appeared to vibrate with melody. Even the servants in distant rooms said that it seemed that an angel was singing. After she ceased, the audience sat spell-bound for a moment, and then followed prolonged thunders of applause, the portly brewer, Mr. Brown himself, leading off again and again.

"Now let the tenor sing alone," he said, for, though a coarse man, he was hearty and good-natured.

The audience emphatically echoed his wish, but Dennis as decidedly shook his head.

Then came a cry, "Miss Ludolph and the tenor again;" and the audience took it up with a clamor that would not be denied.

Christine looked inquiringly at Dennis, and he replied in a low tone, "You command me this evening."

Again she thanked him with her eyes, and from a music stand near chose a magnificent duet from Mendelssohn, in which he must sing several difficult solos.

"Act your pleasure. I am familiar with it," he said, smiling at the way she had circumvented him in his refusal to sing alone.

Christine sat down and played her own accompaniment, while Dennis stood at her side. He determined to do his best and prove that though he swept a store he could also do something else. Many of the strains were plaintive, and his deep and unconscious feeling for his fair companion in song gave to his voice a depth, and at times a pathos, that both thrilled and *touched* the heart, and there were not a few wet eyes in the audience. Unconsciously to himself and all around, he was singing his love; and even Christine, though much preoccupied with her part, wondered at the effect upon herself, and recognized the deep impression made upon the audience.

As the last notes died away the sliding-doors were closed.

Dennis had achieved a greater success than Christine, because, singing from the heart, he had touched the heart. His applause could be read in moist eyes and expressive faces rather than in noisy hands. She saw and understood the result. A sad, disappointed look came into her face, and she said in a low, plaintive tone, as if it were wrung from her: "There must be something wrong about me. I fear I shall never reach true art. I can only win admiration, never touch the heart."

Dennis was about to speak eagerly, when they were overwhelmed by the rush and confusion attendant on the breaking up of the entertainment. Part of the older guests at once left for their homes, and the rest stayed for supper. The parlors were to be cleared as soon as possible for dancing. Christine was joined by her father, who had sat in the audience, scarcely believing his eyes, much less his ears. Was that the young man who was blacking old Schwartz's boots the other day?

His daughter was overwhelmed with compliments, but she took them very coolly and quietly, for her heart was full of bitterness. That which her ambitious spirit most desired she could not reach, and to the degree that she loved art was her disappointment keen. She almost envied poor Dennis, but she knew not the secret of his success; nor did he, either, in truth. His old manner returned, and he busied himself in rapidly packing up everything that he had brought. Mr. Ludolph, who had received a brief explanation from Christine, came and said, kindly, "Why, Fleet, you have blossomed out strongly to-day."

"Indeed, sir, I think I have never had a more rigorous pruning," was the reply.

When the story had been told Mr. Ludolph in full, he understood the remark. Christine was waiting for the crowd to disperse somewhat, in order to speak to Dennis also, for her sense of justice and her genuine admiration impelled her to warm and sincere acknowledgment. But at that moment Mr. Mellen came in, exclaiming, "Miss Ludolph, they are all waiting for you to lead the dance, for to you is given this honor by acclamation, and I plead your promise to be my partner;" and he carried her off, she meaning to return as soon as possible, and supposing Dennis would remain.

A moment after, light, airy music was heard in the front parlor, followed by the rhythmical cadence of light feet and the rustle of silks like a breeze through a forest.

For some reason as she went away Dennis's heart sunk within him. Reaction followed the strong excitements of the day, and a strange sense of weariness and despondency crept over him. The gay music in the other room seemed plaintive and far away, and the tripping feet sounded like the patter of rain on autumn leaves. The very lights appeared to burn dimmer, and the color to fade out of his life. Mechanically he packed up the few remaining articles, to be called for in the morning, and then leaned heavily against a pillar, intending to rest a moment before going out into the night alone.

Some one pushed back the sliding-door a little and passed into the room. Through the opening he caught a glimpse of the gay scene within. Suddenly Christine appeared floating lightly through the waltz in her gauzy drapery, as if in a white, misty cloud. Through the narrow opening she seemed a radiant, living portrait. But her partner whirled her out of the line of vision. Thus in the mazes of the dance she kept appearing and disappearing, flashing in sight one moment, leaving a blank in the crowded room the next.

"So it will ever be, I suppose," he said to himself, bitterly; "chance and stolen glimpses my only privilege."

Again she appeared, smiling archly on the man whose arm clasped her waist.

A frown black as night gathered on Dennis's brow; then a sudden pallor overspread his face to his very lips. The revelation had come! Then for the first time he knew—knew it as if written in letters of fire before him—that he *loved* Christine Ludolph.

At first the knowledge stunned and bewildered him, and his mind was a confused blur; then as she appeared again, smiling upon and in the embrace of another man, a sharp sword seemed to pierce his heart.

Dennis was no faint shadow of a man who had frittered away in numberless flirtations what little heart he originally had. He belonged to the male species, with something of the pristine vigor of the first man, who said of the one woman of all the world, "This is now bone of my bones, and flesh of my flesh;" and one whom he had first seen but a few short months since now seemed to belong to him by the highest and divinest right. But could he ever claim his own?

In his morbid, wearied state, there seemed a "great gulf fixed" between them. For a moment he fairly felt faint and sick, as if he had received a wound. He was startled by hearing Miss Winthrop say at his side: "Mr. Fleet, you will not leave yet. I have many friends wishing an introduction to you. What is the matter? You look as if you were ill."

At her voice he flushed painfully. He was so vividly conscious of his love himself that he felt that every one else must be able to see it, and darkness and solitude now seemed a refuge. Recovering himself by a great effort he said, "Pardon me, I do—I am not well—nothing is the matter—a little rest and I shall be myself again."

"No wonder. You have been taxed every way beyond mortal endurance, and I think that it is a shame the way you have been treated. Pray do not judge Chicago society altogether by what you have seen here. Let me get you some refreshment, and then I will acquaint you with some people who can recognize a gentleman when they meet him."

"No, Miss Winthrop," said Dennis, courteously but firmly; "you are not in your own home, and by staying I should not be accepting your hospitality. I appreciate your kindness deeply, and thank your friends who have expressed a willingness to make my acquaintance. It would not be right to stay longer in this house than is necessary. I do not feel resentful. I have no room in my memory for Miss Brown and her actions, but at the same time self-respect requires that I go at once;" and he took his hat.

"I am not surprised that you feel as you do. But give me the pleasure of welcoming you at my own home as soon as possible," she said, and gave her hand to him in parting.

Dennis took it respectfully and bowed low, saying, "I shall not willingly deny myself so great a pleasure," and was gone.

Christine came in a few moments later, and found only servants clearing the room for dancing.

"Where is Mr. Fleet?" she asked.

"Gone, mum."

"Yes," said Miss Winthrop, coming in at the same time; "he has gone now in very truth; and I don't think the power exists that could lead him to darken these doors again. I doubt if I ever come myself. I never saw a clearer instance of — of — well — *shoddy*."

"It seems to me that you Christians are as proud as any of us."

"Isn't there a difference between pride and self-respect? I am satisfied that if Miss Brown were in trouble, or poor, Mr. Fleet would be the first to help her. O Christine, we have treated him shamefully!"

"You seem to take a wonderful interest in this unknown knight in rusty armor." (Dennis's dress was decidedly threadbare.)

"I do," said the impulsive girl, frankly, "because he is wonderfully interesting. What man of all the large audience present to-night could have acted the part he did? I am satisfied that that man is by birth and education a gentleman. Are you ready, with your aristocratic notions, to recognize chiefly Miss Brown's title to position? What could her coat-of-arms be but the dollar symbol and the beer-barrel?"

"Come, remember she is our hostess."

"You are right; I should not speak so here; but my indignation gets the better of me."

"Would you invite him to your house?"

"Certainly. I have asked him; and what is more, he has promised to come. Supposing that he is poor, are not many of your noblemen as poor as poverty? My parlors shall be haunted only by men of ability and character."

"You are not going to shut out this little heathen," said Christine, putting her arm about her friend.

"Never!" said Miss Winthrop, returning the embrace with double warmth. Then she added, sadly: "You are not an unbeliever from conviction and knowledge, Christine, but from training and association. While I admire and honor your father as a splendid and gifted man, I regret his and your scepticism more deeply than you can ever know."

"Well, Susie," said Christine, with a smile, "if they shut out such as you from your Paradise, I do not wish to go there."

"If, with my clear knowledge of the conditions of entrance, I *shut myself out*, I shall have no right to complain," said Miss Winthrop, sadly.

But the absence of two such belles could not long remain

unnoted; and, having been discovered, they were pounced upon by half a dozen young gentlemen, clamorous for the honor of their hands in the "German."

In spite of herself, Christine was vexed and annoyed. Dennis had seemed, in his obscurity, a nice little bit of personal property, that she could use and order about as she pleased. He had been so subservient and eager to do her will, that she had never thought of him otherwise than as her "humble servant." But now her own hand had suddenly given him the *rôle* of a fine gentleman. Christine was too logical to think of continuing to order about a man who could sing Mendelssohn's music as Dennis had done.

She congratulated herself that the arrangement of the store was nearly completed, and that only one show-room was unfinished.

"I suppose he will be very dignified when we meet again," she thought to herself. "I should not be at all surprised if my impulsive little friend Susie loses her heart to him. Well, I suppose she can to any one she chooses. As for me, rich or poor, stupid or gifted, the men of this land are all alike;" and with a half-sigh she plunged resolutely into the gayeties of the evening, as if to escape from herself.

CHAPTER XXIV.

NIGHT THOUGHTS.

DENNIS passed out of the heavy, massive entrance to the wealthy brewer's mansion with a sense of relief as if escaping from prison. The duskiness and solitude of the street seemed a grateful refuge, and the night wind was to his flushed face like a cool hand laid on a feverish brow. He was indeed glad to be alone, for his was one of those deep, earnest natures that cannot rush to the world in garrulous confidence when disturbed and perplexed. There are many sincere but shallow people who must tell of and talk away every passing emotion. Not of the abundance of their hearts, for abundance there is not, but of the uppermost thing in their hearts their mouths must speak, even though the subjects be of the delicate nature that would naturally be hidden. Such mental constitutions are at least healthful. Concealed trouble never preys upon them like the canker in the bud. Everything comes to the surface and is thrown off.

But at first Dennis scarcely dared to recognize the truth himself, and the thought of telling even his mother was repugnant. For half an hour he walked the streets in a sort of stupor. He was conscious only of a heavy, aching heart and a wearied, confused brain. All the time, however, he knew an event had occurred that must for good or evil affect his entire existence; but he shrunk with nervous dread from grappling with the problem. As the cold air refreshed and revived him, his strong, practical mind took up the question almost without volition, and by reason of his morbid, wearied state, only the dark and discouraging side was presented. The awakening to his love was a very different thing to Dennis, and to the majority in this troubled world, from the blissful consciousness of Adam when for the first time he saw the fair being whom he might woo at his leisure, amid embowering roses, without fear or thought of a rival.

To Dennis the fact of his love, so far from promising to be the source of delightful romance and enchantment, clearly showed itself to be the hardest and most practical question of a life full of such questions.

In his strong and growing excitement he spoke to himself as to a second person: "Oh, I see it all now. Poor, blind fool that I was, to think that by coveting and securing every possible moment in her presence I was only learning to love art! As I saw her to-night, so radiant and beautiful, and yet in the embrace of another man, and that man evidently an ardent admirer, what was art to me? As well might a starving man seek to satisfy himself by wandering through an old Greek temple as for me to turn to art alone. One crumb of warm, manifested love from her would be worth more than all the cold, abstract beauty in the universe. And yet what chance have I? What can I hope for more than a passing thought and a little kindly, condescending interest? Clerk and man-of-all-work in a store, poor and heavily burdened, the idea of my loving one of the most wealthy, admired, and aristocratic ladies in Chicago! It is all very well in story-books for peasants to fall in love with princesses, but in practical Chicago the fact of my attachment to Miss Ludolph would be regarded as one of the richest jokes of the season, and by Mr. Ludolph as such a proof of rusticity and folly as would at once secure my return to pastoral life."

Then hope whispered, "But you can achieve position and wealth as others have done, and then can speak your mind from the standpoint of equality."

But Dennis was in a mood to see only the hopeless side that night, and exclaimed almost aloud: "Nonsense! Can it be even imagined that she, besieged by the most gifted and rich of the city, will wait for a poor unknown admirer? Mr. Mellen, I understand, approaches her from every vantage ground save that of a noble character; but in the fashionable world how little thought is given to this drawback!" and in his perturbation he strode rapidly and aimlessly on, finding some relief in mere physical activity.

Suddenly his hasty steps ceased, and even in the dusk of the street his face gleamed out distinctly, so great was its pallor. Like a ray of light, a passage from the Word of God revealed to him his situation in a new aspect. It seemed to him almost that some one had whispered the words in his ear, so distinctly did they present themselves,—"Be ye not unequally yoked together with unbelievers."

Slowly and painfully he said to himself, as if recognizing the most hopeless barrier that had yet been dwelt upon, "Christine Ludolph is an infidel."

Not only the voice of reason, and of the practical world, but also the voice of God seemed to forbid his love; and the conviction that he must give it all up became as clear as it was painful. The poor fellow leaned his head against the shaggy bark of an elm in a shadowy square which the street-lamps could but faintly penetrate. The night wind swayed the budding branches of the great tree, and they sighed over him as if in sympathy.

The struggle within his soul was indeed bitter, for, though thus far he had spoken hopelessly, he had not been altogether hopeless; but now that conscience raised its impassable wall high as heaven, which he must not break through, his pain was so great as to almost unman him, and such tears as only men can weep fell from his eyes. In anguish he exclaimed, "That which might have been the chief blessing of life has become my greatest misfortune."

Above him the gale caused two fraying limbs to appear to moan in echo of the suffering beneath.

"This then must be the end of my prayers in her behalf, — my ardent hope and purpose to lead her to the truth, — she to walk through honored, sunny paths to everlasting shame and night, and I through dark and painful ways to light and peace, if in this bitter test I remain faithful. Surely there *is* much to try one's faith. And yet it must be so as far as human foresight can judge."

Then a great pity for her swelled his heart, for he felt that her case was the saddest after all, and his tears flowed faster than ever.

Human voices now startled him, — some late revellers passing homeward. The tears and emotion, of which we never think of being ashamed when alone with Nature and its Author, he dreaded to have seen by his fellows, and hastily wiping his eyes, he slunk into the deeper shadow of the tree, and they passed on. Then, an old trait asserting itself, he condemned his own weakness. Stepping from the sheltering trunk against which he was leaning, he stood strong and erect.

The winds were hushed as if expectant in the branches above.

"Dennis Fleet," he said, "you must put your foot on this folly here and now."

He bared his head and looked upward.

"O God," he said, solemnly, "if this is contrary to Thy will — Thy will be done."

He paused a moment reverently, and then turned on his heel and strode resolutely homeward.

A gust of wind crashed the branches overhead together like the clash of cymbals in victory.

The early spring dawn was tingeing the eastern horizon before the gay revel ceased and the mansion of the rich brewer was darkened. All the long night, light, airy music had caused late passers-by to pause a moment to listen, and to pity or envy the throng within, as disposition dictated. Mr. Brown was a man who prided himself on lavish and rather coarse hospitality. A table groaning under costly dishes and every variety of liquor was the crowning feature, the blissful climax of all his entertainments; and society from its highest circles furnished an abundance of anxious candidates for his suppers, who ate and criticised, drank to and disparaged, their plebeian host.

Mrs. Brown was heavy in every sense of the word, and with her huge person draped with acres of silk, and festooned with miles of point-lace, she waddled about and smiled and nodded good-naturedly at everybody and everything.

It was just the place for a fashionable revel, where the gross, repulsive features of coarse excess are veiled and masked somewhat by the glamour of outward courtesy and good-breeding.

At first Christine entered into the dance with great zest and a decided sense of relief. She was disappointed and out of sorts with herself. Again she had failed in the object of her intense ambition, and though conscious that, through the excitement of the occasion, she had sung better than ever before, yet she plainly saw in the different results of her singing and that of Dennis Fleet that there was a depth in the human heart which she could not reach. She could secure only admiration, superficial applause. The sphere of the true artist who can touch and sway the popular heart seemed beyond her ability. By voice or pencil she had never yet attained it. She had too much mind to mistake the character of the admiration she excited, and was far too ambitious to be satisfied with the mere praise bestowed on a highly accomplished girl. She aspired, determined, to be among the first, and to be a second-rate imitator in the world of art was to her the agony of a disappointed life. And yet to imitate with accuracy and skill, not with sympathy, was the only power she had as yet developed. She saw the limitations of her success more clearly than did any one else, and chafed bitterly at the invisible bounds she could not pass.

The excitement of the dance enabled her to banish thoughts that were both painful and humiliating. Moreover, to a nature so active and full of physical vigor, the swift, graceful motion was a source of keen enjoyment.

But when after supper many of the ladies were silly, and the gentlemen were either stupid or excited, according to the action of the "invisible spirit of wine" upon their several constitutions, — when after many glasses of champagne Mr. Mellen began to effervesce in frothy sentimentality and a style of love-making simply nauseating to one of Christine's nature, — she looked around for her father in order to escape from the scenes that were becoming revolting.

Though of earth only in all the sources of her life and hopes, she was not earthy. If her spirit could not soar and sing in the sky, it also could not grovel in the mire of gross materiality. Some little time, therefore, before the company broke up, on the plea of not feeling well she lured her father away from his wine and cigars and a knot of gentlemen who were beginning to talk a little incoherently. Making their adieux amid many protestations against their early departure, they drove homeward.

"How did you enjoy yourself?" asked her father.

"Very much in the early part of the evening, not at all in the latter part. To sum up, I am disgusted with Mr. Mellen and these Browns in general, and myself in particular."

"What is the matter with Mr. Mellen? I understand that the intriguing mammas consider him the largest game in the city."

"When hunting degenerates into the chase and capture of insects, you may style him game. Between his champagne and silly love-making, he was as bad as a dose of ipecac."

Christine spoke freely to her father of her admirers, usually making them the themes of satire and jest.

"And what is the trouble with our entertainers?"

"I am sorry to speak so of any one whose hospitality I have accepted, but unless it is your wish I hope never to accept it again. They all smell of their beer. Everything is so coarse, lavish, and ostentatious. They tell you as through a brazen trumpet on every side, 'We are rich.'"

"They give magnificent suppers," said Mr. Ludolph, in apology.

"More correctly, the French cook they employ gives them. I do not object to the nicest of suppers, but prefer that the Browns be not on the *carte de menu.* From the moment our artistic programme ended, and the entertainment fell into their hands, it began to degenerate into an orgy. Nothing but the instinctive restraints of good-breeding prevents such occasions from ending in a drunken revel."

"You are severe. Mr. Brown's social effort is not a bad type of the entertainments that prevail in fashionable life."

"Well, it may be true, but they never seemed to me so lacking in good taste and refinement before. Wait till we dispense choice viands and wines to choicer spirits in our own land, and I will guarantee a marvellously wide difference. Then the eye, the ear, the mind, shall be feasted, as well as the lower sense."

"Well, I do not see why you should be disgusted with yourself. I am sure that you covered yourself with glory, and were the belle of the occasion."

"That is no great honor, considering the occasion. Father, strange as it may seem to you, I envied your man-of-all-work to-night. Did you not mark the effect of his singing?"

"Yes, and felt it in a way that I cannot explain to myself. His tones seemed to thrill and stir my very heart. I have not been so affected by music for years. At first I thought it was surprise at hearing him sing at all, but I soon found that it was something in the music itself."

"And that something I fear I can never grasp, — never attain."

"Why, my dear, they applauded you to the echo."

"I would rather see one moist eye as the tribute to my singing than to be deafened by noisy applause. I fear I shall never reach high art. Men's hearts sleep when I do my best."

"I think you are slightly mistaken there, judging from your train of admirers," said Mr. Ludolph, turning off a disagreeable subject with a jest. The shrewd man of the world guessed the secret of her failure. She must feel herself, before she could touch feeling. But he had systematically sought to chill and benumb her nature, meaning it to awake at just the time, and under just the circumstances, that should accord with his controlling ambition.

Then reverting to Dennis, he continued: "It won't answer for Fleet to sweep the store any longer after the part he played to-night. Indeed, I doubt if he would be willing to. Not only he, but the world will know that he is capable of better things. What has occurred will awaken inquiry, and may soon secure him good business offers. I do not intend to part readily with so capable a young fellow. He does well whatever is required, and therefore I shall promote him as fast as is prudent. I think I can make him of great use to me."

"That is another thing that provokes me," said Christine. "Only yesterday morning he seemed such a useful, humble creature, and last evening through my own folly he developed into a fine gentleman; and I shall have to say, 'By your leave, sir;' 'Will you please do this?'—if I dare ask anything at all."

"I am not so sure of that," said her father. "My impression is that Fleet has too much good sense to put on airs in the store. But I will give him more congenial work; and as one of the young gentleman clerks, we can ask him up now and then to sing with us. I should much enjoy trying some of our German music with him."

CHAPTER XXV.

DARKNESS.

THE next morning Christine did not appear at the late breakfast at which her father with contracted brow and capricious appetite sat alone. Among the other unexpected results of the preceding day she had taken a very severe cold, and this, with the reaction from fatigue and excitement, caused her to feel so seriously ill that she found it impossible to rise. Her father looked at her, and was alarmed; for her cheeks were flushed with fever, her head was aching sadly, and she appeared as if threatened with one of those dangerous diseases whose earlier symptoms are so obscure and yet so much alike. She tried to smile, but her lip quivered, and she turned her face to the wall.

The philosophy of Mr. Ludolph and his daughter was evidently adapted to fair weather and smooth sailing. Sickness, disease, and the possible results, were things that both dreaded more than they ever confessed to each other. It was most natural that they should, for only in health or life could they enjoy or hope for anything. By their own belief their horizon was narrowed down to time and earth, and they could look for nothing beyond. In Mr. Ludolph's imperious, resolute nature, sickness always awakened anger as well as anxiety. It seemed like an enemy threatening his dearest hopes and most cherished ambition, therefore the heavy frown upon his brow as he pushed away the scarcely tasted breakfast.

To Christine the thought of death was simply horrible, and with the whole strength of her will she ever sought to banish it. To her it meant corruption, dust, nothingness. With a few drawbacks she had enjoyed life abundantly, and she clung to it with the tenacity of one who believed it was all. With the exception of some slight passing indisposition, both she and her father had been seldom ill; and for a number of years now they had voyaged on over smooth, sunny seas of prosperity.

Christine's sudden prostration on the morning following the entertainment was a painful surprise to both.

"I will have Dr. Arten call at once," he said, at parting, "and will come up from the store early in the day to see you;" and Christine was left alone with her French maid.

Her mind was too clouded and disturbed by fever to think coherently, and yet a vague sense of danger — trouble — oppressed her, and while she lay in a half-unconscious state between sleeping and waking, a thousand fantastic visions presented themselves. But in them all the fiery Cross and Dennis Fleet took some part. At times the Cross seemed to blaze and threaten to burn her to a cinder, while he stood by with stern, accusing face. The light from the Cross made him luminous also, and the glare was so terrible that she would start up with a cry of fear. Again, they would both recede till in the far distance they shone like a faint star, and then the black darkness that gathered round her was more dreadful than the light, and with her eyes closed she would reach out her hot hands for the light to return. Once or twice it shone upon her with soft, mellow light, and Dennis stood pointing to it, pleading so earnestly and tenderly that tears gathered in her eyes. Then all was again blurred and distorted.

Within an hour after her father left, she found Dr. Arten feeling her pulse and examining her symptoms. With a great effort she roused herself, and, looking at the doctor with an eager inquiring face, said: "Doctor, tell me the truth. What is the matter?"

He tried to smile and evade her question, but she would not let him.

"Well, really, Miss Ludolph," he said, "we can hardly tell yet what is the matter. You have evidently caught a very severe cold, and I hope that is all. When I come this evening I may be able to speak more definitely. In the mean time I will give you something to soothe and reduce your fever."

The French maid followed the doctor out, leaving the door ajar in her haste, and in an audible whisper said: "I say, docteur, is it not ze small-pox? Zere is so much around. Tell me true, for I must leave zis very minute."

"Hush, you fool!" said the doctor, and they passed out of hearing.

A sickening dread made Christine's heart almost stand still. When the woman returned her mistress watched her most narrowly and asked, "What did the doctor say to you?"

The maid replied in French that he had said she must be still and not talk.

"But you asked him if I had the small-pox. What did he say?"

"Ah, mademoiselle, you make one grand meestake. I ask for a small box to keep your medicine in, zat it make no smell."

From the woman's lie, and from the fact that she was redolent with camphor, and that she kept as far away as possible, near the windows, Christine gathered a most painful confirmation of her fears. For a time she lay almost paralyzed by dread.

Then as the medicine relieved her of fever and unclouded

her mind, thought and conscience awoke with terrible and resistless power. As never before she realized what cold, dark depths were just beneath her gay, pleasure-loving life, and how suddenly skies radiant with the richer promise of the future could become black and threatening. Never had earthly life seemed so attractive, never had her own prospects seemed so brilliant, and her hopes of fame, wealth, and happiness in her future German villa more dazzling, than now when they stood out against the dark background of her fears.

"If, instead of going forward to all this delight, I become an object of terror and loathing even before I die, and something that must be hidden out of sight as soon as possible after, what conceivable fate could be worse? That such a thing is possible proves this to be a dreadful and defective world, with all its sources of pleasure. Surely if there were a God he would banish such horrible evils.

"There is no God, — there can't be any, — at least none such as the Bible reveals. How often I have said this to myself! how often my father has said it to me! and yet the thought of Him torments me often even when well.

"Why does this thought come so persistently now? I settled it long ago, under father's proof, that I did not believe in Him or the superstitions connected with His name. Why doesn't the question stay settled? Other superstitions do not trouble me. Why should that Cross continually haunt me? Why should the *man* who died thereon have the power to be continually speaking to me through His words that I have read? I believe in Socrates as much as I do in Him, and yet I recall the Greek sage's words with an effort, and cannot escape from the Nazarene's. All is mystery and chaos and danger. We human creatures are like frothy bubbles that glisten and dance for a moment on a swift black tide that seems flowing forever, and yet nowhere."

Then her thoughts recurred to Dennis.

"That young Fleet seemed to believe implicitly in what he said yesterday, and he lives up to what he believes. I would give the world for his delusion, were it only for its comforting and sustaining power for this life. If he were very ill, he would be imagining himself on the threshold of some sort of heaven or paradise, and would be calm and perhaps even happy, while I am so supremely wretched. I find that I have nothing, — absolutely nothing to sustain me, — not even the memory of good deeds. I have not even lived the unselfish life that Socrates recommends, much less the holy life of the Bible. I have *pleased myself*. Well, believing as I have been taught, that seemed the most sensible course. Why doesn't it seem so now?"

Thus tossed on a sea of uncertainty and fear, Christine, in darkness and weakness, grappled with those mighty questions which only He can put to rest who said, "Let not your heart be troubled: ye believe in God, believe also in Me."

Dennis walked resolutely home. He felt himself adamant in his stern resolution. He at least had the death-like peace that follows decision. The agony of conflict was over for a time, and, as he thought, forever.

From mere exhaustion he slept heavily, and on the following day with white face and compressed lips entered on his work. And work it now became indeed; for the old glamour was all gone, and life looked as practical and hard as the stones of the street. Even the pictures on the walls seemed to him but things for sale, representing money values; and money appeared the beginning, middle, and ending of the world's creed. Like the unsubstantial mirage had vanished the beautiful, happy life of the past few weeks. Around him were the rocks and sands of the desert, through which he must toil with weary, bleeding feet till he reached the land watered by the river of life. Reason and duty, as he believed, forbade the existence of this foolish passion, and he must and would destroy it; but in his anguish he felt as if he had resolved to torture himself to death.

"And she will never know what I suffer, — never know the wealth of heart I have lavished upon her. I am glad she will not, for the knowledge of my love would make no more impression on her cold, proud nature than a drop of warm summer rain falling on the brow of yonder marble statue of Diana. She would only be amazed at my presumption. She feels that she shines down on me like the sun, and that I am a poor little satellite that she could blot out altogether by causing her father to turn me into the street again, which undoubtedly would be done should I reveal my feelings."

And he was right.

"Come!" said he to himself, breaking from his painful revery, "no weakness! You have your way to make in the world, and your work to do. God will help you, and no creature shall hinder you;" and he plunged resolutely into his duties.

Mr. Ludolph was late in reaching the store that morning, and Dennis found himself secretly hoping, in spite of himself, that Christine would accompany him. His will and heart were now in distinct opposition, and the latter would not obey orders.

When Mr. Ludolph appeared, it was with a frowning, clouded brow. Without a word he passed into his private office, but seemed so restless and troubled in his manner that Dennis felt something was wrong. Why should he take such an interest in this man? Why should he care? The other clerks did not: not one save himself had noticed anything different. Poor Dennis was to learn that he had a disease of many and varied symptoms.

After something over an hour had passed, Mr. Ludolph started from his desk, took his hat and cane as with the purpose of going out,—a very unusual thing at that time. But, as he was passing down the store, he met Dr. Arten opposite Dennis's counter.

"Well?" said Mr. Ludolph, impatiently.

"I will call again this evening," said the doctor, prudently non-committal. "Your daughter has caught a very severe cold. I hope it is nothing more than a cold, but so many troublesome diseases commence with these obscure symptoms that we have to wait till further developments reveal the true nature of the case."

"You doctors make no headway in banishing disease from the world," snarled Mr. Ludolph. "There is small-pox around, is there not?"

"Yes, I am sorry to say there is a great deal of it, but if you remember the history of that one disease, I think you will admit your remark to be unfair."

"I beg your pardon, doctor, but I am anxious, and all out of sorts, as I ever am in sickness" (when affecting himself,—he might justly have added). "It seems such a senseless, useless evil in the world. The idea of you Christians believing a benevolent Being rules the world, and that He permits small-pox. Can it be possible that my daughter has contracted this loathsome horror?"

"Well, it is possible, but I hope not at all probable. We doctors are compelled to look at the practical rather than the theological side of the question. It is possible for *any one* to have this disease. Has your daughter been vaccinated?"

"No!" growled Mr. Ludolph. "I don't believe in vaccination. It is as apt to vitiate the system as to protect it."

"I am sorry for that," said the doctor, looking grave.

Keen Mr. Ludolph saw and read his physician's expression

accurately. Seizing his hand he said, eagerly: "Pardon me, doctor; you can understand a father's feelings. Watch this case night and day. Spare no pains, and be assured I will regret no expense;" and he hastened away to his daughter's bedside.

No prisoner at the bar ever listened with more interest than Dennis. If it had been his own case they were discussing it would not have touched him half so nearly.

But a moment before, Christine in her pride, wealth, and beauty seemed destined to go through life as in a triumphant march. Now he saw her to be a weak human creature, threatened as sorely as the poorest and humblest. Her glorious beauty, even her life, might pass away in Le Grand Hotel as surely as in a tenement house. The very thought thrilled him with fear. Then a great pity rushed into his soul like a tide, sweeping everything before it. His stern resolution to stifle and trample upon his love melted like a snow-wreath, and every interest of life centred in the darkened room where Christine tossed and moaned in the deeper darkness of uncertainty and doubt. The longing to go to her with comfort and help was so intense that it required the utmost effort of reason and will to prevent such rash action. He trembled at himself, — at the strength of his feelings, — and saw that though he might control outward action his heart had gone from him beyond remedy, and that his love, so long unrecognized, was now like the principal source of the Jordan, that springs from the earth a full-grown river, and that he could not help it.

Mr. Ludolph found little comfort at his daughter's bedside. Sending her maid away, who was glad to go, Christine told what she had overheard. Small-pox seemed in the mind of every one, but this was not strange since it was so prevalent in the city.

"O father, what shall I do, — what shall I do, if this

should be the case? Janette will leave me, and there will be no one to take care of me. I know I shall die, and I might as well as to be made hideous by this horrible disease. No, I would rather live, on any terms; for to die is to be nothing. O father, are you sure the Bible is all false? There is so much in it to comfort the sick. If I could only believe in such a life hereafter as Susie Winthrop does, I would as soon die as not."

"No," said Mr. Ludolph, firmly, "your only chance is to get well. There is no use in deceiving ourselves. I have secured the services of the most skilful of physicians, and will see that you have every attention. So try to be as calm as possible, and co-operate with every effort to baffle and banish disease. After all it may be nothing more than a severe cold."

So then in very truth this world was all. In bitterness and dread she realized how slight was her hold upon it. To her healthful body pain was a rare experience, but now her head and every bone ached, and the slightest movement caused increased suffering. But her mental trouble was by far the greatest. Often she murmured to herself, "Oh that I had been trained to the grossest superstitions, so that I might not look down into this black bottomless gulf that unbelief opens at my feet!" and she tossed and moaned most piteously.

Mr. Ludolph returned to the store in an exceedingly worried and anxious state. As he entered he caught Dennis's eager, questioning gaze, and a thought struck him: "Perhaps this young fellow, through his mission school, may know of some good, trustworthy woman who would act as nurse;" and coming to Dennis he explained the situation, and then asked if he knew of any one, or could find a suitable person.

Dennis listened eagerly, thought a moment, and then

said, with a flushed face and in a low tone: "I think my mother would be willing to come. She has had the small-pox and would not be afraid."

"But would she be willing?"

"I think I could persuade her," said Dennis.

Mr. Ludolph thought a moment, then said: "I think she would be the one of all others, for she must be very much of a lady, and I would not like to put my daughter in charge of a common, coarse woman. You may rest assured that I would reward her liberally."

"She would not come for money, sir."

"What then?"

Dennis flushed now more deeply than before. He had been speaking for his mother from his own point of view, and now he hardly knew what to say, for he was not good at evasion. But he told the truth, if not all the truth. "We feel very grateful to you for the means of support, and a chance in life when the world was very dark. You have since promoted me —"

"Nonsense!" said Mr. Ludolph, somewhat touched, though; "you have earned every dollar you have received, and your coming has been of advantage to me also. But if your mother will meet this need, should it occur, neither of you will have cause to regret it;" and he passed on to his office, but soon after went away again and did not return that day.

To Dennis the hours dragged on like years, full of suspense and mental tumult. At times he would bow his head behind his counter, and pray in tearful fervor for the object of his constant thought. The day was rainy, and the store empty of customers, for which he was most thankful, as he would have made the poorest of salesmen. At last the hour for closing arrived, and he was left to himself. In the solitude of his own room he once more looked the situation fairly in the face. With his head bowed in his hands he reflected: "Last night I *thought* to tear this love from my heart, but to-night I find that this would be to tear out my heart itself. I cannot do it. It is my strongest conviction that I can no more stop loving her than I can stop living. Unconsciously this love has grown until now it is my master, and it is folly to make any more resolves, only to be as weak as water when I least expect it. What shall I do?"

Motionless, unconscious of the lapse of time, he remained hour after hour absorbed in painful thought. Circumstances, reason, the Bible, all seemed to frown upon his love; but, though it appeared to be hopeless, his whole nature revolted against the idea of its being wrong.

"It cannot be wrong to love, purely and unselfishly," he muttered. "Such love as mine seems to carry its own conviction of right with it, — an inner consciousness that seems so strong and certain as to be beyond argument, — beyond everything; and yet if God's Word is against it I must be wrong, and my heart is misleading me."

Again in unbroken silence an hour passed away. Then the thought struck him: "It is not contrary to God's action! He so loved the world — unbelievers and all — as to give His best and dearest! Can it be wrong to be God-like?"

"It is not wise, it is not safe," prudence whispered, "to give a worldly, unbelieving spirit the power to influence you that she will have who is first in your heart. What true congeniality can there be? What fellowship hath righteousness with unrighteousness? or what part hath he that believeth with an infidel? As the most intimate friend and companion in life, you should seek one who truly can be *one* with you in all things, and most assuredly so in this vital respect."

"Ah," thought Dennis, "that would have been very good advice to give awhile ago. If from the first I could have understood my feelings and danger, I might have steeled my heart against the influences that have brought me to this. But the mischief is done. The words that now, in spite of myself, continually run in my mind, are, 'What God hath joined together let not man put asunder.' It seems as if some resistless power had joined my soul to hers, and I find no strength within myself to break the bond. I am not usually irresolute; I think I have principle; and yet I feel that I should not dare make the most solemn vow against this love. I should be all the more weak because conscience does not condemn me. It seems to have a light that reason and knowledge know not of. And yet I wish I could be more sure. I wish I could say to myself, I may be loving hopelessly, but not sinfully. I would take the risk. Indeed I cannot help taking it. Oh that I could find light, clear and unmistakable!"

He rose, turned up his light, and opened the Pauline precepts. These words struck his eye, "Art thou bound unto a wife? Seek not to be loosed." Then, above, the words, "How knowest thou, O man, whether thou shalt save thy wife, even though she be an unbeliever?"

"Am I not bound, — bound by that which is God's link in the chain? It does not seem as if the legal contract could change or strengthen my feelings materially, and while honoring the inviolable rite of marriage, which is God's law and society's safety, I know that nothing can more surely bind me to her, so that the spirit, the vital part of the passage, applies to me. Then if through this love I could save her, — if by prayer and effort I could bring her feet into the paths of life, — I should feel repaid for all that I could possibly suffer. She may slight my human love with its human consummation, but God will not let a life of prayer and true love be wasted, and she may learn here, or know hereafter, that though the world laid many rich gifts at her feet I brought the best of all."

He looked out, and saw that the early spring dawn was tingeing the horizon.

"A good omen," he said aloud. "Perhaps the night of this trouble is past, and the dawn is coming. I am convinced that it is not wrong; and I am resolved to make the almost desperate attempt. A mysterious hope, coming from I know not where or what, seems to beckon and encourage me forward."

Dennis was young.

CHAPTER XXVI.

MISS LUDOLPH COMMITS A THEFT.

MR. LUDOLPH on his return found Christine suffering from a nervous horror of the small-pox. From the indiscreet and callous maid, intent on her own safety, and preparing to palliate the cowardice of her flight should her fears prove true, Christine learned that the city was full of this loathsome disease, and her feelings were harrowed by exaggerated instances of its virulent and contagious character.

"But you will surely stay with me," pleaded Christine.

"Mademoiselle could not expect zat."

"Heartless!" muttered Christine. Then she said: "Won't you go for Susie Winthrop? Oh, how I would like to see her now!"

"She vould not come; no von vould come who knew."

Christine wrung her hands and cried, "Oh, I shall die alone and deserted of all!"

"No, you shall not," said her father, entering at that moment; "so do not give way, my dear. — Leave the room, stupid!" (to the maid, who again gladly escaped, resolving not to re-enter till the case was decided). "I have secured the best of physicians, and the best of nurses, and by to-night or to-morrow morning we shall know about what to expect. I cannot help hoping still that it is only a severe cold." And he told her of Dennis's offer of his mother's services.

"I am sure I should like her, for somehow I picture to myself a kind, motherly person. What useful creatures those Fleets are! They are on hand in emergencies when one so needs help. It seemed very nice to have young Fleet my humble servant; but really, father, he deserves promotion."

"He shall have it, and I doubt not will be just as ready to do your bidding as ever. It is only commonplace people whose heads are turned by a little prosperity. Fleet knew he was a gentleman before he came to the store."

"Father, if I should have the small-pox and live, would my beaut — would I become a fright?"

"Not necessarily. Let us hope for the best. Make the most of the world, and never endure evils till they come, are my maxims. Half of suffering is anticipation of possible or probable evil."

"Father," said Christine, abruptly, "I believe you are right, you *must* be right, and have given me the best comfort and hope that truthfully can be given. But this is a strange, cruel world. We seem the sport of circumstances, the victims of hard, remorseless laws. One bad person can frightfully injure another person" (a spasm distorted her father's face). "What accidents may occur! Worst of all are those horrible, subtle, contagious diseases which none can see or guard against! Then to suffer, die, corrupt, — faugh! To what a disgusting end, to what a lame and impotent conclusion, does the noble creature, man, come! My whole nature revolts at it. For instance, here am I a young girl, capable of the highest enjoyment, with everything to live for, and lured forward by the highest hopes and expectations; and yet, in spite of all the safeguards you can place around me, my path is in the midst of dangers, and now perhaps I am to be rendered hideous, if not killed outright, by a disease the very thought of which fills me with loathing. What I fear *has* happened, and may happen again. And what compensation is there for it all? — what can enable one to bear it all? Oh that I could believe in a God and a future happier life!"

"And what kind of a God would He be who, having the power to prevent, permits, or orders, as the Bible teaches, all these evils? I am a man of the world, and pretend to nothing saint-like or chivalric, but do you think I am capable of going to Mr. Winthrop and striking down his daughter Susie with a loathsome disease? And yet if a minister or priest should come here he would begin to talk about the mysterious providence, and submission to God's will. If I am to have a God, I want one at least better than myself."

"You *must* be right," said Christine, with a weary moan. "There is no God, and if there were, in view of what you say, I could only hate and fear Him. How chaotic the world is! But it is hard." After a moment she added, shudderingly: "*It is horrible.* I did not think of these things when well."

"Get well and forget them again, my dear. It is the best you can do."

"If I get well," said Christine, almost fiercely, "I shall get the most I can out of life, cost what it may;" and she turned her face to the wall.

A logical result of his teaching, but for some reason it awakened in Mr. Ludolph a vague foreboding.

The hours dragged on, and late in the afternoon the hard-driven physician appeared, examined his patient, and seemed relieved.

"If there is no change for the worse," he said, cheerily, "if no new symptoms develop by to-morrow, I can pronounce this merely a severe cold, caused by the state of the system and too sudden check of perspiration;" and the doctor gave an opiate and bowed himself out.

Long and heavily Christine slept. The night that Dennis

filled with agonizing prayer and thought was to her a blank. While he in his strong Christian love brought heaven nearer to her, while he resolved on that which would give her a chance for life, happy life, here and hereafter, she was utterly unconscious. No vision or presentiment of good, like a struggling ray of light, found access to her darkened spirit. So heavy was the stupor induced by the opiate, that her sleep seemed like the blank she so feared, when her brilliant, ambitious life should end in nothingness.

So I suppose God's love meditates good, and resolves on life and joy for us, while our hearts are sleeping, dead to Him, benumbed and paralyzed so that only His love can awaken them. Like a vague yet hope-inspiring dream, this truth often enters the minds of those who are wrapped in the spiritual lethargy that may end in death. God wakes, watches, loves, and purposes good for them. When we are most unconscious, perhaps another effort for our salvation has been resolved upon in the councils of heaven.

But ambition more than love, earthly hopes rather than heavenly, kept Mr. Ludolph an anxious watcher at Christine's side that night. A smile of satisfaction illumined his somewhat haggard face as he saw the fever pass away and the dew of natural moisture come out on Christine's brow, but there was no thankful glance upward. Immunity from loathsome disease was due only to chance and the physician's skill, by his creed.

The sun was shining brightly when Christine awoke and by a faint call startled her father from a doze in the great arm-chair.

"How do you feel, my dear?" he asked.

She languidly rubbed her heavy eyes, and said she thought she was better, — she felt no pain. The opiate had not yet lost its effect. But soon she greatly revived, and when the doctor came he found her decidedly better, and concluded that she was merely suffering from a severe cold, and would soon regain her usual health.

Father and daughter were greatly relieved, and their spirits rose.

"I really feel as if I ought to thank somebody," said Christine. "I am not going to thank the doctor, for I know what a bill is coming, so I will thank you. It was very kind of you to sit up the long night with me."

Even Mr. Ludolph had to remember that he had in his anxiety thought as much of himself as of her.

"Another lease of life," said Christine, dreamily looking into the future; "and, as I said last night, I mean to make the most of it."

"I can best guide you in doing that," said her father, looking into his daughter's face with keen scrutiny.

"I believe you, and intend to give you the chance. When can we leave this detested land, this city of shops and speculators? To think that I, Christine Ludolph, am sick, idle, and perhaps have endangered all by reason of foolish exposure in a brewer's tawdry, money-splashed house! Come, father, when is the next scene in the brief drama to open? I am impatient to go *home* to our beloved Germany and enter on real life."

"Well, my dear, if all goes well, we can enter on our true career a year from next fall, — a short year and a half. Do not blame the delay, for it will enable us to live in Germany in almost royal style. I never was making money so rapidly as now. I have invested in that which cannot depreciate, and thus far has advanced beyond belief, — buildings in the business part of the city. Rents are paying me from twenty to a hundred per cent. At the same time I could sell out in a month. So you see you have only to co-operate with me, — to preserve health and strength, — to enjoy all that money can insure; and money can buy almost everything."

Christine's eyes sparkled as the future opened before her, and she said, with emphasis, "If *I* could preserve health and strength, I would live a thousand years."

"You can do much toward it. Every chance is in favor of prudence and wise action;" and, much relieved, her father went to the store.

Business had accumulated, and in complete absorption he gave himself to it. With an anxiety beyond expression, Dennis, flushed and trembling, ventured to approach. Merely glancing to see who it was, Mr. Ludolph, with his head bent over his writing, said, "Miss Ludolph is better — no fear of small-pox, I think — you need not write to your mother — greatly obliged."

It was well for Dennis that his employer did not look up. The open face of Mr. Ludolph's clerk expressed more than friendly interest in his daughter's health. The young man went to his tasks with a mountain of fear lifted from his heart.

But the thought of the beloved one lying alone and sick at the hotel seemed very pathetic to him. Love filled his heart with more sympathy for Christine upon her luxurious couch, in rapid convalescence, than for all the hopeless suffering of Chicago. What could he do for her? She seemed so far off, so high and distant, that he could not reach her. If he ventured to send anything, prudence whispered that she would regard it as an impertinence. But love can climb every steep place, and prudence is not its grand-vizier.

Going by a fruit-store in the afternoon he saw some fine strawberries, the first in from the South. He bought a basket, decorated it with German ivy obtained at a flower-stand, and spirited it upstairs to his room as if it were the most dangerous of contraband. In a disguised hand he wrote on a card, "For Miss Ludolph." Calling Ernst, who had little to do at that hour of the day, he said: "Ernst, my boy, take this parcel to Le Grand Hotel, and say it is for Miss Christine Ludolph. Tell them to send it right up, but on no account — remember, on no account — tell any one who sent it. Carry it carefully in just this manner."

Ernst was soon at his destination, eager to do anything for his friend.

After all, the day had proved a long one for Christine. Unaccustomed to the restraints of sickness, she found the enforced inaction very wearisome. Mind and body both seemed weak. The sources of chief enjoyment when well seemed powerless to contribute much now. In silken robe she reclined in an arm-chair, or languidly sauntered about the room. She took up a book only to throw it down again. Her pencil fared no better. Ennui gave to her fair young face the expression of one who had tried the world for a century and found it wanting. She was leaning her elbow on the window sill, gazing vacantly into the street, when Ernst appeared.

"Janette," she said, suddenly, "do you see that boy? He is employed at the store. Go bring him up here; I want him;" and with more animation than she had shown that day she got out materials for a sketch.

"I must get that boy's face," she said, "before good living destroys all his artistic merit."

Ernst was unwilling to come, but the maid almost dragged him up.

"What have you got there?" asked Miss Ludolph, with a reassuring smile.

"Something for Miss Ludolph," stammered the boy, looking very much embarrassed.

Christine carefully opened the parcel and then exclaimed with delight: "Strawberries, as I live! the very ambrosia of the gods. Papa sent them, did he not?"

"No," said the boy, hanging his head.

"Who did, then?" said Christine, looking at him keenly.

He shuffled uneasily, but made no answer.

"Come, I insist on knowing," she cried, her wilful spirit and curiosity both aroused.

The boy was pale and frightened, and she was mentally taking notes of his face. But he said, doggedly, "I can't tell."

"But I say you must. Don't you know that I am Miss Ludolph?"

"I don't care what you do to me," said the little fellow, beginning to cry, "I won't tell."

"Why won't you tell, my boy?" said Christine, cunningly, in a wheedling tone of voice.

Before he knew it, the frightened, bewildered boy fell into the trap, and he sobbed, "Because Mr. Fleet told me not to, and I wouldn't disobey him to save my life."

A look of surprise, and then a broad smile, stole over the young girl's face, — at the gift, the messenger, and at him who sent it. It was indeed a fresh and unexpected little episode, breaking the monotony of the day, — as fresh and pleasing to her as one of the luscious berries so grateful to her parched mouth.

"You need not tell me," she said, soothingly, "if Mr. Fleet told you not to."

The boy saw the smile, and in a moment realized that he had been tricked out of the forbidden knowledge.

His little face glowed with honest indignation, and looking straight at Miss Ludolph, with his great eyes flashing through the tears, he said, "You stole that from me."

Even she colored a little and bit her lip under the merited charge. But all this made him all the more interesting as an art study, and she was now sketching away rapidly. She coolly replied, however, "You don't know the world very well yet, my little man."

The boy said nothing, but stood regarding her with his unnaturally large eyes filled with anger, reproach, and wonder.

"Oh," thought Christine, "if I could only paint that expression!"

"You seem a great friend of Mr. Fleet," she said, studying and sketching him as if he had been an inanimate object.

The boy made no answer.

"Perhaps you do not know that I am a friend,—friendly," she added, correcting herself, "to Mr. Fleet also."

"Mr. Fleet never likes to have his friends do wrong," said the boy, doubtingly.

Again she colored a little, for Ernst's pure and reproachful face made her feel that she had done a mean thing, but she laughed and said: "You see I am not in his mission class, and have never had the instruction that you have. But, after all, why do you think Mr. Fleet better than other people?"

"By what he does."

"That is a fair test; what has he done?"

"He saved us all from starving, and worse than starving."

Then with feminine tact she drew from him his story, and it was told with deep feeling and the natural pathos of childhood, and his gratitude caused him to dwell with a simple eloquence on the part Dennis had taken, while his rich and loved German accent made it all the more interesting to Christine. She dropped her pencil, and, when he finished, her eyes, that were seldom moistened by the dew of sympathy, were wet.

"Good-by, my child," she said, in a voice so kind and sweet that it seemed as if another person had spoken. "You shall come again, and then I shall finish my sketch. When I get well I shall go to see your father's picture. Do not be afraid; neither you nor Mr. Fleet will fare the worse for the strawberries, and you may tell him that they have done me much good."

When Dennis, wondering at Ernst's long absence, heard from him his story, his mind was in a strange tumult, and yet the result of his effort seemed favorable. But he learned more fully than ever that Christine was not perfect, and that her faultless beauty and taste were but the fair mask of a deformed spirit. But he dwelt in hope on the feeling she had shown at Ernst's story.

"She seemed to have two hearts," said the boy,—"a good, kind one way inside the cold, hard outside one."

"That is about the truth," thought Dennis. "Good-night, Ernst. I don't blame you, my boy, for you did the best you could."

He had done better than Dennis knew.

CHAPTER XXVII.

A MISERABLE TRIUMPH.

AFTER Ernst's departure Christine reclined wearily in her chair, quite exhausted by even the slight effort she had made, but her thoughts were busy.

"What a unique character that Dennis Fleet is! And yet, in view of what he believes and professes, he is both natural and consistent. He seems humble only in station, and that is not his fault. Everything he does seems marked by unusual good taste and intelligence. His earlier position and treatment in the store must have been very galling. I can hardly believe that the gentleman I sang Mendelssohn's music with the other evening was the same that I laughed at as he blacked old Schwartz's boots. And yet he saw me laugh, and blacked the boots, conscious that he was a gentleman. It must have been very hard. And yet I would rather do such work myself than live on charity, and so undoubtedly he felt. It is very fortunate that we nearly finished the rearrangement of the pictures before all this occurred, for I could not order him about now as I have done. The fact is, I like servants, not dignified helpers; and knowing what I do, even if he would permit it, I could not speak to him as formerly. But he did show wonderful taste and skill in his help. See now that little ivy-twined basket of luscious fruit: it looks just like him. If he were only rich and titled, what a genuine nobleman he would make! He is among the few men who do not weary or disgust me; so many are coarse and commonplace. I cannot understand it, but I, who fear and care for no one except my father, almost feared him when under Miss Brown's insolence he looked as few men can. What a jumble the world is! He sweeps the store, while insignificant atoms of men are conspicuous in their littleness by reason of high position.

"It was very kind of him to send me this tasteful gift after the miserable experience I caused him the other day. I suppose he does it on the principle of returning good for evil, as his creed teaches. Moreover, he seems grateful that father gave him employment, and a chance to earn twice what he receives. He certainly must be promoted at once.

"Perhaps," thought she, smiling to herself, while a faint tinge of color came into her cheeks, — "perhaps, like so many others, he may be inclined to be a little sentimental also, though he will never be as silly as some of them.

"What a noble part he acted toward those Bruders! The heart of a pagan could not fail to be touched by that poor little fellow's story, and it has made me believe that I have more heart than I supposed. Sometimes, especially when I hear or read of some such noble deed, I catch glimpses of a life infinitely better than the one I know, like the sun shining through a rift in the clouds; then they shut down again, and father's practical wisdom seems the best there is.

"At any rate," she said aloud, getting up and walking the floor with something of the old restless energy, "I intend to live while I live, and crowd into life's brief day all that I can. I thank Mr. Fleet for a few sensations in what would otherwise have been a monotonous, dreary afternoon."

"What, strawberries!" said Mr. Ludolph, coming in. "Where did you get these? They are the first I have seen."

"Your man-of-all-work sent them to me," said Christine, daintily dipping one after another in sugar.

"Well, that is a good joke."

"A most excellent one, which I am enjoying, and in which you may share. Help yourself."

"And what has led him to this extravagant favor?"

"Consistency, I suppose. As a good Christian he would return good for evil; and I certainly caused him many and varied tortures the other day."

"No, he is grateful; from first to last the callow youth has been overwhelmed with gratitude that I have permitted him to be worth to me double what I paid him."

"Well, you have decided to promote him, have you not?"

"Yes, he shall have charge of the hanging of new pictures, and the general arrangement of the store, so as to keep up your tasteful and artistic methods. Moreover, he shall meet customers at the door, and direct them just where to find what they want. He is fine-looking, polite, speaks English perfectly, and thus takes well. I can gradually work him in as general salesman, without creating troublesome jealousies."

"What will old Schwartz say?"

"Schwartz is good at finance and figures. I can trust him, and he must relieve me more in this respect. He of course knows that this is the more important work, and will feel honored. As to the others, if they do not like it I can find plenty who will. Fleet's good fortune will take him quite by surprise. He was performing his old humble duties as briskly and contentedly as usual to-day."

"I am surprised at that, for I should have supposed that he would have been on his dignity somewhat, indicating by manner at least that the time for a change had come. He can indicate a great deal by manner, as you might have learned had you seen him under Miss Brown's insults and my lack of courtesy. Well, it does me good to find one American whose head is not turned by a little success. You are right though, I think, father; that young fellow can be very useful to you, and a decided help in hastening the time when we can leave this shop life, and enter our true sphere. I am more impatient to go than words can express, for life seems so brief and uncertain that we must grasp things as soon as possible or we lose them forever. Heavens! what a scare I have had! Everything seemed slipping from under my feet yesterday, and I sinking I know not where. Surely by concentrating every energy we can be ready to go by a year from next fall."

"Yes, that is my plan now."

On the following day Dennis was again promoted and his pay increased. A man more of the Pat Murphy type was found to perform the coarse work of the store. As Mr. Ludolph had said, Dennis could hardly realize his good fortune. He felt like one lifted out of a narrow valley to a breezy hillside. He was now given a vantage-point from which it seemed that he could climb rapidly, and his heart was light as he thought of what he would be able to do for his mother and sisters. Hope grew sanguine as he saw how he would now have the means to pursue his beloved art-studies to far greater advantage. But, above all, his promotion brought him nearer the object of his all-absorbing passion. What he feared would take him one or two years to accomplish he had gained in a day. Hope whispered that perhaps it was through her influence in some degree that he had obtained this advance. Could she have seen and read his ardent glances? Lovers' hopes will grow like Jonah's gourd, and die down as quickly. Words could not express his longing to see her again, but for several days she did not come to the store. She merely sent him word to complete the unfinished show-room in accordance with the plan on which they had been working, leaving space on the sides of the room opposite each other for two large pictures. Though much disappointed, Dennis had carefully carried out her bidding.

Every evening the moment his duties permitted he sought his instructor, Mr. Bruder, and, with an eagerness that his friends could not understand, sought to educate hand and eye. Dennis judged rightly that mere business success would never open to him a way to the heart of such a girl as Christine. His only hope of winning even her attention was to excel in the world of art, where she hoped to shine as a queen. Then to his untiring industry and eager attention he added real genius for his tasks, and it was astonishing what progress he made. When at the close of his daily lesson Dennis had taken his departure, Mr. Bruder would shake his head, and cast up his eyes in wonder, and exclaim: "Dot youth vill astonish de vorld yet. Never in all Germany haf I seen such a scholar."

Often till after midnight he would study in the solitude of his own little room. And now, relieved of duties in the early morning, he arranged an old easel in the attic of the store, a sort of general lumber-room, yet with a good light for his purpose. Here he secured two good hours daily, and often more, for painting; and his hand grew skilful, and his eye true, under his earnest efforts. But his intense application caused his body to grow thin and his face pale.

Christine had rapidly recovered from her illness, her vital and elastic constitution rebounding back into health and vigor like a bow rarely bent. She, too, was working scarcely less eagerly than Dennis, and preparing for a triumph which she hoped would be the earnest of the fame she meant to achieve. She no longer came to the store with her father in the morning, but spent the best and early hours of the day in painting, riding out along the lake and in the park in the afternoon. Occasionally she came to the store in the after part of the day, glanced sharply round to see that her tasteful arrangement was kept up, and ever seemed satisfied.

Dennis was usually busy with customers at that time, and, though conscious of her presence the moment she entered, found no excuse or encouragement to approach. The best he ever received from her was a slight smile and a cold bow of recognition, and in her haste and self-absorption she did not always give these. She evidently had something on her mind by which it was completely occupied.

"She does not even think of me," sighed Dennis; "she evidently imagines that there is an immeasurable distance between us yet."

He was right; she did not think of him, and scarcely thought of any one else, so absorbed was she in the hope of a great success that now was almost sure. She had sent her thanks for the berries by her father, which so frightened Dennis that he had ventured on no more such favors. She had interceded for his promotion. Surely she had paid her debt, and was at quits. So she would have been if he had only given her a basket of strawberries, but having given his heart, and life-long love, he could scarcely be expected to be satisfied. But he vowed after each blank day all the more resolutely that he would win her attention, secure recognition of his equality, and so be in position for laying siege to her heart.

But a deadly blight suddenly came over all his hopes.

One bright morning late in May two large flat boxes were brought to the store. Dennis was busy with customers, and Mr. Schwartz said, in his blunt, decided way, that he would see to the hanging of those pictures. They were carried to the show-room in the rear of the store, and Dennis at once concluded that they were something very fine, designed to fill the spaces he had left, and was most anxious to see them. Before he was disengaged they were lifted from their casing and were standing side by side on the floor, opposite the entrance, the warm rich morning light falling upon them with fine effect. Mr. Schwartz seemed unusually excited and perplexed for him, and stared first at one picture, then at the other, in a manner indicating that not their beauty, but some other cause disturbed him.

Dennis had scarcely had time to exclaim at the exquisite loveliness and finish of the two paintings before Mr. Ludolph entered, accompanied by Mr. Cornell, a well-known artist, Mr. French, proprietor of another large picture-store, and several gentlemen of taste, but of lesser note, whom Dennis had learned to know by sight as *habitués* of the "Temple of Art." He also saw that Christine was advancing up the store with a lady and gentleman. Feeling that his presence might be regarded as obtrusive, he passed out, and was about to go away, when he heard his name called.

Looking up he saw Miss Winthrop holding out her hand, and in a moment more she presented him to her father, who greeted him cordially. Christine also gave him a brief smile, and said: "You need not go away. Come and see the pictures."

Quick-eyed Dennis observed that she was filled with suppressed excitement. Her cheeks, usually but slightly tinged with pink, now by turns glowed and were pale. Miss Winthrop seemed to share her nervousness, though what so excited them he could not divine. The paintings, beautiful as they were, could scarcely be the adequate cause; and yet every eye was fastened on them.

One seemed the exact counterpart of the other in frame and finish as well as subject. A little in the background, upon a crag overhanging the Rhine, was a castle, massive, frowning, and built more for security and defence than comfort. The surrounding landscape was bold, wild, and even gloomy. But in contrast with these rugged and sterner features, was a scene of exquisite softness and tenderness. Beneath the shadow of some great trees not far from the castle gate, a young crusader was taking leave of his fair-haired bride. Her pale, tearful face, wherein love and grief blent indescribably, would move the most callous heart, while the struggle between emotion and the manly pride that would not permit him to give way, in the young chieftain's features, was scarcely less touching. Beautiful as were the accessories of the pictures, their main point was to portray the natural, tender feeling induced by a parting that might be forever. At first they all gazed quietly and almost reverently at the vivid scene of human love and sorrow, save old Schwartz, who fidgeted about as Dennis had never seen him before. Clearly something was wrong.

"Mr. Schwartz," said Mr. Ludolph, "you may hang the original picture on the side as we enter, and the copy opposite. We would like to see them up, and in a better light."

"Dat's it," snorted Mr. Schwartz; "I'd like to know vich is vich."

"You do not mean to say that you cannot tell them apart? The original hung here some time, and you saw it every day."

"I do mean to say him," said Mr. Schwartz, evidently much vexed with himself. "I couldn't have believed dat any von in de vorld could so impose on me. But de two pictures are just de same to a pin scratch in frame, subject, and treatment, and to save my life I cannot tell dem apart."

Christine's face fairly glowed with triumph, and her eyes were all aflame as she glanced at her friend. Miss Winthrop came and took her cold, quivering hands into her own warm palms, but was scarcely less excited. Dennis saw not this side scene, so intent was he on the pictures.

"Do you mean to say," said Mr. Cornell, stepping forward,

"that one of these paintings is a copy made here in Chicago, and that Mr. Schwartz cannot tell it from the original?"

"He says he cannot," said Mr. Ludolph.

"And I'd like to see the von who can," said old Schwartz, gruffly.

"Will you please point out the original," said one of the gentlemen, "that we may learn to distinguish them? For my part they seem like the twins whose mother knew them apart by pink and white ribbons, and when the ribbons got mixed she could not tell which was which."

Again Christine's eyes glowed with triumph.

"Well, really, gentlemen," said Mr. Ludolph, "I would rather you would discover the copy yourselves. Mr. Cornell, Mr. French, and some others, I think, saw the original several times."

"Look at Mr. Fleet," whispered Miss Winthrop to Christine.

She looked, and her attention was riveted to him. Step by step, he had drawn nearer, and his eyes were eagerly glancing from one picture to the other as if following up a clue. Instinctively she felt that he would solve the question, and her little hands clenched, and her brow grew dark.

"Really," said Mr. Cornell, "I did not know that we had an artist in Chicago who could copy the work of one of the best European painters so that there need be a moment's hesitancy in detecting differences, but it seems I am mistaken. I am almost as puzzled as Mr. Schwartz."

"The frames are exactly alike," said Mr. French.

"There is a difference between the two pictures," said Mr. Cornell, slowly. "I can feel it rather than see it. They seem alike, line for line and feature for feature, in every part; and just where the difference lies and in what it consists I cannot tell for the life of me."

With the manner of one who had settled a difficult problem, Dennis gave a sigh of relief so audible that several glanced at him.

"Perhaps Mr. Fleet from his superior knowledge and long experience can settle this question," said Christine, sarcastically.

All eyes were turned toward him. He flushed painfully, but said nothing.

"Speak up," said Mr. Ludolph, good-naturedly, "if you have any opinion to give."

"I would not presume to give my opinion among so many more competent judges."

"Come, Mr. Fleet," said Christine, with a covert taunt in her tone, "that is a cheap way of making a reputation. I fear the impression will be given that you have no opinion."

Dennis was now very pale, as he ever was under great excitement. The old look came again that the young ladies remembered seeing at Miss Brown's entertainment.

"Come, speak up if you can," said Mr. Ludolph, shortly.

"Your porter, Mr. Ludolph?" said Mr. Cornell, remembering Dennis only in that capacity. "Perhaps he has some private marks by which he can enlighten us."

Dennis now acted no longer as porter or clerk, but as a man among men.

Stepping forward and looking Mr. Cornell full in the face he said; "I can prove to you, sir, that your insinuation is false by simply stating that I never saw those pictures before. The original had been removed from the store before I came. I have had therefore no opportunity of knowing the copy from the original. But the pictures are different, and I can tell precisely wherein I think the difference lies."

"Tell it then," said several voices. Christine stood a little back and on one side, so that he could not see her face, or he would have hesitated long before he spoke. In the firm, decided tones of one thoroughly aroused and sure of his ground, he proceeded.

"Suppose this the copy," said he, stepping to one of the pictures. (Christine breathed hard and leaned heavily against her friend.) "I know of but one in Chicago capable of such exquisite work, and he did not do it; indeed he could not, though a master in art."

"You refer to Mr. Bruder?" said Mr. Cornell.

Dennis bowed and continued: "It is the work of one in whom the imitative power is wonderfully developed; but one having never felt — or unable to feel — the emotions here presented cannot portray them. This picture is but the beautiful corpse of that one. While line for line, and feature for feature, and even leaf for leaf on the trees is faithfully exact, yet the soul, the deep, sorrowful tenderness that you feel in that picture rather than see, is wanting in this. In that picture you forget to blame or praise, to criticise at all, so deeply are your sympathies touched. It seems as if in reality two human hearts were being torn asunder before you. This you know to be an exquisite picture only, and can coolly criticise and dwell on every part, and say how admirably it is done."

And Dennis bowed and retired.

"By Jove, he is right," exclaimed Mr. Cornell; and approving faces and nodding heads confirmed his judgment. But Dennis enjoyed not his triumph, for as he turned he met Christine's look of agony and hate, and like lightning it flashed through his mind, "She painted the picture."

CHAPTER XXVIII.

LIFE WITHOUT LOVE.

AS Dennis realized the truth, and remembered what he had said, his face was scarcely less full of pain than Christine's. He saw that her whole soul was bent on an imitation that none could detect, and that he had foiled her purpose. But Christine's wound was deeper than that. She had been told again, clearly and correctly, that the sphere of high, true art was beyond her reach. She felt that the verdict was true, and her own judgment confirmed every word Dennis uttered. But she had done her best; therefore her suffering was truly agony, — the pain and despair at failure in the most cherished hope of life. There seemed a barrier which, from the very limitations of her being, she could not pass. She did not fail from the lack of taste, culture, or skill, but in that which was like a sixth sense, — something she did not possess. Lacking the power to touch and move the heart, she knew she could never be a great artist.

Abruptly and without a word she left the room and store, accompanied by the Winthrops. Dennis felt as if he could bite his tongue out, and Christine's face haunted him like a dreadful apparition. Wherever he turned he saw it so distorted by pain, and almost hate, that it scarcely seemed the same that had smiled on him as he entered at her invitation.

"Truly God is against all this," groaned he, to himself; "and what I in my weakness could not do He has accomplished by this unlooked-for scene. She will now ever regard me with aversion."

Dennis, like many another, thought he saw God's plan clearly from a mere glimpse of a part of it. He at once reached this miserable conclusion, and suffered as greatly as if it had been God's will, instead of his own imagination. To wait and trust is often the latest lesson we learn in life.

Mr. Ludolph's guests, absorbed in the pictures, at first scarcely noticed the departure of the others.

Christine, with consummate skill and care, kept her relationship to the picture unknown to all save the Winthrops, meaning not to acknowledge it unless she succeeded. But in Dennis's startled and pained face she saw that he had read her secret, and this fact also annoyed her much.

"I should like to know the artist who copied this painting," said Mr. Cornell.

"The artist is an amateur, and not willing to come before the public at present," said Mr. Ludolph, so decidedly that no further questions were asked.

"I am much interested in that young clerk of yours," said Mr. French. "He seems to understand himself. It is so hard to find a good discriminating judge of pictures. Do you expect to keep him?"

"Yes, I do," said Mr. Ludolph, with such emphasis that his rival in trade pressed that point also no further.

"Well, really, Mr. Ludolph," said one of the gentlemen, "you deal in wonders, mysteries, and all sorts of astonishing things here. We have an unknown artist in Chicago deserving an ovation; you have in your employ a prince of critics, and if I mistake not he is the same who sang at Brown's some little time ago. Miss Brown told me that he was your porter."

"Yes, I took him as a stranger out of work and knew nothing of him. But he proved to be an educated and accomplished man, who will doubtless be of great use to me in time. Of course I promoted him when I found him out." These last remarks were made for Mr. French's benefit rather than for any one's else. He intended that his rival should knowingly violate all courtesy if he sought to lure Dennis away. After admiring the paintings and other things recently received, the gentlemen bowed themselves out.

On leaving the store Mr. Winthrop — feeling awkward in the presence of the disappointed girl — had pleaded business, and bidden her adieu with a warm grasp of the hand and many assurances that she had succeeded beyond his belief.

"I know you mean kindly in what you say," said Christine while not the slightest gleam lighted up her pale, sad face "Good-by."

She, too, was relieved, and wished to be alone. Miss Winthrop sought to comfort her friend as they walked homeward.

"Christine, you look really ill. I don't see why you take this matter so to heart. You have achieved a success that would turn any head but yours. I could not believe it possible had I not seen it. Your ambition and ideal are so lofty that you will always make yourself miserable by aiming at the impossible. As Mr. Fleet said, I do not believe there is another in the city who could have done so well, and if you can do that now, what may you not accomplish by a few years more of work?"

"That's the terrible part of it," said Christine, with a long sigh. "Susie, I have attained my growth. I can never be a real artist, and no one living can ever know the bitterness of my disappointment. I do not believe in the immortality that you do, and this was my only chance to live beyond the brief hour of my life. If I could only have won for myself a place among the great names that the world will ever honor, I might with more content let the candle of my existence flicker out when it must. But I have learned to-day what I have often feared, — that Christine Ludolph must soon end in a forgotten handful of dust."

"O Christine, if you could only believe!"

"I cannot. I tried in my last sickness, but vainly. I am more convinced than ever of the correctness of my father's views."

Miss Winthrop sighed deeply. "Why are you so despondent?" she at last asked.

As if half speaking to herself, Christine repeated the words, "'Painted by one having never felt, or unable to feel, the emotions presented, and therefore one who cannot portray them.' That is just the trouble. I tried to speak in a language I do not know. Susie, I believe I am about half ice. Sometimes I think I am like Undine, and have no soul. I know I have no heart, in the sense that you have.

"I live a very cold sort of life," she continued, with a slight shudder. "I seem surrounded by invisible barriers that I cannot pass. I can see, beyond, what I want, but cannot reach it. O Susie, if you knew what I suffered when so ill! Everything seemed slipping from me. And yet why I should so wish to live I hardly know, when my life is so narrowed down."

"You see the disease, but not the remedy," sighed Susie.

"What is the remedy?"

"*Love.* Love to God, and I may add love for some good man."

Christine stopped a moment and almost stamped her foot impatiently.

"You discourage me more than any one else," she cried. "As to loving God, how can I love merely a name? and, even if He existed, how could I love a Being who left His world so full of vile evils? As to human love, faugh! I have had enough of romantic attachments."

"Do you never intend to marry?"

"Susie, you are the friend of my soul, and I trust you and you only with our secret. Yes, I expect to marry, but not in this land. You know that in Germany my father will eventually be a noble, the representative of one of the most ancient and honorable families. We shall soon have sufficient wealth to resume our true position there. A husband will then be found for me. I only stipulate that he shall be able to give me position among the first, and gratify my bent for art to the utmost."

"Well, Christine, you are a strange girl, and your dream of the future is stranger still."

"Sometimes I think that all is a dream, and may end like one. Nothing seems certain or real, or turns out as one expects. Think of it. A nobody who swept my father's store the other day has this morning made such havoc in my dream that I am sick at heart."

"But you cannot blame Mr. Fleet. He did it unconsciously; he was goaded on to it. No *man* could have done otherwise. You surely do not feel hardly toward him?"

"We do not naturally love the lips and bless the voice that tell us of an incurable disease. Oh, no," she added, "why should I think of him at all? He merely happened to point out what I half suspected myself. And yet the peculiar way this stranger crosses my path from time to time almost makes me superstitious."

"And you seem to have peculiar power over him. He would have assuredly left us in the lurch at our tableau party had it not been for you, and I should not have blamed him. And to-day he seemed troubled and pained beyond expression when he read from your face, as I imagine, that you were the author of the picture."

"Yes, I saw that he discovered the fact, and this provokes me also. If he should speak his thoughts —"

"I do not think he will. I am sure he will not if you caution him."

"That I will not do; and I think on the whole he has too much sense to speak carelessly of what he imagined he saw in a lady's face. And now, Susie, good-by. I shall not inflict my miserable self longer upon you to-day, and I am one who can best cure my wounds in solitude."

"Do you cure them, Christine? or do you only cover them up? If I had your creed nothing could cure my wounds. Time might deaden the pain, and I forget them in other things, but I do not see where any cure could come from. O Christine! you did me good service when in the deepening twilight of Miss Brown's parlor you showed me my useless, unbelieving life. But I do believe now. The cross is radiant to me now, — more radiant than the one that so startled us then. Mr. Fleet's words were true, I know, as I know my own existence. I could die for my faith."

Christine frowned and said, almost harshly: "I don't believe in a religion so full of crosses and death. Why could not the all-powerful Being you believe in take away the evil from the world?"

"That is just what He came to do. In that very character he was pointed out by His authorized forerunner: 'Behold the Lamb of God, that taketh away the sin of the world.'"

"Why does He not do it then?" asked Christine, petulantly. "Centuries have passed. Patience itself is wearied out. He has had time enough, if He ever meant or had the power to fulfil the promise. But the world is as full of evil and suffering as ever. Susie, I would not disturb your credulous faith, for it seems to do you good; but to me Christ was a noble but mistaken man, dead and buried centuries ago. He can do for me no more than Socrates. They vigorously attacked evil in their day, but evil was too much for them, as it is for us. We must just get the most we can out of life, and endure what we cannot prevent or escape. An angel could not convert me to-day, — no, not even Susie Winthrop, and that is saying more still;" and with a nasty kiss she vanished.

Susie looked wistfully after her, and then bent her steps homeward with a pitying face.

Christine at once went to her own private room. Putting on a loose wrapper she threw herself on a lounge, and buried her face in the cushions. Her life seemed growing narrow and meagre. Hour after hour passed, and the late afternoon sun was shining into her room when she arose from her bitter revery, and summed up all in a few words spoken aloud, as was her custom when alone.

"Must I, after all, come down to the Epicurean philosophy, 'Let us eat, drink, and be merry, for to-morrow we die'? I seem on a narrow island, the ocean is all around me, and the tide is rising, *rising*. It will cover *soon* my standing-place, and then what becomes of Christine Ludolph?"

A look of anguish came into the fair young face, and a slight shudder passed over her. She glanced around a room furnished in costly elegance. She saw her lovely person in the mirror opposite, and exclaimed: "What a mystery it all is! I have so much, and yet so utterly fail of having that which contents. I have all that wealth can purchase; and multitudes act as if that were enough. I know I am beautiful. I can see that yonder for myself, as well as read it in admiring eyes. And yet my maid is better contented than I, and the boy who blacks the boots better satisfied with his lot than either of us. I am raised so high that I can see how much more there is or might be beyond. I feel like one led into a splendid vestibule, only to find that the palace is wanting, or that it is a mean hovel. All that I have only mocks me, and becomes a means of torture. All that I am and have ought to be, might be, a mere prelude, an earnest and a preparation for something better beyond. But I am told, and must believe, that this is all, and I may lose this in a moment and forever. It is as if a noble strain of music commenced sweetly, and then suddenly broke down into a few discordant notes and ceased. It is like my picture, — all very well; but that which would speak to and move the heart, year after year, when the mere beauty ceased to please, — that life or something is wanting. What were his words? — 'This picture is but the beautiful corpse of the other;' and my life is but a cold marble effigy of a true life. And yet is there any true and better life? If there is nothing better beyond, I have been carried forward too far. Miss Brown thoroughly enjoys champagne and flirtations. Susie Winthrop is happy in her superstition, as any one might be who could believe what she does. But I have gone past the power of taking up these things, as I have gone past my childhood's sports. And now what is there for me? My most dear and cherished hope — a hope that shone above my life like a sun — has been blown away by the breath of my father's clerk (it required no greater power to bring me down to my true level), and I hoped to be a queen among men, high-born, but crowned with the richer coronet of genius. I, who hoped to win so high a place that men would speak of me with honest praise, now and in all future time, must be contented as a mere accomplished woman, deemed worthy perhaps in time to grace some nobleman's halls who in the nice social scale abroad may stand a little higher than myself. I meant to shine and dazzle, to stoop to give in every case; but now I must take what I can get, with a humble 'Thank you;'" and she clenched her little powerless hands in impotent revolt at what seemed very cruel destiny.

She appeared at the dinner-table outwardly calm and quiet. Her father did not share in her bitter disappointment, and she saw that he did not, and so felt more alone. He regarded her success as remarkable (as it truly was), having never believed that she could copy a picture so exactly as to deceive an ordinarily good observer. When, therefore, old Schwartz and others were unable to distinguish between the pictures, he was more than satisfied. He was sorry that Dennis had spoiled the triumph, but could not blame him. At the same time he recognized in Fleet another and most decided proof of intelligence on questions of art, for he knew that his criticism was just. He believed that when the true knight that his ambition would choose appeared, with golden spurs and jewelled crest, then her deeper nature would awaken, and she far surpass all previous effort. Moreover, he did not fully understand or enter into her lofty ambition. To see her settled in life, titled, rich, and a recognized leader in the aristocracy of his own land, was his highest aspiration so far as she was concerned.

He began, therefore, in a strain of compliment to cheer his daughter and rally her courage; but she shook her head sadly, and said so decidedly, "Father, let us change the subject," that with some surprise at her feelings he yielded to her wish, thinking that a little time and experience would moderate her ideas and banish the pain of disappointment. It was a quiet meal, both being occupied by their own thoughts. Soon after he was absorbed for the evening by his cigar and some business papers.

It was a mild, summer-like night, and a warm, gentle rain was falling. Even in the midst of a great city the sweet odors of spring found their way to the private parlor where Christine sat by the window, still lost in painful thoughts.

"Nature is full of hope, and the promise of coming life. So ought I to be in this my spring-time. Why am I not? If I am sad and disappointed in my spring, how dreary will be my autumn, when leaf after leaf of beauty, health, and strength drops away!"

A muffled figure, seemingly regardless of the rain, passed slowly down the opposite side of the street. Though the person cast but a single quick glance toward her window, and though the twilight was deepening, something in the passer-by suggested Dennis Fleet. For a moment she wished she could speak to him. She felt very lonely. Solitude had done her no good. Her troubles only grew darker and more real as she brooded over them. She instinctively felt that her father could not understand her, and she had never been able to go to him for sympathy. He was not the kind of person that any one would seek for such a purpose. Christine was not inclined to confidence, and there was really no one who knew her deeper feelings, and who could enter into her real hopes for life. She was so proud and cold that few ever thought of giving her confidence, much less of asking hers.

Up to the time of her recent illness she had been strong, self-confident, almost assured of success. At times she recognized dimly that something was wrong; but she shut her eyes to the unwelcome truth, and determined to succeed. But her sickness and fears at that time, and now a failure that seemed to destroy the ambition of her life, all united in greatly shaking her self-confidence.

This evening, as never before, she was conscious of weak ness and dependence. With the instinct of one sinking, her spirit longed for help and support. Then the thought suddenly occurred to her, "Perhaps this young stranger, who so clearly pointed out the disease, may also show the way to some remedy."

But the figure had passed on. In a moment mere pride and conventionality resumed sway, and she smiled bitterly, saying to herself, "What a weak fool I am to-night! Of all things let me not become a romantic miss again."

She went to her piano and struck into a brilliant strain. For a few moments the music was of a forced and defiant character, loud, gay, but with no real or rollicking mirth in it, and it soon ceased. Then in sharp contrast came a sad, weird German ballad, and this was real. In its pathos her burdened heart found expression, and whoever listened then would not merely have admired, but would have felt. One song followed another. All the pent-up feeling of the day seemed to find natural flow in the plaintive minstrelsy of her own land.

Suddenly she ceased and went to her window. The muffled figure stood in the shadow of an angle in the attitude of a listener. A moment later it vanished in the dusk toward the business part of the city. The quick footsteps died away, and only the patter of the falling rain broke the silence. Christine felt sure that it was Dennis. At first her feeling was one of pleasure. His coming and evident interest took somewhat, she scarcely knew why, from her sense of loneliness. Soon her pride awoke, however, and she said: "He has no business here to watch and listen. I will show him that, with all his taste and intelligence, we have no ground in common on which he can presume."

Her father had also listened to the music, and said to himself: "Christine is growing a little sentimental. She takes this disappointment too much to heart. I must touch her pride with the spur a little, and that will make her ice and steel in a moment. It is no slight task to keep a girl's heart safe till you want to use it. I will wait till the practical daylight of to-morrow, and then she shall look at the world through my eyes again."

CHAPTER XXIX.

DENNIS'S LOVE PUT TO PRACTICAL USE.

THE day following his unlucky criticism of the pictures was one of great despondency to Dennis. He had read in Christine's face that he had wounded her sorely; and, though she knew it to be unintentional, would it not prejudice her mind against him, and snap the slender thread by which he hoped to draw across the gulf between them the cord, and then the cable, that might in time unite their lives?

In the evening his restless, troubled spirit drove him, in spite of the rain, to seek to be at least nearer to her. He felt sure that in the dusk and wrapped in his greatcoat he would not be noticed, but was mistaken, as we have seen. He was rewarded, for he heard her sing as never before, as he did not believe she could sing. For the first time her rich, thoroughly trained voice had the sweetness and power of feeling. To Dennis her song seemed like an appeal, a cry for help, and his heart responded in the deepest sympathy. As he walked homeward he said to himself: "She could be a true artist, perhaps a great one, for she can feel. She has a heart. She has a taste and skill in touch that few can surpass. I can scarcely believe the beautiful coloring and faultless lines of that picture are her work."

He longed for a chance to speak with her and explain. He felt that he had so much to say, and in a thousand imaginary ways introduced the subject of her painting. He hoped he might find her sketching in some of the rooms again. He thought that he knew her better for having heard her sing, and that he could speak to her quite frankly.

The next day she came to the store, but passed him without the slightest notice. He hoped she had not seen him, and, as she passed out, so placed himself that she must see him, and secured for his pains only a slight, cold inclination of the head.

"It is as I feared," he said, bitterly. "She detests me for having spoiled her triumph. She is not just," he added, angrily. "She has no sense of justice, or she would not blame me. What a mean-spirited craven I should have been had I shrunk away under her taunts yesterday. Well, I can be proud too."

When she came in again he did not raise his eyes, and when she passed out he was in a distant part of the store. Christine saw no tall muffled figure under her window again, though she had the curiosity to look. That even this humble admirer, for whom she cared not a jot, should show such independence rather nettled and annoyed her for a moment. But she paid no more heed to him than to the other clerks.

But what was the merest jar to Christine's vanity cost Dennis a desperate struggle. It required no effort on her part to pass him by without a glance. To him it was torture. In a few days she ceased to think about him at all, and only remembered him in connection with her disappointment. But she was restless, could settle down to no work, and had lost her zest in her old pleasures. She tried to act as usual, for she saw her father's eye was on her. He had not much indulgence for any one's weaknesses save his own, and often by a little cold satire would sting her to the very quick. On the other hand his admiration, openly expressed in a certain courtly gallantry, nourished her pride but not her heart. Though she tried to keep up her usual routine her manner was forced before him and languid when alone. But he said, "All this will pass away like a cold snap in spring, and the old zest will come again in a few days."

It did, but from a cause which he could not understand, and which his daughter with consummate skill and care concealed. He thought it was only the old enthusiasm rallying after a sharp frost of disappointment.

Dennis's pride gave way before her cool and unstudied indifference. It was clearly evident to him that he had no hold upon her life whatever, and how to gain any he did not see. He became more and more dejected.

"She must have a heart, or I could not love her so; but it is so incased in ice I fear I can never reach it."

That something was wrong with Dennis any friend who cared for him at all might see. The Bruders did, and, with the quick intuitions of woman, Mrs. Bruder half guessed the cause. Mr. Bruder, seeing preoccupation and sometimes weary apathy in Dennis's face, would say, "Mr. Fleet is not well."

Then, as even this slight notice of his different appearance seemed to give pain, Mr. Bruder was patiently and kindly blind to his pupil's inattention.

Dennis faithfully kept up all his duties on Sunday as during the week; but all was now hard work. Some little time after the unlucky morning which he could never think of without an expression of pain, he went to his mission class as usual. He heard his boys recite their lessons, said a few poor lame words in explanation, and then leaned his head listlessly and wearily on his hand. He was startled by hearing a sweet voice say, "Well, Mr. Fleet, are you not going to welcome a new laborer into your corner of the vineyard?"

With a deep flush he saw that Miss Winthrop was in

charge of the class next to him, and that he had been oblivious to her presence nearly an hour. He tried to apologize. But she interrupted him, saying: "Mr. Fleet, you are not well. Any one can see that."

Then Dennis blushed as if he had a raging fever, and she was perplexed.

The closing exercises of the school now occupied them, and then they walked out together.

"Mr. Fleet," she said, "you never accepted my invitation. We have not seen you at our house. But perhaps your circle of friends is so large that you do not wish to add to it."

Dennis could not forbear a smile at the suggestion, but he said, in apology, "I do not visit any one, save a gentleman from whom I am taking lessons."

"Do you mean to say that you have no friends at all in this great city?"

"Well, I suppose that is nearly the truth; that is, in the sense you use the term. My teacher and his wife — "

"Nonsense! I mean friends of one's own age, people of the same culture and status as yourself. I think we require such society, as truly as we need food and air. I did not mean those whom business or duty brought you in contact with, or who are friendly or grateful as a matter of course."

"I have made no progress since my introduction to society at Miss Brown's," said Dennis.

"But you had the sincere and cordial offer of introduction," said Miss Winthrop, looking a little hurt.

"I feel hardly fit for society," said Dennis, all out of sorts with himself. "It seems that I can only blunder and give pain. But I am indeed grateful for your kindness."

Miss Winthrop looked into his worn, pale face, and instinctively knew that something was wrong, and she felt real sympathy for the lonely young man, isolated among thousands. She said, gently but decidedly: "I did mean my invitation kindly, and I truly wished you to come. The only proof you can give that you appreciate my courtesy is to accept an invitation for to-morrow evening. I intend having a little musical entertainment."

Quick as light flashed the thought, "Christine will be there." He said, promptly: "I will come, and thank you for the invitation. If I am awkward, you must remember that I have never mingled in Chicago society, and for a long time not in any."

She smiled merrily at him, and said, "Don't do anything dreadful, Mr. Fleet."

He caught her mood, and asked what had brought her down from her theological peak to such a valley of humiliation as a mission school.

"You and Miss Ludolph," she answered, seriously. "Between you, you gave me such a lesson that afternoon at Miss Brown's that I have led a different life ever since. Christine made all as dark as despair, and against that darkness you placed the fiery Cross. I have tried to cling to the true cross ever since. Now He could not say to me, 'Inasmuch as ye did it not.' And oh!" said she, turning to Dennis with a smile full of the light of heaven, "His service is so very sweet! I heard last week that teachers were wanted at this mission school, so I came, and am glad to find you a neighbor."

Dennis's face also kindled at her enthusiasm, but after a moment grew sad again.

"I do not always give so lifeless a lesson as to-day," he said, in a low voice.

"Mr. Fleet, you are not well. I can see that you look worn and greatly wearied. Are you not in some way overtaxing yourself?"

Again that sensitive flush, but he only said: "I assure you

I am well. Perhaps I have worked a little hard. That is all."

"Well, then, come to our house and play a little to-morrow evening," she answered from the platform of a street car, and was borne away.

Dennis went to his lonely room, full of self-reproach.

"Does she find Christ's service so sweet, and do I find it so dull and hard? Does human love alone constrain me, and not the love of Christ? Truly I am growing weak. Every one says I look ill. I think I am, in body and soul, and am ceasing to be a man; but with God's help I will be one,—and what is more, a Christian. I thank you, Miss Winthrop; you have helped me more than I have helped you. I will accept your invitation to go out into the world. I will no longer mope, brood, and perish in the damp and shade of my own sick fancies. If I cannot win her, I can at least be a man without her;" and he felt better and stronger than he had done for a long time. The day was breaking again.

In accordance with a custom that was growing with him ever since the memorable evening when Bill Cronk befriended him, he laid the whole matter before his Heavenly Father, as a child tells an earthly parent all his heart. Then he added one simple prayer, "Guide me in all things."

The next day was brighter and better than its forerunners. "For some reason I feel more like myself," he thought. After the excitement and activity of a busy day, he said, "I can conquer this, if I must."

But when he had made his simple toilet, and was on his way to Miss Winthrop's residence, his heart began to flutter strangely, and he knew the reason. Miss Winthrop welcomed him most cordially, and put him at his ease in a moment, as only a true lady can. Then she turned to receive other guests. He looked around. Christine was not there; and his heart sunk like lead. "She will not be here," he sighed. But the guests had not ceased coming, and every new arrival caused a flutter of hopes and fears. He both longed and dreaded to meet her. At last, when he had almost given up seeing her, suddenly she appeared, advancing up the parlor on her father's arm. Never had she seemed so dazzlingly beautiful. He was just then talking to Mr. Winthrop, and for a few moments that gentleman was perplexed at his incoherent answers and the changes in his face. Having paid their respects to the daughter, Mr. and Miss Ludolph came toward Mr. Winthrop, and of course Dennis had to meet them. Having greeted them warmly, Mr. Winthrop said, "Of course you do not need an introduction to Mr. Fleet."

Dennis had shrunk a little into the background, and at first they had not noticed him. Mr. Ludolph said, good-naturedly, "Glad to see you, Mr. Fleet, and will be still more glad to hear your fine voice."

But Christine merely bowed as to one with whom her acquaintance was slight, and turned away. At first Dennis had blushed, and his heart had fluttered like a young girl's; but, as she turned so coolly away, his native pride and obstinacy were aroused.

"She shall speak to me and do me justice," he muttered. "She must understand that I spoke unconsciously on that miserable morning, and am not to be blamed. As I am a man, I will speak boldly and secure recognition." But as the little company mingled and conversed before the music commenced, no opportunity offered. He determined to show her, however, that he was no country boor, and with skill and taste made himself agreeable.

Christine furtively watched him. She was surprised to see him, as the idea of meeting him in society as an equal had scarcely been suggested before. But when she saw that he greeted one after another with grace and ease, and that all seemed to enjoy his conversation, so that a little knot of Miss Winthrop's most intelligent guests were about him at last, she felt that it would be no great condescension on her part to be a little more affable. In her heart, though, she had not forgiven the unconscious words that had smitten to the ground her ambitious hopes.

Then again, his appearance deeply interested her. A suppressed excitement and power, seen in the glow and fire of his dark eyes, and felt in his tones, stirred her languid pulses.

"He is no vapid society-man," she said to herself; and her artist eye was gratified by the changes in his noble face.

"Look at Fleet," whispered her father; "could you believe he was sweeping the store the other day? Well, if we don't find out his worth and get what we can from him, the world will. We ought to have had him up to sing before this, but I have been so busy since your illness that it slipped my mind."

Miss Winthrop now led Christine to the piano, and she played a classical piece of music in faultless taste. Then followed duets, solos, quartets, choruses, and instrumental pieces, for nearly all present were musical amateurs. Under the inspiration of this soul-stirring art, coldness and formality melted away, and with jest and brilliant repartee, alternating with song, there gathered around Miss Winthrop's piano such a group as could never grace the parlors of Miss Brown. Sometimes they would carry a new and difficult piece triumphantly through; again they would break down, with much laughter and good-natured rallying.

Dennis, as a stranger, held back at first; but those who remembered his singing at the tableau party were clamorous to hear him again, and they tested and tried his voice during the evening in many and varied ways. But he held his own, and won greener laurels than ever. He did his very best, for he was before one whom he would rather please than all the world; moreover, her presence seemed to inspire him to do better than when alone. Christine, like the others, could not help listening with delight to his rich, clear tenor, and Mr. Ludolph was undisguised in his admiration.

"I declare, Mr. Fleet, I have been depriving myself of a good deal of pleasure. I meant to have you up to sing with us before, but we have been under such a press of business of late! But the first evening I am disengaged you must surely come."

Christine had noticed how quietly and almost indifferently Dennis had taken the many compliments showered on him before, but now, when her father spoke, his face flushed, and a sudden light came into his eyes. Dennis had thought, "I can then see and speak to her." Every now and then she caught his eager, questioning, and almost appealing glance, but he made no advances. "He thinks I am angry because of his keen criticism of my picture. For the sake of my own pride, I must not let him think that I care so much about his opinion;" and Christine resolved to let some of the ice thaw that had formed between them. Moreover, in spite of herself, when she was thrown into his society, he greatly interested her. He seemed to have just what she had not. He could meet her on her own ground in matters of taste, and then, in contrast with her cold, negative life, he was so earnest and positive. "Perhaps papa spoke for us both," she thought, "and I have been depriving myself of a pleasure also, for he certainly interests while most men only weary me."

Between ten and eleven supper was announced; not the prodigal abundance under which the brewer's table had groaned, but a dainty, elegant little affair, which inspired and promoted social feeling, though the "spirit of wine" was absent. The eye was feasted as truly as the palate. Christine had stood near Dennis as the last piece was sung, and he turned and said in a low, eager tone, "May I have the pleasure of waiting on you at supper?"

She hesitated, but his look was so wistful that she could not well refuse, so with a slight smile she bowed assent, and placed the tips of her little gloved hand on his arm, which so trembled that she looked inquiringly and curiously into his face. It was very pale, as was ever the case when he felt deeply. He waited on her politely but silently at first. She sat in an angle, somewhat apart from the others. As he stood by her side, thinking how to refer to the morning in the show-room, she said: "Mr. Fleet, you are not eating anything, and you look as if you had been living on air of late, — very unlike your appearance when you so efficiently aided me in the rearrangement of the store. I am delighted that you keep up the better order of things."

Dennis's answer was quite irrelevant.

"Miss Ludolph," he said, abruptly, "I saw that I gave you pain that morning in the show-room. If you only knew how the thought has pained me!"

Christine flushed almost angrily, but said, coldly, "Mr. Fleet, that is a matter you can never understand, therefore we had better dismiss the subject."

But Dennis had determined to break the ice between them at any risk, so he said, firmly but respectfully: "Miss Ludolph, I did understand all, the moment I saw your face that day. I do understand how you have felt since, better than you imagine."

His manner and words were so assured that she raised a startled face to his, but asked coldly and in an indifferent manner, "What can you know of my feelings?"

"I know," said Dennis, in a low tone, looking searchingly into her face, from which cool composure was fast fading, —

"I know your dearest hope was to be among the first in art. You staked that hope on your success in a painting that required a power which you do not possess." Christine became very pale, but from her eyes shone a light before which most men would have quailed. But Dennis's love was so true and strong that he could wound her for the sake of the healing and life he hoped to bring, and he continued, —"On that morning this cherished hope for the future failed you, not because of my words, but because your artist eye saw that my words were true. You have since been unhappy—"

"What right have *you*,—you who were but a few days since—who are a stranger,—what right have you to speak thus to me?"

"I know what you would say, Miss Ludolph," he answered, a slight flush coming into his pale face. "Friends may be humble and yet true. But am I not right?"

"I have no claim on your friendship," said Christine, coldly. "But, for the sake of argument, grant that you are right, what follows?" and she looked at him more eagerly than she knew. She felt that he had read her very soul and was deeply moved, and again the superstitious feeling crept over her, "That young man is in some way connected with my destiny."

Dennis saw his power and proceeded rapidly, for he knew they might be interrupted at any moment; and so they would have been had anything less interesting than eating occupied the attention of others.

"I saw in the picture what in your eyes and mine would be a fatal defect,—the lack of life and true feeling,—the lack of power to live. I did not know who painted it, but felt that any one who could paint as well as that, and yet leave out the soul, as it were, had not the power to put it in. No artist of such ability could willingly or ignorantly have permitted such a defect."

Christine's eyes sunk, their fire faded out, and her face had the pallor of one listening to her doom. This deeper feeling mastered the momentary resentment against the hand that was wounding her, and she forgot him, and all, in her pain and despair.

In a low, earnest tone Dennis continued: "But since I have come to know who the artist is, since I have studied the picture more fully, and have taken the liberty of some observation," — Christine hung on his lips breathlessly, and Dennis spoke slowly, marking the effect of every word, — "I have come to the decided belief that the lady who painted that picture *can* reach the sphere of true and highest art."

The light that stole into Christine's face under his slow, emphatic words was like a rosy dawn in June; and the thought flashed through Dennis's mind, "If an earthly hope can so light up her face, what will be the effect of a heavenly one?"

For a moment she sat as one entranced, looking at a picture far off in the future. His words had been so earnest and assured that they seemed reality. Suddenly she turned on him a look as grateful and happy as the former one had been full of pain and anger, and said: "Ah, do not deceive me, do not flatter. You cannot know the sweetness and power of the hope you are inspiring. To be disappointed again would be death. If you are trifling with me I will never forgive you," she added, in sudden harshness, her brow darkening.

"Nor should I deserve to be forgiven if I deceived you in a matter that to you is so sacred."

"But how — how am I to gain this magic power to make faces feel and live on canvas?"

"You must believe. You must feel yourself."

She looked at him with darkening face, and then in a

sudden burst of passion said: "I don't believe; I can't feel. All this is mockery, after all."

"No!" said Dennis, in the deep, assured tone that ever calms and secures attention. "This is not mockery. I speak the words of truth and soberness. You do not believe, but that is not the same as cannot. And permit me to contradict you when I say you *do* feel. On this subject so near your heart you feel most deeply, — feel as I never knew any one feel before. This proves you capable of feeling on other and higher subjects, and what you feel your trained and skilful hand can portray. You felt on the evening of that miserable day, and sang as I never heard you sing before. Your tones then would move any heart, and my tears fell with the rain in sympathy: I could not help it."

Her bosom rose and fell tumultuously, and her breath came hard and quick.

"Oh, if I could believe you were right!"

"I know I am right," he said, so decidedly that again hope grew rosy and beautiful in her face.

"Then again," he continued, eagerly, "see what an advantage you have over the most of us. Your power of imitation is wonderful. *You can copy anything you see.*"

"Good-evening, Miss Ludolph. Where have you been hiding? I have twice made the tour of the supper-room in my search," broke in the voluble Mr. Mellen. Then he gave Dennis a cool stare, who acted as if unconscious of his presence. An expression of disgust flitted across Christine's face at the interruption, or the person, — perhaps both, — and she was about to shake him off that Dennis might speak further, when Miss Winthrop and others came up, and there was a general movement back to the parlors.

"Why, Christine, what is the matter?" asked her friend. "You look as if you had a fever. What has Mr. Fleet been saying?"

"Oh, we have had an argument on my hobby, art, and of course don't agree, and so got excited in debate."

Miss Winthrop glanced keenly at them and said, "I would like to have heard it, for it was Greek meeting Greek."

"To what art or *trade* did Mr. Fleet refer?" asked Mr. Mellen, with an insinuation that all understood.

"One that you do not understand," said Christine, keenly.

The petted and spoiled millionnaire flushed angrily a moment, and then said with a bow: "You are right, Miss Ludolph. Mr. Fleet is acquainted with one or two arts that I have never had the pleasure of learning."

"He has at least learned the art of being a gentleman," was the sharp retort.

The young man's face grew darker, and he said, "From the *sweeping* nature of your remarks, I perceive that Mr. Fleet is high in your favor."

"A poor pun made in poorer taste," was all the comfort he got from Christine.

Dennis was naturally of a very jealous disposition where his affections were concerned. His own love took such entire possession of him that he could not brook the interference of others, or sensibly consider that they had the same privilege to woo, and win if possible, that he had. Especially distasteful to him was this rich and favored youth, whose presence awakened all his combativeness, which was by no means small.

Mr. Mellen's most inopportune interruption and covert taunts provoked him beyond endurance. His face was fairly white with rage, and for a moment he felt that he could stamp his rival out of existence. In the low, concentrated voice of passion he said, "If Mr. Mellen should lose his property, as many do, I gather from his remarks that he would still keep up his idea of a gentleman on charity."

Mr. Mellen flushed to the roots of his hair, his hands clenched. In the flashing eyes and threatening faces of the young men those witnessing the scene foresaw trouble. A light hand fell on Dennis's arm, and Miss Winthrop said, "Mr. Fleet, I wish to show you a picture, and ask your judgment in regard to it."

Dennis understood the act, and in a moment more his face was crimson with shame.

"Miss Winthrop, you ought to send me home at once. I told you I was unfit for society. Somehow I am not myself. I humbly ask your pardon."

"So sincere a penitent shall receive absolution at once. You were greatly provoked. I trust you for the future."

"You may," was the emphatic answer. After that pledge Mr. Mellen might have struck him and received no more response than from a marble statue.

Mr. Mellen also took a sober second thought, remembering that he was in a lady's parlor. He walked away with his ears tingling, for the flattered youth had never had such an experience before. The few who witnessed the scene smiled significantly, as did Christine half contemptuously; but Miss Winthrop soon restored serenity, and the remaining hours passed away in music and dancing. Christine did not speak to Dennis again, — that is, by word of mouth, — but she thought of him constantly, and their eyes often met; — on his part that same eager, questioning look. She ever turned hers at once away. But his words kept repeating themselves continually, especially his last sentence, when the unlucky Mr. Mellen had broken in upon them, — "You can copy anything you see."

"How noble and expressive of varied feeling his face is!" she thought, watching it change under the playful badinage of Miss Winthrop.

"How I would like to copy it! Well, you can, — 'You

can copy anything you see.'" Then like a flash came a suggestion,—"You can make him love you, and copy feeling, passion, life—from the *living* face. Whether I can believe or feel, myself, is very doubtful. This I can do: he himself said so. I cannot love, myself,—I must not; I do not wish to now, but perhaps I can inspire love in him, and then make his face a study. As to my believing, he can never know how utterly impossible his faith is to me."

Then conscience entered a mild protest against the cruelty of the project. "Nonsense!" she said to herself; "most girls flirt for sport, and it is a pity if I cannot with such a purpose in view. He will soon get over a little puncture in his heart after I have sailed away to my bright future beyond the sea, and perhaps Susie will comfort him;" and she smiled at the thought. Dennis saw the smile and was entranced by its loveliness. How little he guessed the cause!

Having resolved, Christine acted promptly. When their eyes again met, she gave him a slight smile. He caught it instantly and looked bewildered, as if he could not believe his eyes. Again, when a little later, at the urgent request of many, he sung alone for the first time, and again moved his hearers deeply by the real feeling in his tones, he turned from the applause of all, with that same questioning look, to her. She smiled an encouragement that she had never given him before. The warm blood flooded his face instantly. All thought that it was the general chorus of praise. Christine knew that she had caused it, and surprise and almost exultation came into her face. "I half believe he loves me now," she said. She threw him a few more kindly smiles from time to time, as one might throw some glittering things to an eager child, and every moment assured her of her power.

"I will try one more test," she said, and by a little effort she lured to her side the offended Mr. Mellen, and appeared much pleased by his attention. Then unmistakably the pain of jealousy was stamped on Dennis's face, and she was satisfied. Shaking off the perplexed Mr. Mellen again, she went to the recess of a window to hide her look of exultation.

"The poor victim loves me already," she said. "The mischief is done. I have only to avail myself of what exists from no fault of mine, and surely I ought to; otherwise the passion of the infatuated youth will be utterly wasted, and do no one any good."

Thus in a somewhat novel way Christine obtained a new master in painting, and poor Dennis and his love were put to use somewhat as a human subject might be if dissected alive.

CHAPTER XXX.

THE TWO HEIGHTS.

DENNIS went home in a strange tumult of hopes and fears, but hope predominated, for evidently she cared little for Mr. Mellen. "The ice is broken at last," he said. It was, but he was like to fall through into a very cold bath, though he knew it not. He was far too excited to sleep, and sat by his open window till the warm June night grew pale with the light of coming day.

Suddenly a bright thought struck him; a moment more and it became an earnest purpose. "I think I can paint something that may express to her what I dare not put in words."

He immediately went up into the loft and prepared a large frame, so proportioned that two pictures could be painted side by side, one explanatory and an advance upon the other. He stretched his canvas over this, and sketched and outlined rapidly under the inspiration of his happy thought.

Christine came with her father to the store, as had been her former custom, and her face had its old expression. The listless, disappointed look was gone. She passed on, not appearing to see him while with her father, and Dennis's heart sunk again. "She surely knew where to look for me if she cared to look," he said to himself. Soon after he went to the upper show-room to see to the hanging of a new picture.

"I am so glad your taste, instead of old Schwartz's mathematics, has charge of this department now," said a honeyed voice at his side. He was startled greatly.

"What is the matter? Are you nervous, Mr. Fleet? I had no idea that a lady could so frighten you."

He was blushing like a girl, but said, "I have read that something within, rather than anything without, makes us cowards."

"Ah, then you confess to a guilty conscience?" she replied, with a twinkle in her eye.

"I do not think I shall confess at all till I have a merciful confessor," said Dennis, conscious of a deeper meaning than his light words might convey.

"'The quality of mercy is not strained,' therefore it is unfit for my use. I'll none of it, but for each offence impose unlimited penance."

"But suppose one must sin?"

"He must take the consequences then. Even your humane religion teaches that;" and with this parting arrow she vanished, leaving him too excited to hang his picture straight.

It all seemed a bewildering dream. Being so thoroughly taken by surprise and off his guard, he had said far more than he meant. But had she understood him? Yes, better than he had himself, and laughed at his answers with their covert meanings.

She spent the next two days in sketching and outlining his various expressions as far as possible from memory. She would learn to catch those evanescent lines, — that something which makes the human face eloquent, though the lips are silent.

Dennis was in a maze, but he repeated to himself jubilantly again, "The ice is broken." That evening at Mr. Bruder's he asked for studies in ice.

"Vy, dat is out of season," said Mr. Bruder, with a laugh.

"No, now is just the time. It is a nice cool subject for this hot weather. Please oblige me; for certain reasons I wish to be able to paint ice perfectly."

Arctic scenery was Mr. Bruder's forte, on which he specially prided himself. He was too much of a gentleman to ask questions, and was delighted to find the old zest returning in his pupil. They were soon constructing bergs, caves, and grottos of cold blue ice. Evening after evening, while sufficient light lasted, they worked at this study. Dennis's whole soul seemed bent on the formation of ice. After a month of labor Mr. Bruder said, "I hope you vill get over dis by fall, or ve all freeze to death."

"One of these days I shall explain," said Dennis, smiling.

The evening of the second day after the little rencounter in the show-room, Mr. Ludolph sat enjoying his cigar, and Christine was at the piano playing a difficult piece of music.

"Come, father," she said, "here is a fine thing just from Germany. There is a splendid tenor solo in it, and I want you to sing it for me."

"Pshaw!" said her father, "why did I not think of it before?" and he rang the bell. "Here, Brandt, go down to the store, and if Mr. Fleet is there ask him if he will come up to my rooms for a little while."

Brandt met Dennis just starting for his painting lesson, but led him a willing captive, to give Christine instruction unconsciously.

She, whose strategy had brought it all about, smiled at her success. It was not her father's tenor she wanted, but Dennis's face; and her father should unknowingly work her will. The girl had learned so much from the wily man of the world that she was becoming his master.

Dennis came and entered with a thrill of delight what was to him enchanted ground. Mr. Ludolph was affable, Christine kind, but she looked more than she said.

Dennis sung the solo, after one or two efforts, correctly. Then Mr. Ludolph brought out a piece of music that he wished to try; Christine found others; and before they knew it the evening had passed. Quite a knot of delighted listeners gathered in the street opposite. This Christine pointed out to her father with evident annoyance.

"Well, my dear," he said, "hotel life in a crowded city renders escape from such things impossible."

But a purpose was growing in her mind of which she spoke soon after. Throughout the evening she had studied Dennis's face as much as she could without attracting notice, and the thought grew upon her that at last she had found a path to the success she so craved.

"You seem to have gone to work with your old interest," said her father, as he came out of his room the next morning and found Christine at her easel.

"I shall try it again," she said, briefly.

"That is right," said he. "The idea of being daunted by one partial failure! I predict for you such success as will satisfy even your fastidious taste."

"We shall see," she said. "I hope, too." But she would not have her father know on what grounds. He might regard the experiment as a dangerous one for herself as well as for Dennis, and she decided to keep her plan entirely secret.

She now came to the store daily, and rarely went away without giving Dennis a smile or word of recognition. But he noticed that she ever did this in a casual manner, and in a way that would not attract attention. He also took the hint, and never was obtrusive or demonstrative, but it was harder work for his frank nature. When unobserved, his glances grew more ardent day by day. So far from checking these, she encouraged them, but, when in any way he sought to put his feelings into words, she changed the subject instantly and decidedly. This puzzled him, for he did not understand that looks could be painted, but not words. The latter were of no use to her. But she led him on skilfully, and, from the unbounded power his love gave her, played upon his feelings as adroitly as she touched her grand piano.

Soon after the company at Miss Winthrop's, she said to him, "You received several invitations the other evening, did you not?"

"Yes."

"Accept them. Go into society. It will do you good."

Thus he soon found himself involved in a round of sociables, musicales, and now and then a large party. Christine was usually present, radiant, brilliant, the cynosure of all eyes, but ever coolly self-possessed. At first she would greet him with distant politeness, or pretend not to see him at all, but before the evening was over would manage to give him a half-hour in which she would be kind and even gentle at times, but very observant. Then for the rest of the evening he would find no chance to approach. It appeared that she was deeply interested in him, enjoyed his society, and was even becoming attached to him, but that for some reason she determined that no one should notice this, and that matters should only go so far. Poor Dennis could not know that he was only her unconscious instructor in painting, paid solely in the coin of false smiles and delusive hopes. At times, though, she would torture him dreadfully. Selecting one of her many admirers, she would seem to smile upon his suit, and poor Dennis would writhe in all the agonies of jealousy, for he was very human, and had all the normal feeling of a strong man. She would then watch his face grow pale and his manner restless, as quietly and critically as an entomologist regards the struggles of an insect beneath his microscope. Again, she would come to him all grace and sweetness, and his fine face would light up with hope and pleasure. She would say honeyed nothings, but study him just as coolly in another aspect.

Thus she kept him hot and cold by turns, — now lifting him to the pinnacle of hope, again casting him down into the valley of fear and doubt. What she wanted of him was just what she had not, — feeling, intense, varied feeling, so that, while she remained ice, she could paint as if she felt; and with a gifted woman's tact, and with the power of one loved almost to idolatry, she caused every chord of his soul, now in happy harmony, now in painful discord, to vibrate under her skilful touch. But such a life was very wearing, and he was failing under it. Moreover, he was robbing himself of sleep in the early morning, that he might work on his picture in the loft of the store, for which he asked of poor Mr. Bruder nothing but ice.

Mrs. Bruder worried over him continually.

"You vork too hart. Vat shall ve do for you? O my fren, if you love us do not vork so hart," she would often say. But Dennis would only smile and turn to her husband in his insatiable demand for painted ice. At last Mr. Bruder said, "Mr. Fleet, you can paint ice, as far as I see, as vell as myself."

Then Dennis turned short around and said, "Now I want warm rosy light and foliage; give me studies in these."

"By de hammer of Thor, but you go to extremes."

"You shall know all some day," said Dennis, entering on his new tasks with increasing eagerness.

But day by day he grew thinner and paler. Even Christine's heart sometimes relented; for, absorbed as she was in her own work and interests, she could not help noticing how sadly he differed from the vigorous youth who had lifted the heavy pictures for her but a few short weeks ago. But she quieted herself by the thought that he was a better artistic subject, and that he would mend again when the cool weather came.

"Where shall we go for the two hot months?" asked her father the morning after the Fourth.

"I have a plan to propose," replied Christine. "Suppose we go to housekeeping."

"What!" said her father, dropping his knife and fork, and looking at her in astonishment. "Go to all the expense of furnishing a house, when we do not expect to stay here much more than a year? We should hardly be settled before we left it."

"Listen to me patiently till I finish, and then I will abide by your decision. But I think you will give me credit for having a slight turn for business as well as art. You remember Mr. Jones's beautiful house on the north side, do you not? It stands on —— Street, well back, surrounded by a lawn and flowers. There is only one other house on the block. Well, Mr. Jones is embarrassed, and his house is for sale. From inquiry I am satisfied that a cash offer would obtain the property cheaply. The furniture is good, and much of it elegant. What we do not want — what will not accord with a tasteful refurnishing — can be sent to an auction-room. At comparatively slight expense, if you can spare Mr. Fleet to help me during the time when business is dull, I can make the house such a gem of artistic elegance that it will be noted throughout the city, and next fall some rich snob, seeking to vault suddenly into social position, will give just what you are pleased to ask. In the mean time we have a retired and delightful home.

"Moreover, father," she continued, touching him on his weak side, "it will be a good preparation for the more difficult and important work of the same kind awaiting me in my own land."

"Hum*p*h!" said Mr. Ludolph, meditatively, "there is

more method in your madness than I imagined. I will think of it, for it is too important a step to be taken hastily."

Mr. Ludolph did think of it, and, after attending to pressing matters in the store, went over to see the property. A few days afterward he came up to dinner and threw the deed for it into his daughter's lap. She glanced it over, and her eyes grew luminous with delight and triumph.

"See how comfortable and happy I will make you in return for this kindness," she said.

"Oh, come," replied her father, laughing, "that is not the point. This is a speculation, and your business reputation is at stake."

"I will abide the test," she answered, with a significant nod.

Christine desired the change for several reasons. There was a room in the house that would just suit her as a studio. She detested the publicity of a hotel. The furnishing of an elegant house was a form of activity most pleasing to her energetic nature, and she felt a very strong wish to try her skill in varied effect before her grand effort in the Ludolph Hall of the future.

But in addition to these motives was another, of which she did not speak to her father. In the privacy of her own home she could pursue that peculiar phase of art study in which she was absorbed. Her life had now become a most exciting one. She ever seemed on the point of obtaining the power to portray the eloquence of passion, feeling, but there was a subtile something that still eluded her. She saw it daily, and yet could not reproduce it. She seemed to get the features right, and yet they were dead, or else the emotion was so exaggerated as to suggest weak sentimentality, and this of all things disgusted her. Every day she studied the expressive face of Dennis Fleet, the mysterious power seemed nearer her grasp. Her effort was now gaining all the excitement of a chase. She saw before her just what she wanted, and it seemed that she had only to grasp her pencil or brush, and place the fleeting expressions where they might always appeal to the sympathy of the beholder. Nearly all her studies now were the human face and form, mainly those of ladies, to disarm suspicion. Of course she took no distinct likeness of Dennis. She sought only to paint what his face expressed. At times she seemed about to succeed, and excitement brought color to her cheek and fire to her eye that made her dazzlingly beautiful to poor Dennis. Then she would smile upon him in such a bewitching, encouraging way that it was little wonder his face lighted up with all the glory of hope.

If once more she could have him about her as when rearranging the store, and, without the restraint of curious eyes, could play upon his heart, then pass at once to her easel with the vivid impression of what she saw, she might catch the coveted power, and become able to portray, as if she felt, that which is the inspiration of all the highest forms of art, — feeling.

That evening, Dennis, at Mr. Ludolph's request, came to the hotel to try some new music. During the evening Mr. Ludolph was called out for a little time. Availing himself of the opportunity, Dennis said, "You seem to be working with all your old zest and hope."

"Yes," she said, "with greater hope than ever before."

"Won't you show me something that you are doing?"

"No, not yet. I am determined that when you see work of mine again the fatal defect which you pointed out shall be absent."

His eyes and face became eloquent with the hope she inspired. Was her heart, awakening from its long winter of doubt and indifference, teaching her to paint? Had she recognized the truth of his assurance that she must feel, and then she could portray feeling? and had she read in his face and manner that which had created a kindred impulse in her heart? He was about to speak, the ice of his reserve and prudence fast melting under what seemed good evidence that her smiles and kindness might be interpreted in accordance with his longings. She saw and anticipated.

"With all your cleverness, Mr. Fleet, I may prove you at fault, and become able to portray what I do not feel or believe."

"You mean to say that you work from your old standpoint merely?" asked Dennis, feeling as if a sunny sky had suddenly darkened.

"I do not say that at all, but that I do not work from yours."

"And yet you hope to succeed?"

"I think I am succeeding."

Perplexity and disappointment were plainly written on his face. She, with a merry and half-malicious laugh, turned to the piano, and sung: —

From Mount Olympus' snowy height
  The gods look down on human life:
Beneath contending armies fight;
  All undisturbed they watch the strife.

Dennis looked at her earnestly, and after a moment said, "Will you please play that accompaniment again?"

She complied, and he sung: —

Your Mount Olympus' icy peak
  Is barren waste, by cold winds swept:
Another height I gladly see,
  Where God o'er human sorrow wept.

She turned a startled and almost wistful face to him, for he had given a very unexpected answer to her cold, selfish philosophy, which was so apt and sudden as to seem almost inspired.

"Do you refer to Christ's weeping over Jerusalem?" she asked.

"Yes."

She sat for a little time silent and thoughtful, and Dennis watched her keenly. Suddenly her brow darkened, and she said, bitterly: "Delusion! If He had been a God He would not have idly wept over sorrow. He would have banished it."

Dennis was about to reply eagerly, when Mr. Ludolph entered, and music was resumed. But it was evident that Dennis's lines had disturbed the fair sceptic's equanimity.

CHAPTER XXXI.

BEGUILED.

DENNIS returned to his room greatly perplexed. There was something in Christine's actions which he could not understand. From the time of their first conversation at Miss Winthrop's, she had evidently felt and acted differently. If her heart remained cold and untouched, if as yet neither faith nor love had any existence therein, what was the inspiring motive? Why should deep discouragement change suddenly to assured hope?

Then again her manner was equally inexplicable. From that same evening she gave him more encouragement than he had even hoped to receive for months, but yet he made no progress. She seemed to enjoy meeting him, and constantly found opportunity to do so. Her eyes were continually seeking his face, but there was something in her manner in this respect that puzzled him more than anything else. She often seemed looking at his face, rather than at *him*. At first Christine had been furtive and careful in her observations, but as the habit grew upon her, and her interest increased, she would sometimes gaze so steadily that poor Dennis was deeply embarrassed. Becoming conscious of this, she would herself color slightly, and be more careful for a time.

In her eagerness for success, Christine did not realize how dangerous an experiment she was trying. She could not look upon such a face as Dennis Fleet's, eloquent with that which should never fail to touch a woman's heart with sympathy, and then forget it when she chose. Moreover, though she knew it not, in addition to her interest in him as an art study, his strong, positive nature affected her cool, negative one most pleasantly. His earnest manifested feeling fell like sunlight on a heart benumbed with cold.

Thus, under the stimulus of his presence, she found that she could paint or sketch to much better purpose than when alone. This knowledge made her rejoice in secret over the opportunity she could now have, as Dennis again assisted her in hanging pictures, and affixing to the walls ornaments of various kinds.

Coming to him one morning in the store, she said, "I am going to ask a favor of you again."

Dennis looked as if she were conferring the greatest of favors. His face always lighted up when she spoke to him.

"It is very kind of you to ask so pleasantly for what you can command," he said.

"To something of the same effect you answered before, and the result was the disagreeable experience at Miss Brown's."

Dennis's brow contracted a little, but he said, heroically, "I will go to Miss Brown's again if you wish it."

"How self-sacrificing you are!" she replied, with a half-mischievous smile.

"Not as much so as you imagine," he answered, flushing slightly.

"Well, set your mind at rest on that score. Though not very merciful, as you know, I would put no poor soul through that ordeal again. In this case you will only have to encounter one of the tormentors you met on that occasion, and I will try to vouch for her better behavior." Then she added, seriously: "I hope you will not think the task beneath you. You do not seem to have much of the foolish pride that stands in the way of so many Americans, and then" — looking at him with a pleading face — "I have so set my heart upon it, and it would be such a disappointment if you were unwilling!"

"You need waste no more ammunition on one ready to surrender at discretion," he said.

"Very well; then I shall treat you with all the rigors of a prisoner of war. I shall carry you away captive to my new castle on the north side, and put you at your old menial task of hanging pictures and decorating in various ways. As eastern sovereigns built their palaces and adorned their cities by the labors of those whom the fortunes of war threw into their hands, so your skill and taste shall be useful to me; and I, your head task-mistress," she added, with her insinuating smile, "will be ever present to see that there is no idling, nothing but monotonous toil. Had you not better have stood longer on the defensive?"

Dennis held out his hands in mock humility and said: "I am ready for my chains. You shall see with what fortitude I endure my captivity."

"It is well that you should show it somewhere, for you have not done so in your resistance. But I parole you on your honor, to report at such times as I shall indicate and papa can spare you;" and with a smile and a lingering look that seemed, as before, directed to his face rather than himself, she passed out.

That peculiar look often puzzled him, and at times he would go to a glass and see if there was anything wrong or unusual in his appearance. But now his hopes rose higher than ever. She had been very gracious, certainly, and invited intimate companionship. Dennis felt that she must have read his feelings in his face and manner, and, to his ingenuous nature, any encouragement seemed to promise all he hoped.

For a week after this he scarcely saw her, for she was very busy making preliminary arrangements for the occupation of her new home. But one afternoon she suddenly appeared, and said, with affected severity, "Report to-morrow at nine A. M."

Dennis bowed humbly. She gave him a pleasant smile over her shoulder, and passed away as quickly as she had come. It seemed like a vision to him, and only a trace of her favorite perfume (which indeed ever seemed more an atmosphere than a perfume) remained as evidence that she had been there.

At five minutes before the time on the following day he appeared at the new Ludolph mansion. From an open window Christine beckoned him to enter, and welcomed him with characteristic words, — "In view of your foolish surrender to my power, remember that you have no rights that I am bound to respect."

"I throw myself on your mercy."

"I have already told you that I do not possess that trait; so prepare for the worst."

She was dressed in some light summer fabric, and her rounded arms and neck were partially bare. She looked so white and cool, so self-possessed, and, with all her smiles, so devoid of warm human feeling, that Dennis felt a sudden chill at heart. The ancient fable of the sirens occurred to him. Might she not be luring him on to his own destruction? At times he almost hoped that she loved him; again, something in her manner caused him to doubt everything But there were not, as in the case of Ulysses and his crew, friendly hands to bind and restrain, or to put wax in his ears, and soon the music of her voice, the strong enchantment of the love she had inspired, banished all thought of prudence. His passion was now becoming a species of intoxication, a continued and feverish excitement, and its influence was unhappy on mind and body. There was no rest, peace, or assurance in it, and the uncertainty, the tantalizing inability to obtain a definite satisfying word, and yet the apparent nearness of the prize, wore upon him. Sometimes, when late at night he sat brooding over his last interview, weighing with the nice scales of a lover's anxiety her every look and even accent, his own haggard face would startle him.

Then again her influence was not morally good, and his interest declined in everything save what was connected with her.

Conscience at times told him that he was more bent on gaining her love for himself than in winning it for God. He satisfied himself by trying to reason that when he had won her affection his power for good would be greater, and thus, while he ever sought to look and suggest his own love in nameless little ways, he made less and less effort to remind her of a better love than even his. Moreover, she never encouraged any approach to sacred themes, sometimes repelling it decidedly, and so, though he would scarcely acknowledge it, the traitorous fear sprung up, that in speaking of God's love he might mar his chances of speaking of his own.

In the retirement of his own room, his reveries grew longer, and his prayers shorter and less inspired by faith and earnestness. At the mission school, Susie Winthrop noticed with regret that the lesson was often given in a listless, preoccupied manner; and even the little boys themselves missed something in the teacher once so interesting and animated. From witnessing his manner when with Christine, Miss Winthrop had more than suspected his secret for some time, and she felt at first a genuine sympathy for him, believing his love to be hopeless. From the first she had found Dennis very fascinating, but when she read his secret in his ardent glances toward Christine, she became conscious that her interest was rather greater than passing acquaintance warranted, and, like the good, sensible girl that she was, fought to the death the incipient fancy. At first she felt that he ought to know that Christine was pledged to a future that would render his love vain. But her own feelings made her so exceedingly sensitive that it was impossible to attempt so difficult and delicate a task. Then, as Christine seemed to smile upon him, she said to herself: "After all, what is their plan, but a plan, and to me a very chimerical one? Perhaps Mr. Fleet can give Christine a far better chance of happiness than her father's ambition. And, after all, these are matters in which no third person can interfere." So, while remaining as cordial as ever, she prudently managed to see very little of Dennis.

As we have seen, under Christine's merry and half-bantering words (a style of conversation often assumed with him), even the thought of caution vanished. She led him over the moderately large and partially furnished house. There were women cleaning, and mechanics at work on some of the rooms. As they passed along she explained the nature of the decorations she wished. They consisted largely of rich carvings in wood, and unique frames.

"I wish you to help me design these, and see that they are properly put up, and to superintend the fresco-painters and mechanics in general. Indeed, I think you are more truly my prime-minister than my captive."

"Not less your captive," said Dennis, with a flush.

She gave him a bewildering smile, and then studied its effect upon him. He was in Elysium, and his eyes glowed with delight at her presence and the prospect before him. At last she led him into two large apartments on the second floor that opened into each other, and said, "These are my rooms; that yonder is my studio," as was evident from the large easel with canvas prepared upon it.

They at once had to Dennis all the sacredness of a shrine.

"I intend to make these rooms like two beautiful pictures," said Christine, "and here shall be the chief display of your taste."

Dennis could scarcely believe his ears, or realize that the cold, beautiful girl who a few short months ago did not notice him now voluntarily gave him such opportunities to urge his suit. The success that a man most covets seemed assured, and his soul was intoxicated with delight. He said, "You intimated that my tasks might be menial, but I feel as I imagine a Greek artist must have done, when asked to decorate the temple of a goddess."

"I think I told you once before that your imagination overshadowed your other faculties."

Her words recalled the painted girl whom she by a strange coincidence so strongly resembled. To his astonishment he saw the same striking likeness again. Christine was looking at him with the laughing, scornful expression that the German lady bent upon the awkward lover who knelt at her feet. His face darkened in an instant.

"Have I offended you?" she asked, gently; "I remember now you did not admire that picture."

"I liked everything about it save the expression of the girl's face. I think you will also remember that I said that such a face should be put to nobler uses."

Christine flushed slightly, and for a moment was positively afraid of him. She saw that she must be more careful, for she was dealing with one of quick eye and mind. At the same time her conscience reproached her again. The more she saw of him the more she realized how sincere and earnest he was; how different from ordinary society-men, to whom an unsuccessful suit to a fair lady is a mere annoyance. But she was not one to give up a purpose readily for the sake of conscience or anything else, and certainly not now, when seemingly on the point of success. So she said, with a slight laugh, "Do not compare me to any of those old pagan myths again;" and having thus given a slight reason, or excuse, for her unfortunate expression, she proceeded to beguile him more thoroughly than ever by the subtile witchery of smiles, glances, and words, that might mean everything or nothing.

"You seem to have a study on your easel there," said Dennis, as they stood together in the studio. "May I see it?"

"No," said she; "you are to see nothing till you see a triumph in the portrayal of feeling and life-like earnestness that even your critical eye cannot condemn."

She justly feared that, should he see her work, he might discover her plan; for, however she might disguise it, something suggesting himself entered into all her studies.

"I hope you will succeed, but doubt it."

"Why?" she asked, quickly.

"Because we cannot portray what we cannot feel. The stream cannot rise higher than its fountain." Then he added, with heightened color and some hesitation, "I fear — your heart is still sleeping;" and he watched with deep anxiety how she would take the questioning remark.

At first she flushed almost angrily; but, recovering self-possession in a moment, she threw upon him an arch smile, suggesting all that a lover could wish, and said: "Be careful, Mr. Fleet; you are seeking to penetrate mysteries that we most jealously guard. You know that in the ancient temple there was an inner sanctuary which none might enter."

"Yes, *one* might," said Dennis, significantly.

With her long lashes she veiled the dark blue eyes that expressed anything but tender feeling, and yet, so shaded, they appeared as a lover would wish, and in a low tone she answered, "Well, he could not enter when he would, only when permitted."

She raised her eyes quickly to see the effect; and she did see an effect that she would have given thousands to be able to transfer to canvas.

His face, above all she had ever seen, seemed designed to express feeling, passion; and his wearing life had made it so thin, and his eyes were so large and lustrous, that the spiritual greatly predominated, and she felt as if she could almost see the throbs of the strong, passionate heart.

Apart from her artistic purposes, contact with such warm, intense life had for Christine a growing fascination. She had not realized that in kindling and fanning this flame of honest love to sevenfold power and heat, she might be kindled herself. When, therefore, she saw the face of Dennis Fleet eloquent with the deepest, strongest feeling that human features can portray, another chord than the artistic one was touched, and there was a low, faint trill of that music which often becomes the sweetest harmony of life.

"And at some time in the future may I hope to enter?" he asked, tremulously.

She threw him another smile over her shoulder as she turned to her easel, — a smile that from a true woman would mean, You may, but which from many would mean nothing, and said, vaguely, "What is life without hope?" and then, as matters were going too fast and far, decisively changed the subject.

Seated at her easel she painted eagerly and rapidly, while he measured the space over and around the fireplace with a view to its ornamentation. She kept the conversation on the general subject of art, and, though Dennis knew it not, every glance at his face was that of a portrait-painter.

CHAPTER XXXII.

BITTER DISAPPOINTMENT.

DENNIS went back to the store in a maze of hopes and fears, but hope predominated. Christine could not be indifferent and treat him as she did, if she had a particle of sincerity, and with a lover's faith he would not believe her false, though he knew her to be so faulty.

"At any rate," he said to himself, "in this new arrangement I have all the opportunity a man could ask, and if I cannot develop her plainly manifested interest into something more decisive by such companionship, I may as well despair;" and he determined to avail himself of every advantage within his reach in making the most of what he deemed a rare stroke of fortune. His greatly increased salary enabled him to dress with that taste and even elegance so pleasing to a lady's eye, and he had withal acquired that ease and grace of manner which familiarity with the best society bestows.

It is also well to tell the reader that after some hesitation Dennis had confided his feelings to his mother, and received from her the warmest sympathy. To Ethel Fleet's unworldly nature, that he should fall in love with and marry his employer's daughter seemed eminently fitting, with just a spice of beautiful romance. And it was her son's happiness and Christine's beauty that she thought of, not Mr. Ludolph's money. In truth, such was her admiration for her son, she felt that with all her wealth the young lady would receive a greater honor than she conferred. Though Dennis wrote with the partiality of a lover, he could not so portray Christine's character but that his mother felt the deepest anxiety, and often sighed in sad foreboding of serious trouble in the future.

From Mrs. Fleet's knowledge of her son's passion, Christine, though she knew it not, received another advantage of incalculable value. Dennis had painted an excellent little cabinet likeness of her, and sent it to his mother. In the quiet of the night she would sit down before that picture, and by her strong imagination summon her ideal of Christine, and then lead her directly to Christ, as parents brought their children of old. Could such prayers and faith be in vain? Faith is often sorely tried in this world, but never tried in vain.

Day after day Dennis went to Mr. Ludolph's new home during the morning hours, and Christine's spell worked with bewildering and increasing power. While she tortured him with many doubts and fears, his hope grew to be almost a certainty that he had at last made a place for himself in her heart. Sometimes the whole story of his love trembled on his lips, but she never permitted its utterance. That she determined should be reserved for the climax. He usually met her alone, but noticed that in the presence of others she was cool and undemonstrative. Mr. Ludolph rarely saw them together, and, when he did, there was nothing in his daughter's manner to awaken suspicion. This perfectly acted indifference in the presence of others, and equally well acted regard when alone, often puzzled Dennis sorely. But at last he concluded: "She is wiser than I. She knows that I am in no condition now to make proposals for her hand; therefore it is better that there should be no recognized understanding between us;" and he resolved to be as prudent as she. Then again she would so awaken his jealousy and fears that he would feel that he must know his fate, — that anything was better than such torturing uncertainty.

As for Christine, two processes were going on in her mind, — one that she recognized, and one that she did not.

Her artistic aims were clear and definite. In the first place she meant perfectly to master the human face as it expressed emotions, especially such as were of a tender nature; and in the second place she intended to paint a picture that in itself would make her famous. She chose a most difficult and delicate subject, — of the character she had ever failed in, — a declaration of love.

When Dennis began to work again in her presence, the picture was well advanced.

In a grand old hall, whose sides were decorated with armor and weapons, a young man stood pleading his cause with a lady whose hand he held. The young girl's face was so averted that only a beautiful profile was visible, but her form and attitude were grace itself. The lovers stood in an angle of the hall near an open window, through which was seen a fine landscape, a picture within a picture. But Christine meant to concentrate all her power and skill on the young knight's face. This should be eloquent with all the feeling and passion that the human face could express, and she would insure its truthfulness to life by copying life itself, — the reality. Dennis Fleet was the human victim that she was offering on the altar of her ambition.

Much of the picture was merely in outline, but she finished the form and features of the suppliant in all save the expression, and this she meant to paint from his face whenever she was in the right mood and could bring matters to a crisis.

After he had been coming to the house two or three times a week for nearly a month, she felt that she was ready for the final scene, and yet she dreaded it, she had staked so much hope upon it. It also provoked her to find that she was really afraid of him. His was such a strong, sincere nature, that she felt increasingly the wrong of trifling with it. In vain she tried to quiet herself by saying, "I do not care a straw for him, and he will soon get over his infatuation on discovering the truth."

But she had a lesson to learn as well as he, for as we have intimated, unrecognized as yet, there was a process going on in her mind that in time would make strange havoc in her cold philosophy. Her heart's long winter was slowly breaking up; her girlish passion, intense as it was foolish, proved that she had a heart. Everything had been against her. Everything in her experience and education, and especially in her father's strong character and prejudices, had combined to deaden and to chill her; and had these influences continued, she would undoubtedly have become as cold and hard as some whom we find in advanced life with natures like the poles, where the ice gathers year after year, but never melts.

But in Dennis Fleet she met a nature as positive as she was becoming negative. He was so warm and earnest that when she commenced to fan his love into a stronger flame for purely artistic purposes, as she vowed to herself, some sparks of the sacred fire fell on the cold altar of her own heart and slowly began to kindle.

But this awakening would not now be that of a child, but of a *woman*. Therefore, Mr. Ludolph, beware!

But she had yet much to learn in the hard, strange school of experience before she would truly know herself or her own needs.

Success in art, however, was still her ruling passion. And though strange misgivings annoyed and perplexed her, though her respect for Dennis daily increased, and at times a sudden pity and softness made her little hands hesitate before giving an additional wrench to the rack of uncertainty upon which she kept him; still, she would not for the world have abandoned her purpose, and such compunctions were as yet but the little back eddies of the strong current.

One day, in the latter part of August, Christine felt herself in the mood to give the finishing touch to the principal figure in her picture. The day was somewhat hazy, the light subdued and favorable for artistic work. Though she had prolonged Dennis's labors, to his secret delight and great encouragement, she could not keep him employed much longer.

She sent for him to come over in the afternoon. "Some brackets, carvings, and pictures had come for her studio, and she wished him to put them up," she said, coolly, as he entered.

He had come glowing with hope and almost assurance, for, the last time they had parted, she had dismissed him with unusual kindness. But here was one of those capricious changes again that he could not understand.

She took her seat at her easel, saying, with a nod and a smile, "I can direct you here, for I am in a mood for work this afternoon."

He bowed quietly and went on with his task. Her rather cool reception oppressed him, and the tormenting question presented itself, for the hundredth time, "Can she in any degree feel as I do?" He longed to settle the matter by plain, straightforward action.

Her maid knocked at the door, saying, "The mail, mademoiselle."

A dainty note was handed her, which seemed decidedly pleasing, and Dennis noticed as she read it that she wore on her finger a solitaire diamond that he had not seen before. His latent jealousy was aroused. She saw that her spell was working, and smiled. Soon she said: "Mr. Fleet, you seem very grave. What is the matter?"

He answered, curtly, "Nothing."

She looked at him with a pretty, pained surprise. At the same time her heart smote her. His face was so pale and thin, and indicated such real suffering, that she pitied him more than ever. But she would have suffered much herself for the sake of success, and she was not one to hesitate long over the suffering of another. She compressed her lips as she said, mentally: "Art is first, and these transient feelings are secondary. There is little in the world but that has cost some one deeply." She did not know how profound a truth this was.

After a few moments Dennis said, in a tone that had a jealous tinge, "Miss Ludolph, your correspondent seems to interest you deeply."

"And you also, I think," she replied, with an arch smile; "and you will be interested still more when you have read this;" and she offered him the note.

"I have no right, — do not think me prying," said he, flushing.

"I give the right. You know a lady can give many rights — if she chooses," she added, significantly.

He looked at her eagerly.

Her eyes fell consciously, and her cheeks glowed with excitement, for she felt that the critical moment had come. But instantly her proud, resolute nature aroused as never before, and she determined to make the most of the occasion, let the consequences be what they might. Therefore she worked eagerly and watched him closely. Never had she been so conscious of power. She felt inspired, capable of placing on the canvas anything she chose. If in this mood she could succeed in bringing into his face just the expression she desired, she could catch it and fix it forever, and with it make a laurel (not a hymeneal) wreath for her own brow. But what could Dennis know of all this? To him the glowing cheek and eyes so lustrous told a different tale; and hope — sweet, exquisite, almost assured — sprung up in his heart.

And he meant that it should be assured. He would speak that day if it were possible, and *know* his happiness, instead of fondly believing and hoping that all was sure. Then he would be as prudent and patient as she desired. Thus Christine was destined to have her wish fulfilled.

She continued: "The note is from a special friend of yours; indeed I think you form a little mutual-admiration society, and you are spoken of, so I think you had better read it."

"I shall not read the note," said Dennis; "but you may tell me, if you choose, what you think the writer will have no objection to my knowing."

"And do you mean to suggest that you do not know who wrote the note? I can inform you that you are to be invited to a moonlight sail and musicale on the water. Is not that a chance for romance?"

"And will *you* go?" asked Dennis, eagerly.

"Yes, if *you* will," she said, in a low tone, giving him a sidelong glance.

This was too much for Dennis, the manner more than the words, and taken together they would have led any earnest man to committal. He was about to speak eagerly, but she was not quite ready.

"Moreover," she continued, quickly, while Dennis stood before her with cheeks alternately hot and pale, "this special friend who invites you will be there. Now don't pretend ignorance of her name."

"I suppose you mean Miss Winthrop," said Dennis, flushing.

"Ah, you blush, do you? Well, it is my turn to ask pardon for seeming curiosity."

He drew a few steps nearer to her, and the expression she had so longed to see came into his face. She looked at him earnestly with her whole soul in her eyes. She would photograph him on memory, if possible. For a moment or two he hesitated, embarrassed by her steady gaze, and seemingly at a loss for words. Then, in a low, deep tone he said, "You, better than any one, know that I have no cause to blush at the mention of Miss Winthrop's name."

She did not answer, but was painting rapidly. He thought this was due to natural excitement expressing itself in nervous action. But she did not discourage him, and this he felt was everything. With his heart in his eyes and tones, he said: "O Christine, what is the use of wearing this transparent mask any longer? Your quick woman's eye has seen for weeks the devoted love I cherish for you. I have heard much of woman's intuitions. Perhaps you saw my love before I recognized it myself, since your grace and beauty caused it to grow unconsciously while I was your humble attendant. But, Christine, believe me, if you will but utter in words what I fondly believe I have read in your kindly glances and manner, though so delicately veiled,— if you will give me the strength and rest which come of assured hope,— I know that not far in the future I shall be able to place at your feet more than mere wealth. I, too, hope to be an artist, and you have been my chief inspiration. I could show you a picture now that would tell more of what I mean than can my poor words. There is a richer and happier world than you have yet known, and oh, how I have prayed that I might lead you into it!" and in words of burning eloquence he proceeded to tell the story of his love.

She heard him as in a dream. She understood his words, remembered them afterward, but so intent was she on her darling purpose that she heeded them not. His voice sounded far away, and every power of mind and body was concentrated to transfer his expression to the canvas before her. Even he, blinded as he was by his emotions, occupied by the long pent-up torrent of feeling that he was pouring into her unheeding ear, wondered at her strange, dazzling beauty and peculiar manner.

After speaking a moment or two, the blur over his eyes and the confusion of his mind began to pass away, and he was perplexed beyond measure at the way she was receiving the open declaration of his love. She was painting through it all, not with the nervous, random stroke of one who sought to hide excitement and embarrassment in occupation. She was working earnestly, consciously, with precision, and, what was strangest of all, she seemed so intent upon his face that his words, which would have been such music to any woman that loved, were apparently unheard. He stopped, but the break in his passionate flow of language was unnoted.

"Christine, listen to me!" he cried, in an agony of fear and perplexity. The tone of his appeal might have stirred a marble bosom to pity, but she only raised her left hand deprecatingly as if warding off an interruption, while she worked with intense eagerness with her right.

"Christine!" a frown contracted her brow for a second, but she worked on.

He looked at her as if fearing she had lost her reason, but there was no madness in her swift, intelligent strokes Then like a flash the thought came to him: "It is my face, not myself, that she wants! This, then, has been the secret of her new hope as an artist. She would not feel, as I told her she must, but she would call out and copy my emotion; and this scene, which means life or death to me, is to her but a lesson in art, and I am no more than the human subject under the surgeon's knife. But surely no anatomist is so cruel as to put in his lancet before the man is dead."

Every particle of color receded from his face, and he watched her manner for the confirmation of his thought.

Her face was indeed a study. A beautiful smile parted her lips, her eyes glowed with the exultation of assured and almost accomplished success, and she looked like an inspired priestess at a Greek oracle.

But a bitterness beyond words was filling his heart.

A few more skilful strokes, and she threw down her brush, crying in ecstatic tones, "Eureka! Eureka!" as she stood before the painting in rapt admiration. In an instant he stood by her side. With all the pride of triumph she pointed to the picture, and said: "Criticise that, if you can! Deny that there is soul, life, feeling there, if you dare! Is that painting but a 'beautiful corpse'?"

Dennis saw a figure and features suggesting his own, pleading with all the eloquence of true love before the averted face of the maiden in the picture. It was indeed a triumph, having all the power of the reality.

He passed his hand quickly across his forehead, as if to repel some terrible delusion, while yet he whispered its reality to himself, in silent, despairing confession: "Ah, my God! How cold she must be when she can see any one look like that, and yet copy the expression as from a painted face upon the wall!"

Then, his own pride and indignation rising, he determined at once to know the truth; whether he held any place in her heart, or whether the picture was all, and he nothing.

Drawing a step nearer, as if to examine more closely, he seized a brush of paint and drew it over the face that had cost both him and Christine so much, and then turned and looked at her.

For a moment she stood paralyzed, so great seemed the disaster. Then she turned on him in fury. "How dare you!" she exclaimed.

Only equal anger, and the consciousness of right, could have sustained any man under the lightning of her eyes.

"Rather, let me ask, how dare you?" he replied, in the deep, concentrated voice of passion; and lover and lady stood before the ruined picture with blazing eyes. In the same low, stern voice he continued, "I see the secret of your artistic hope now, Miss Ludolph, but permit me to say that you have made your first and last success, and there in that black stain, most appropriately black, is the result."

She looked as if she could have torn him to atoms.

"You have been false," he continued. "You have acted a lie before me for weeks. You have deceived in that which is most sacred, and with sacrilegious hands have trifled with that which every true man regards as holy."

She trembled beneath his stern, accusing words. Conscience echoed them, anger and courage were fast deserting her in the presence of the aroused and more powerful spirit of her wronged lover. But she said, petulantly, "Nonsense! You know well that half the ladies of the city would have flirted with you from mere vanity and love of power; my motive was infinitely beyond this."

Until now this had almost seemed sufficient reason to excuse her action, but she distrusted it even to loathing as she saw the look of scorn come out on his noble face.

"And is that your best plea for falsehood? A moment since I loved you with a devotion that you will never receive again. But now I despise you."

"Sir!" she cried, her face scarlet with shame and anger, "leave this room!"

"Yes, in a moment, and never again to enter it while Christine Ludolph is as false in character as she is beautiful in person. But before I go, you, in your pride and luxury, shall hear the truth for once. Not only have you been false, but you have been what no true woman ever can be, — cruel as death. Your pencil has been a stiletto with which you have slowly felt for my heart. You have dipped your brush in human suffering as if it were common paint. Giotto stabbed a man and mercifully took him off by a few quick pangs, that he might paint his dying look. You, more cruel, accomplish your purpose by slow, remorseless torture. Merciful Heaven only knows what I have suffered since you smiled and frowned on me by turns, but I felt that if I could only win your love I would gladly endure all. You falsely made me believe that I had won it, and yet all the while you were dissecting my heart, as a surgeon might a living subject. And now what have you to offer to solace the bitterness of coming years? Do you not know that such deeds make men bad, faithless, devilish? Never dream of success till you are changed utterly. Only the noble in deed and in truth can reach high and noble art."

She sat before the disfigured picture with her face bowed in her hands.

She thought he was gone, but still remained motionless like one doomed. A few moments passed and she was startled by hearing his voice again. It was no longer harsh and stern, but sad, grave, and pitiful.

"Miss Ludolph, may God forgive you."

She trembled. Pride and better feeling were contending for the mastery. After a few moments she sprung up and reached out her hands; but he was gone now in very truth.

CHAPTER XXXIII.

THE TWO PICTURES.

WHEN Christine saw that Dennis was not in the room, she rushed to a window only in time to see his retreating form passing down the street. For a moment she felt like one left alone to perish on a sinking wreck. His words, so assured in their tones, seemed like those of a prophet. Conscience echoed them, and a chill of fear came over her heart. What if he were right? What if she had let the one golden opportunity of her life pass? Even though she had stolen her inspiration from him through guile and cruelty, had he not enabled her to accomplish more than in all her life before? To what might he not have led her, if she had put her hand frankly and truthfully in his? There are times when to those most bewildered in mazes of error light breaks, clear and unmistakable, defining right and wrong with terrible distinctness. Such an hour was this to Christine. The law of God written on her heart asserted itself, and she trembled at the guilty thing she saw herself to be. But there seemed no remedy save in the one she had driven away, never to return, as she believed. After a brief but painful revery she exclaimed: "But what am I thinking of? What can he or any man of this land be to me?"

Then pride, her dominant trait, awoke as she recalled his words.

"He despises me, does he? I will teach him that I

belong to a sphere he cannot touch, — the poor infatuated youth! And did he dream that I, Christine Ludolph, could give him my hand? He shall learn some day that none in this land could receive that honor, and none save the proudest in my own may hope for it. The idea of my giving up my ancient and honorable name for the sake of this unknown Yankee youth."

Bold, proud words that her heart did not echo.

But pride and anger were now her controlling impulses, and with the strong grasp of her resolute will she crushed back her gentler and better feelings, and became more icy and hard than ever.

By such choice and action, men and women commit moral suicide.

With a cold, white face, and a burnished gleam in her eyes, she went to the easel and commenced painting out the ominous black stain.

"I'll prove him a false prophet also. I will be an artist without passing through all his sentimental and superstitious phases that have so amused me during the past weeks. I have seen his lovelorn face too often not to be able to reproduce it and its various expressions."

Her strokes were quick and almost fierce.

"Mrs. Dennis Fleet, ha! ha! ha!" and her laugh was as harsh and discordant as the feeling that prompted it.

Again, a little later: "He despises me! Well, he is the first man that ever dared to say that;" and her face was flushed and dark with anger.

Dennis at first walked rapidly from the scene of his bitter disappointment, but his steps soon grew slow and feeble. The point of endurance was passed. Body and mind acting and reacting on each other had been taxed beyond their powers, and both were giving way. He felt that they were and struggled to reach the store before the crisis should come. Weak and trembling, he mounted the steps, but fell fainting across the threshold. One of the clerks saw him fall and gave the alarm. Mr. Ludolph, Mr. Schwartz, and others hastened to the spot. Dennis was carried to his room, and a messenger was despatched for Dr. Arten. Ernst, with flying feet, and wild, frightened face, soon reached his home in DeKoven Street, and startled his father and mother with the tidings.

The child feared that Dennis was dead, his face was so thin and white. Leaving the children in Ernst's care, both Mr. and Mrs. Bruder, prompted by their strong gratitude to Dennis, rushed through the streets as if distracted. Their intense anxiety and warm German feeling caused them to heed no more the curious glances cast after them than would a man swimming for life note the ripple he made.

When Dennis regained consciousness, they, and Mr. Ludolph and Dr. Arten, were around him. At first his mind was confused, and he could not understand it all.

"Where am I?" he asked, feebly, "and what has happened?"

"Do not be alarmed; you have only had a faint turn," said the doctor.

"O Mr. Fleet, you vork too hart, you vork too hart; I knew dis vould come," sobbed Mrs. Bruder.

"Why, his duties in the store have not been so onerous of late," said Mr. Ludolph, in some surprise.

"It is not der vork in der store, but he vork nearly all night too. Den he haf had trouble, I know he haf. Do he say no vort about him?"

Dennis gave Mrs. Bruder a sudden warning look, and then, through the strong instinct to guard his secret, roused himself.

"Is it anything serious, doctor?" he asked.

The physician looked grave, and said, "Your pulse and whole appearance indicate great exhaustion and physical depression, and I also fear that fever may set in."

"I think you are right," said Dennis. "I feel as if I were going to be ill. My mind has a tendency to wander. Mr. Ludolph, will you permit me to go home? If I am to be sick, I want to be with my mother."

Mr. Ludolph looked inquiringly at the doctor, who said significantly, in a low tone, "I think it would be as well."

"Certainly, Fleet," said his employer; "though I hope it is only a temporary indisposition, and that you will be back in a few days. You must try and get a good night's rest, and so be prepared for the journey in the morning."

"With your permission I will go at once. A train leaves now in an hour, and by morning I can be at home."

"I scarcely think it prudent," began the doctor.

"O certainly not to-night," said Mr. Ludolph, also.

"Pardon me, I must go at once," interrupted Dennis, briefly and so decidedly that the gentlemen looked at each other and said no more.

"Mr. Bruder," he continued, "I must be indebted to you for a real proof of your friendship. In that drawer you will find my money. The key is in my pocketbook. Will you get a carriage and take me to the depot at once? and can you be so kind as to go on home with me? I cannot trust myself alone. Mrs. Bruder, will you pack up what you think I need?"

His faithful friends hastened to do his bidding.

"Mr. Ludolph, you have been very kind to me. I am sorry this has occurred, but cannot help it. I thank you gratefully, and will now trespass on your valuable time no longer."

Mr. Ludolph, feeling that he could be of no further use, said: "You will be back in a week, Fleet. Courage. Good-by."

Dennis turned eagerly to the doctor and said: "Can you not give me something that will reduce the fever and keep me sane a little longer? I know that I am going to be delirious, but would reach the refuge of home first."

A prescription was given and immediately procured, and the doctor went away shaking his head.

"This is the way people commit suicide. They know no more about, or pay no more heed to, the laws of health than the laws of China. Here is the result: This young fellow has worked in a way that would break down a cast-iron machine, and now may never see Chicago again."

But Dennis might have worked even in his intense way for months and years without serious harm, had not a fair white hand kept him on the rack of uncertainty and fear.

Not work, but worry, makes havoc of health.

In the gray dawn Ethel Fleet, summoned from her rest, received her son, weak, unconscious, muttering in delirium, and not recognizing even her familiar face. He was indeed a sad, painful contrast to the ruddy, buoyant youth who had left her a few short months before, abounding in hope and life. But she comforted herself with the thought that neither sin nor shame had brought him home.

We need not dwell on the weary weeks that followed. Dennis had every advantage that could result from good medical skill and the most faithful nursing. But we believe that his life lay rather in his mother's prayers of faith. In her strong realization of the spiritual world she would go continually into the very presence of Jesus, and say, "Lord, he whom Thou lovest is sick;" or, like parents of old, she would seem by her importunity to bring the Divine Physician to his very bedside.

Mr. Bruder, too, insisted on remaining, and watched with the unwearied faithfulness of one who felt that he owed to Dennis far more than life. It was indeed touching to see this man, once so desperate and depraved, now almost as patient and gentle as the mother herself, sitting by his unconscious friend, often turning his eyes heavenward and muttering in deep guttural German as sincere a prayer as ever passed human lips, that Dennis might be spared.

The hand of God seemed about to take him from them, but their strong, loving faith laid hold of that hand, and put upon it the restraint that only reverent, believing prayer can. Dennis lived. After many days delirium ceased, and the confused mind became clear. But during his delirium Ethel and Mr. Bruder learned from the oft-repeated words, "Cruel, cruel Christine!" the nature of the wound that had nearly destroyed his life.

Mr. Ludolph was late in reaching his home on the evening after Dennis was taken sick. Christine sat in the dusk on the ivy-shaded piazza, awaiting him. He said, abruptly, "What have you been doing to Fleet, over here?"

For a second her heart stood still, and she was glad the increasing gloom disguised her face. By a great effort she replied, in a cool, matter-of-fact tone: "I do not understand your question. Mr. Fleet was here this afternoon, and gave some finishing touches to my studio. I do not think I shall need him any more."

Her quiet, indifferent voice would have disarmed suspicion itself.

"It is well you do not, for he seems to have received some 'finishing touches' himself. He fell across the threshold of the store in a dead faint, and has gone home, threatened with a serious illness."

Even her resolute will could not prevent a sharp, startled exclamation.

"What is the matter?" said her father, hastily; "you are not going to faint also, are you?"

"No," said Christine, quietly again; "but I am tired and nervous, and you told your news so abruptly! Why, it seemed but a moment ago he was here at work, and now he is dangerously ill. What an uncertain stumbling forward in the dark life is!"

This was a style of moralizing peculiarly distasteful to Mr. Ludolph, — all the more repugnant because it seemed true, and brought home in Dennis's experience. Anything that interfered with his plans and interests, even though might be God's providence, always angered him. And now he was irritated at the loss of one of his best clerks, just as he was becoming of great value; so he said, sharply: "I hope you are not leaning toward the silly cant of mysterious providence. Life is uncertain stumbling only to fools who can't see the chances that fortune throws in their way, or recognize the plain laws of health and success. This young Fleet has been putting two days' work in one for the past four months, and now perhaps his work is done forever, for the doctor looked very grave over him."

Again the shadow of night proved most friendly to Christine. Her face had a frightened, guilty look that it was well her father did not see, or he would have wrung from her the whole story. She felt the chill of a terrible dread at heart. If he should die, her conscience would give a fearful verdict against her. She stood trembling, feeling almost powerless to move.

"Come," said her father, sharply, "I am hungry and tired."

"I will ring for lights and supper," said Christine, hastily, and then fled to her own room.

When she appeared, her father was sitting at the table impatiently awaiting her. But her face was so white, and there was such an expression in her eyes, that he started and said, "What is the matter?"

His question irritated her, and she replied as sharply as he had spoken.

"I told you I was tired, and I don't feel well. I have been a month in constant effort to get this house in order, and I am worn out, I suppose."

He looked at her keenly, but said more kindly, "Here, my dear, take this wine;" and he poured out a glass of old port.

She drank it eagerly, for she felt she must have something that would give her life, warmth, and courage. In a way she could not understand, her heart sunk within her.

But she saw her father was watching her, and knew she must act skilfully to deceive him. Rallied and strengthened by the generous wine, her resolute will was soon on its throne again, and Mr. Ludolph with all his keen insight was no match for her. In a matter-of-fact tone she said: "I do not see how we have worked Mr. Fleet to death. Does he charge anything of the kind?"

"Oh, no! but he too seems possessed with the idea of becoming an artist. That drunken old Bruder, whom he appears to have reformed, was giving him lessons, and after working all day he would study much of the night and paint as soon as the light permitted in the morning. He might have made something if he had had a judicious friend to guide him" ("And such you might have been," whispered her conscience), "but now he drops away like untimely fruit."

"It is a pity," said she, coolly, and changed the subject, as if she had dismissed it from her mind.

Mr. Ludolph believed that Dennis was no more to his daughter than a useful clerk.

The next morning Christine rose pale and listless.

Her father said, "I will arrange my business so that we can go off on a trip in a few days."

When left alone she sat down at her easel and tried to restore the expression that had so delighted her on the preceding day. But she could not. Indeed she was greatly vexed to find that her tendency was to paint his stern and scornful look, which had made a deeper impression on her mind than any she had ever seen on his face, because so unexpected and novel. She became irritated with herself, and cried, fiercely: "Shame on your weakness! You are unworthy of your blood and ancestry. I will reproduce that face as it was before he so insolently destroyed it;" and she bent over her easel with an expression not at all in harmony with her work. Unconsciously she made a strange contrast, with her severe, hard face and compressed lips, to the look of love and pleading she sought to paint. For several days she wrought with resolute purpose, but found that her inspiration was gone.

At last she threw down her brush in despair, and cried: "I cannot catch it again. The wretch either smiles or frowns upon me. I fear he was right: I have made my first and last success;" and she leaned her head sullenly and despairingly on her hand. Again the whole scene passed before her, and she dwelt upon every word, as she was beginning often to do now, in painful revery. When she came to the words, "I too mean to be an artist. I could show you a picture that would tell you far more of what I mean than can my poor words," she started up, and, hastily arraying herself for the street, was soon on her way to the Art Building.

No one heeded her movements there, and she went directly upstairs to his room. Though simple and plain, it had unmistakably been the abode of a gentleman and a person of taste. It was partially dismantled, and in disorder from his hasty departure, and she found nothing which satisfied her quest there. She hastened away, glad to escape from a place where everything seemed full of mute reproach, and next bent her steps to the top floor of the building. In a part half-filled with antiquated lumber, and seldom entered, she saw near a window facing the east an easel with canvas upon it. She was startled at the throbbing of her heart.

"It is only climbing these long stairs," she said; but her words were belied by the hesitating manner and eager face with which she approached and removed the covering from the canvas.

She gazed a moment and then put out her hands for something by which to steady herself. His chair was near, and she sunk into it, exclaiming: "He has indeed painted more than he — more than any one — could put into words. He has the genius that I have not. All here is striking and original;" and she sat with her eyes riveted to a painting that had revealed to her — herself.

Here was the secret of Dennis's toil and early work. Here were the results of his insatiable demand for the incongruous elements of ice and sunlight.

Side by side were two emblematic pictures. In the first there opened before Christine a grotto of ice. The light was thin and cold but very clear. Stalactites hung glittering from the vaulted roof. Stalagmites in strange fantastic forms rose to meet them. Vivid brightness and beauty were on every side, but of that kind that threw a chill on the beholder. All was of cold blue ice, and so natural was it that the eye seemed to penetrate its clear crystal. To the right was an opening in the grotto, through which was caught a glimpse of a summer landscape, a vivid contrast to the icy cave.

But the main features of the picture were two figures. Sleeping on a couch of ice was the form of a young girl. The flow of the drapery, the contour of the form, was grace itself, and yet all was ice. But the face was the most wonderful achievement. Christine saw her own features, as beautiful as in her vainest moments she had ever dared to hope. So perfect was the portrait that the delicate blue veins branched across the temple in veiled distinctness. It was a face that lacked but two things, life and love; and yet in spite of all its beauty the want of these was painfully felt, — all the more painfully, even as a lovely face in death awakens a deeper sadness and regret.

One little icy hand grasped a laurel wreath, also of ice. The other hand hung listless, half open, and from it had dropped a brush that formed a small stalagmite at her side.

Bending over her in most striking contrast was the figure of a young man, all instinct with life, power, and feeling. Though the face was turned away, Dennis had suggested his own form and manner. His left hand was extended toward the sleeping maiden, as if to awaken her, while with the right he pointed toward the opening through which was seen the summer landscape, and his whole attitude indicated an eager wish to rescue her. This was the first picture.

The second one was still more suggestive. At the entrance of the grotto, which looked more cold than ever, in its partial shadow, Christine saw herself again, but how changed! She now had a beauty which she could not believe in, — could not understand.

The icy hue and rigidity were all gone. She stood in the warm sunlight, and seemed all warmth and life. Her face glowed with feeling, yet was full of peace.

Instead of the barren ice, flowers were at her feet, and fruitful trees bent over her. Birds were seen flitting through their branches. The bended boughs, her flowing costume, and the tress of golden hair lifted from her temple, all showed that the summer wind was blowing.

Everything, in contrast with the frozen, death-like cave, indicated life, activity. Near her, a plane-tree, which in nature's language is the emblem of genius, towered into the sky; around its trunk twined the passion-flower, meaning, in Flora's tongue, "Holy love;" while just above her head, sipping the nectar from an open blossom, was a bright-hued butterfly, the symbol of immortality. By her side stood the same tall, manly form, with face still averted. He was pointing, and her eyes, softened, and yet lustrous and happy, were following where a path wound through a long vista, in alternate light and shadow, to a gate, that in the distance looked like a pearl. Above and beyond it, in airy outline, rose the walls and towers of the Holy City, the New Jerusalem.

For a long time she sat in rapt attention. Moment by moment the paintings in their meaning grew upon her. At last her eyes filled with tears, her bosom rose and fell with an emotion most unwonted, and in low tones she murmured: "Heavenly delusion! and taught with the logic I most dearly love. Oh that I could believe it! I would give ten thousand years of the life I am leading to know that it is true. Is there, can there be a path that leads through light or shade to a final and heavenly home? If this is true, in spite of all my father's keen and seemingly convincing arguments, what a terrible mistake our life is!"

Then her thoughts reverted to the artist.

"What have I done in driving him away with contempt in his heart for me? I can no more affect haughty superiority to the man who painted those pictures. Though he could not be my lover, what a friend he might have been! I fear I shall never find his equal. Oh this world of chaos and confusion! What is right? What is best? *What is truth?* He might have taught me. But the skilful hand that portrayed those wonderful scenes may soon turn to dust, and I shall go to my grave burdened with the thought that I have quenched the brightest genius that will ever shine upon me;" and she clasped her hands in an agony of regret.

Then came the thought of securing the pictures. Dropping a veil over her red eyes, she went down and got some large sheets of paper, and by fastening them together made a secure covering. Then she carried the light frame with the canvas to the second floor, and, summoning Ernst, started homeward with her treasure. The boy obeyed with reluctance. Since the time she had surprised him out of his secret in regard to the strawberries, he had never liked her, and now he felt that in some way she was the cause of the sickness of his dearest friend. Christine could not bear the reproach of his large, truthful eyes, and their walk was a silent one. At parting she handed him a bank note, but he shook his head.

"Have you heard from Mr. Fleet?" she asked, with a flush.

The boy's lip quivered at the mention of that name, and he answered, hastily: "Fader wrote moder Mr. Fleet was no better. I fear he die;" and in an agony of grief he turned and ran sobbing away.

From under her veil Christine's tears were falling fast also, and she entered her elegant home as if it had been a prison.

CHAPTER XXXIV.

REGRET.

THE next day was the Sabbath, and a long, dreary one it was to Christine. But late in the afternoon Susie Winthrop came with a pale, troubled face.

"O Christine, have you heard the news?" she exclaimed.

Christine's heart stood still with fear, but by a great effort she said, composedly, "What news?"

"Mr. Fleet has gone home very ill; indeed, he is not expected to live."

For a moment she did not answer, and when she did it was with a voice unnaturally hard and cold: "Have you heard what is the matter?"

Miss Winthrop wondered at her manner, but replied, "Brain fever, I am told."

"Is he delirious?" asked Christine, in a low tone.

"Yes, all the time. Ernst, the little office-boy, told me he did not know his own mother. It seems that the boy's father is with Mrs. Fleet, helping take care of him."

Christine's face was averted and so colorless that it seemed like marble.

"O Christine, don't you care?" said Susie, springing up and coming toward her.

"Why should I care?" was the quick answer.

Susie could not know that it was in reality but an incoherent cry of pain, — the blind, desperate effort of pride to shield itself. But the tone checked her steps and filled her face with reproach.

"Perhaps you have more reason to care than you choose to admit," she said, pointedly.

Christine flushed, but said, coldly: "Of course I feel an interest in the fate of Mr. Fleet, as I do in that of every passing acquaintance. I feel very sorry for him and his friends;" but never was sympathy expressed in a voice more unnaturally frigid.

Susie looked at her keenly, and again saw the telltale flush rising to her cheek. She was puzzled, but saw that her friend had no confidence to give, and she said, with a voice growing somewhat cold also: "Well, really, Christine, I thought you capable of seeing as much as the rest of us in such matters, but I must be mistaken, if you only recognized in Dennis Fleet a passing acquaintance. Well, if he dies I doubt if either you or I look upon his equal again. Under right influences he might have been one of the first and most useful men of his day. But they need not tell me it was overwork that killed him. I know it was trouble of some kind."

Christine was very pale, but said nothing; and Susie, pained and mystified that the confidence of other days was refused, bade her friend a rather cold and abrupt adieu.

Left alone, Christine bowed her white face in her hands and sat so still that it seemed as if life had deserted her. In her morbid state she began to fancy herself the victim of some terrible fatality. Her heart had bounded when Susie Winthrop was announced, believing that from her she would gain sympathy; but in strange perversity she had hidden her trouble from her friend, and permitted her to go away in coldness. Christine could see as quickly and as far as any, and from the first had noted that Dennis was very interesting to her friend. Until of late she had not cared, but now for some reason the fact was not pleasing, and she felt a sudden reluctance to speak to Susie of him.

Now that she was alone a deeper sense of isolation came over her than she had ever felt before. Her one confidential friend had departed, chilled and hurt. She made friends but slowly, and, having once become estranged, from her very nature she found it almost impossible to make the first advances toward reconciliation.

Soon she heard her father's steps, and fled to her room to nerve herself for the part she must act before him. But she was far from successful; her pale face and abstracted manner awakened his attention and his surmises as to the cause. Having an engagement out, he soon left her to welcome solitude; for when she was in trouble he was no source of help or comfort.

Monday dragged wearily to a close. She tried to work, but could not. She took up the most exciting book she could find, only to throw it down in despair. For ever before the canvas or the page would rise a pale thin face, at times stern and scornful, again full of reproach, and then of pleading.

Even at night her rest was disturbed, and in dreams she heard the mutterings of his delirium, in which he continually charged her with his death. At times she would take his picture from its place of concealment, and look at it with such feelings as would be awakened by a promise of some priceless thing now beyond reach forever. Then she would become irritated with herself, and say, angrily: "What is this man to me? Why am I worrying about one who never could be much more to me living than dead? I will forget the whole miserable affair."

But she could not forget. Tuesday morning came, but no relief. "Whether he lives or dies he will follow me to my grave!" she cried. "From the time I first spoke to him there has seemed no escape, and in strange, unexpected ways he constantly crosses my path!"

She felt that she must have some relief from the oppression on her spirit. Suddenly she thought of Ernst, and at once went to the store and asked if he had heard anything later. He had not, but thought that his mother would receive a letter that day.

"I want to see your father's picture, and will go home that way, if you will give me the number."

The boy hesitated, but at last complied with her wish.

A little later Christine knocked at Mr. Bruder's door. There was no response, though she heard a stifled sound within. After a little she knocked more loudly. Then the door slowly opened, and Mrs. Bruder stood before her. Her eyes were very red, and she held in her hand an open letter. Christine expected to find more of a lady than was apparent at first glance in the hard-working woman before her, so she said, "My good woman, will you tell Mrs. Bruder I would like to see her?"

"Dis is Mrs. Bruder," was the answer.

Then Christine noticed the letter, and the half-effaced traces of emotion, and her heart misgave her; but she nerved herself to say, "I came to see your husband's picture."

"It is dere," was the brief reply.

Christine began to expatiate on its beauty, though perhaps for the first time she looked at a fine picture without really seeing it. She was at a loss how to introduce the object of her visit, but at last said, "Your husband is away?"

"Yes."

"He is taking care of one of my father's — of Mr. Fleet, I am told. Have you heard from him as to Mr. Fleet's health?"

"Dis is Miss Ludolph?"

"Yes."

"You can no read Sherman?"

"Oh, yes, I can. German is my native tongue."

"Strange dot him should be so."

"Why?"

"Der Shermans haf hearts."

Christine flushed deeply, but Mrs. Bruder without a word put her husband's letter into her hand, and Christine read eagerly what, translated, is as follows: —

"My dear Wife: — Perhaps before this reaches you our best friend, our human savior, will be in heaven. There is a heaven, I believe as I never did before; and when Mrs. Fleet prays the gate seems to open, and the glory to stream right down upon us. But I fear now that not even her prayers can keep him. Only once he knew her; then he smiled and said, 'Mother, it is all right,' and dropped asleep. Soon fever came on again, and he is sinking fast. The doctor shakes his head and gives no hope. My heart is breaking. Marguerite, Mr. Fleet is not dying a natural death; he has been slain. I understand all his manner now, all his desperate hard work. He loved one above him in wealth, — none could be above him in other respects, — and that one was Miss Ludolph. I suspected it, though, till delirious, he scarcely ever mentioned her name. But now I believe she played with his heart — the noblest that ever beat — and then threw it away, as if it were a toy instead of the richest offering ever made to a woman. Proud fool that she was; she has done more mischief than a thousand such frivolous lives as hers can atone for. I can write no more; my heart is breaking with grief and indignation."

As Christine read she suffered her veil to drop over her face. When she looked up she saw that Mrs. Bruder's gaze was fixed upon her as upon the murderer of her best friend. She drew her veil closer about her face, laid the letter down, and left the room without a word. She felt so guilty and miserable on her way home that it would scarcely have surprised her had a policeman arrested her for the crime with which her own conscience, as well as Mr. Bruder's letter, charged her; and yet her pride revolted at it all.

"Why should this affair take so miserable a form with me?" she said. "To most it ends with a few sentimental sighs on one side, and as a good joke on the other. All seems to go wrong of late, and I am destined to have everything save happiness and the success upon which I set my heart. There is no more cruel mockery than to give one all save the very thing one wants; and, in seeking to grasp that, I have brought down upon myself this wretched, blighting experience. Oh this chaotic world! The idea of there being a God! Why, I could make a better world myself!" and she reached her home in such a morbid, unhappy state, that none in the great city need have envied the rich and flattered girl. Mechanically she dressed and came down to dinner.

During the afternoon Ernst, while out on an errand, had slipped home and heard the sad news. He returned to Mr. Ludolph's office crying. To the question, "What is the matter?" he had answered, "Oh, Mr. Fleet is dying; he is dead by dis time!"

Mr. Ludolph was sadly shocked and pained, for as far as he could like anybody besides himself and daughter, he had been prepossessed in favor of his useful and intelligent clerk, and he was greatly annoyed at the thought of losing him. He returned full of the subject, and the first words with which he greeted Christine were, "Well, Fleet will hang no more pictures for you, and sing no more songs."

She staggered into a chair and sat before him pale and panting, for she thought he meant that death had taken place.

"Why, what is the matter?" cried he.

She stared at him gaspingly, but said nothing.

"Here, drink this," he said, hastily pouring out a glass of wine.

She took it eagerly. After a moment he said: "Chri

tine, I do not understand all this. I was merely saying that my clerk, Mr. Fleet, was not expected — "

The point of endurance and guarded self-control was past, and she cried, half-hysterically: "Am I never to escape that man? Must every one I meet speak to me as if I had murdered him?"

Then she added, almost fiercely: "Living or dead, never speak to me of him again! I am no longer a child, but a woman, and as such I insist that his name be dropped between us forever!"

Her father gave a low exclamation of surprise, and said, "What! was he one of the victims?" (this being his term for Christine's rejected suitors).

"No," said she; "I am the victim. He will soon be at rest, while I shall be tormented to the grave by — " She hardly knew what to say, so mingled and chaotic were her feelings. Her hands clenched, and with a stamp of her foot she hastily left the room.

Mr. Ludolph could hardly believe his eyes. Could this passionate, thoroughly aroused woman be his cold, self-contained daughter? He could not understand, as so many cannot, that such natures when aroused are tenfold more intense than those whom little things excite. A long and peculiar train of circumstances, a morbid and overwrought physical condition, led to this outburst from Christine, which was as much a cause of surprise to herself afterward as to her father. He judged correctly that a great deal had occurred between Dennis and herself of which he had no knowledge, and again his confidence in her was thoroughly shaken.

At first he determined to question her and extort the truth. But when, an hour later, she quietly entered the parlor, he saw at a glance that the cold, proud, self-possessed woman before him would not submit to the treatment accepted by the little Christine of former days. The wily man read from her manner and the expression of her eye that he might with her consent lead, but could not command without awakening a nature as imperious as his own.

He was angry, but he had time to think. Prudence had given a decided voice in favor of caution.

He saw what she did not recognize herself, that her heart had been greatly touched, and in his secret soul he was not sorry now to believe that Dennis was dying.

"Father," said Christine, abruptly, "how soon can we start on our eastern trip?"

"Well, if you particularly wish it," he replied, "I can leave by the evening train to-morrow."

"I do wish it very much," said Christine, earnestly, "and will be ready."

After an evening of silence and constraint they separated for the night.

Mr. Ludolph sat for a long time sipping his wine after she had gone.

"After all it will turn out for the best," he said. "Fleet will probably die, and then will be out of the way. Or, if he lives, I can easily guard against him, and it will go no farther. If she had been bewitched by a man like Mr. Mellen, the matter would have been more difficult.

"In truth," he continued, after a little, "now that her weak woman's heart is occupied by an impossible lover, there is no danger from possible ones;" and the man of the world went complacently to his rest, believing that what he regarded as the game of life was entirely in his own hands.

The next evening the night express bore Christine from the scene of the events she sought to escape; but she was to learn, in common with the great host of the sinning and suffering, how little change of place has to do with change of feeling. We take memory and character with us from land to land, from youth to age, from this world to the other, from time through eternity. Sad, then, is the lot of those who ever carry the elements of their own torture with them.

It was Christine's purpose, and she had her father's consent, to make a long visit in New York, and, in the gayety and excitement of the metropolis, to forget her late wretched experience.

As it was still early in September, they resolved to stop at West Point and participate in the gayest season of that fashionable watering-place. At this time the hotels are thronged with summer tourists returning homeward from the more northern resorts. Though the broad piazzas of Cozzens's great hotel were crowded by the *élite* of the city, there was a hum of admiration as Christine first made her round on her father's arm; and in the evening, when the spacious parlor was cleared for dancing, officers from the post and civilians alike eagerly sought her hand, and hundreds of admiring eyes followed as she swept through the mazes of the dance, the embodiment of grace and beauty. She was very gay, and her repartee was often brilliant, but a close observer would have seen something forced and unnatural in all. Such an observer was her father. He saw that the sparkle of her eyes had no more heart and happiness in it than that of the diamonds on her bosom, and that with the whole strength of her resolute nature she was laboring to repel thought and memory. But, as he witnessed the admiration she excited on every side, he became more determined than ever that his fair daughter should shine a star of the first magnitude in the *salons* of Europe. At a late hour, and wearied past the power of thought, she gladly sought refuge in the blank of sleep.

The next morning they drove out early, before the sun was high and warm. It was a glorious autumn day. Recent rains had purified the atmosphere, so that the unrivalled scenery of the Hudson stood out in clear and grand out line.

As Christine looked about her she felt a thrill of almost delight, — the first sensation of the kind since that moment of exultation which Dennis had inspired, but which he had also turned to the bitterness of disaster and humiliation. She was keenly alive to beauty, and she saw it on every side.

The Ludolph family had ever lived among the mountains on the Rhine, and the heart of this latest child of the race yearned over the rugged scenery before her with hereditary affection, which had grown stronger with each successive generation.

The dew, like innumerable pearls, gemmed the grass in the park-like lawn of the hotel, and the slanting rays of the sun flecked the luxuriant foliage. Never before had this passion for the beautiful in nature been so gratified, and all the artist feeling within her awoke.

On reaching the street the carriage turned southward, and, after passing the village of Highland Falls, entered on one of the most beautiful drives in America. At times the road led under overarching forest-trees, shaded and dim with that delicious twilight which only myriads of fluttering leaves can make. Again it would wind around some bold headland, and the broad expanse of the Hudson would shine out dotted with white sails. Then through a vista its waters would sparkle, suggesting an exquisite cabinet picture. On the right the thickly-wooded mountains rose like emerald walls, with here and there along their base a quiet farm-house. With kindling eye and glowing cheeks she drank in view after view, and at last exclaimed, "If there were only a few old castles scattered among these Highlands, this would be the very perfection of scenery."

Her father watched her closely, and with much satisfaction.

"After all, her wound is slight," he thought, "and new scenes and circumstances will soon cause her to forget."

Furtively, but continually, he bent his eyes upon her, as if to read her very soul. A dreamy, happy expression rested on her face, as if a scene were present to her fancy even more to her taste than the one her eyes dwelt upon. In fact she was living over that evening at Miss Winthrop's, when Dennis had told her that she could reach truest and highest art, — that she could feel, — could copy anything she saw; and exhilarated by the fresh morning air, inspired by the scenery, she felt for the moment, as never before, that it might all be true.

Was he who gave those blissful assurances also exerting a subtile, unrecognized power over her? Certainly within the last few weeks she had been subject to strange moods and reveries. But the first dawning of a woman's love is like the aurora, with its strange, fitful flashes. The phenomena have never been satisfactorily explained.

But, as Mr. Ludolph watched complacently and admiringly, her expression suddenly changed, and a frightened, guilty look came into her face. The glow upon her cheeks gave place to extreme pallor, and she glanced nervously around as if fearing something, then caught her father's eye, and was conscious of his scrutiny. She at once became cold and self-possessed, and sat at his side pale and quiet till the ride ended. But he saw from the troubled gleam of her eyes that beneath that calm exterior were tumult and suffering.

Few in this life are so guilty and wretched as not to have moments of forgetfulness, when the happier past comes back and they are oblivious of the painful present. Such a brief respite Christine enjoyed during part of her morning ride. The grand and swiftly varying scenery crowded her mind with pleasant images, which had been followed by a delicious revery. She felt herself to be a true priestess of Nature, capable of understanding and interpreting her voices and hidden meanings, — of catching her evanescent beauty and fixing it on the glowing canvas. The strong consciousness of such power was indeed sweet and intoxicating. Her mind naturally reverted to him who had most clearly asserted her possession of it.

"He, too, would have equal appreciation of this scenery," she said to herself.

Then came the sudden remembrance, shrivelling her pretty dreams as the lightning scorches and withers.

"*He — he is dead! — he must be by this time!*"

And dread and guilt and something else which she did not define, but which seemed more like a sense of great loss, lay heavy at her heart. No wonder her father was perplexed and provoked by the sad change in her face. At first he was inclined to remonstrate and put spurs to her pride. But there was a dignity about the lady at his side, even though she was his daughter, that embarrassed and restrained him. Moreover, though he understood much and suspected far more, — more indeed than the truth, — there was nothing acknowledged or tangible that he could lay hold of, and she meant that it should be so. For reasons she did not understand she felt a disinclination to tell her troubles to Susie Winthrop, and she was most resolute in her purpose never to permit her father to speak on the subject.

If Mr. Ludolph had been as coarse and ignorant as he was hard and selfish, he would have gone to work at the case with sledge-hammer dexterity, as many parents have done, making sad, brutal havoc in delicate womanly natures with which they were no more fit to deal than a blacksmith with hair-springs. But though he longed to speak, and bring his remorseless logic to bear, Christine's manner raised a barrier which a man of his fine culture could not readily pass.

She joined her father at a late breakfast, smiling and brilliant, but her gayety was clearly forced. The morning was spent in sketching, she seeming to crave constant occupation or excitement.

In the afternoon father and daughter drove up the river to the military grounds to witness a drill. Mr. Ludolph did his best to rally Christine, pointing out everything of interest. First, the grand old ruin of Fort Putnam frowned down upon them. This had been the one feature wanting, and Christine felt that she could ask nothing more. Her wonder and admiration grew as the road wound along the immediate bluff and around the plain by the river fortifications. But when she stood on the piazza of the West Point Hotel, and looked up through the Highlands toward Newburgh, tears came to her eyes, and she trembled with excitement. From her recent experiences her nerves were morbidly sensitive. But her father could only look and wonder, she seemed so changed to him.

"And is the Rhine like this?" she asked.

"Well, the best I can say is, that to a German and a Ludolph it seems just as beautiful," he replied.

"Surely," said she, slowly and in half-soliloquy, "if one could live always amid such scenes as these, the Elysium of the gods or the heaven of the Christians would offer few temptations."

"And among just such scenes you shall live after a short year passes," he answered, warmly and confidently. But with anger he missed the wonted sparkle of her eyes when these cherished plans were broached.

In bitterness Christine said to herself: "A few weeks since this thought would have filled me with delight. Why does it not now?"

Silently they drove to the parade-ground. At the sally-port of the distant barracks bayonets were gleaming. There was a burst of martial music, then each class at the Academy — four companies — came out upon the grassy plain upon the double-quick. Their motions were light and swift, and yet so accurately timed that each company seemed one perfect piece of mechanism. A cadet stood at a certain point with a small color flying. Abreast of this their advance was checked as suddenly as if they had been turned to stone, and the entire corps was in line. Then followed a series of skilful manœuvres, in which Christine was much interested, and her old eager manner returned.

"I like the army," she exclaimed; "the precision and inflexible routine would just suit me. I wish there was war, and I a man, that I might enter into the glorious excitements."

Luxurious Mr. Ludolph had no tastes in that direction, and, shrugging his shoulders, said: "How about the hardships, wounds, and chances of an obscure death? These are the rule in a campaign; the glorious excitements the exceptions."

"I did not think of those," she said, shrinking against the cushions. "Everything seems to have so many miserable drawbacks!"

The pageantry over, the driver turned and drove northward through the most superb scenery.

"Where are we going?" asked Christine.

"To the cemetery," was the reply.

"No, no! not there!" she exclaimed, nervously.

"Nonsense! Why not?" remonstrated her father.

"I don't wish to go there!" she cried, excitedly. "Please turn around."

Her father reluctantly gave the order, but added, "Christine, you certainly indulge in strange moods and whims of late."

She was silent a moment, and then she began a running fire of questions about the Academy, that left no space for explanations.

That evening she danced as resolutely as ever, and by her beauty and brilliant repartee threw around her many bewildering spells that even the veterans of the Point could scarcely resist.

But when alone in her own room she looked at her white face in the mirror, and murmured in tones full of unutterable dread and remorse, "He is dead, — he must be dead by this time!"

CHAPTER XXXV.

REMORSE.

CHRISTINE had a peculiar experience while at West Point. She saw on every side what would have brought her the choicest enjoyment, had her mind been at rest. To her artist nature, and with her passion and power for sketching, the Highlands on the Hudson were paradise. But though she saw in profusion what once would have delighted her, and what she now felt ought to be the source of almost unmingled happiness, she was still thoroughly wretched. It was the old fable of Tantalus repeating itself. Her sin and its results had destroyed her receptive power. The world offered her pleasures on every side; she longed to enjoy them, but could not, for her heart was preoccupied, — filled and overflowing with fear, remorse, and a sorrow she could not define.

A vain, shallow girl might soon have forgotten such an experience as Christine had passed through. Such a creature would have been sentimental or hysterical for a little time, according to temperament, and then with the old zest have gone to flirting with some new victim. There are belles so weak and wicked that they would rather plume themselves on the fact that one had died from love for them. But in justice to all such it should be said that they rarely have mind enough to realize the evil they do. Their vanity overshadows every other faculty, and almost destroys those sweet, pitiful, unselfish qualities which make a true woman what a true man most reverences next to God.

Christine was proud and ambitious to the last degree, but she had not this small vanity. She did not appreciate the situation fully, but she was unsparing in her self-condemnation.

If Dennis had been an ordinary man, and interested her no more than had other admirers, and had she given him no more encouragement, she would have shrugged her shoulders over the result and said she was very sorry he had made such a fool of himself.

But as she went over the past (and this now she often did), she saw that he was unusually gifted; nay, more, the picture she discovered in the loft of the store proved him possessed of genius of a high order. And such a man she had deceived, tortured, and even killed! This was the verdict of her own conscience, the assertion of his own lips. She remembered the wearing life of alternate hope and fear she had caused him. She remembered how eagerly he hung on her smiles and sugared nothings, and how her equally causeless frowns would darken all the world to him. She saw day after day how she had developed in a strong, true heart, with its native power to love unimpaired, the most intense passion, and all that her own lesser light might burn a little more brightly. Then, with her burning face buried in her hands, she would recall the bitter, shameful consummation. Worse than all, waking or sleeping, she continually saw a pale, thin face, that even in death looked upon her with unutterable reproach. In addition to the misery caused by her remorse, there was a deeper bitterness still. Within the depths of her soul a voice told her that the picture was true; that he might have awakened her, and led her out into the warmth and light of a happy life, — a life which she felt ought to be possible, but which as yet had been but a vague and tantalizing dream. Now the world seemed to her utter chaos, — a place of innumerable paths leading nowhere;

and her own hands had broken the clew that might have brought her to something assured and satisfactory. She was very wretched, for her life seemed but a little point between disappointment on one side and the blackness of death and nothingness on the other.

The very beauty of the landscapes about her often increased her pain. She felt that a few weeks ago she would have enjoyed them keenly, and found in their transference to canvas a source of unfailing pleasure. With a conscious blush she thought that if he were present to encourage, to stimulate her, by the very vitality of his earnest, loving nature, she would be in the enjoyment of paradise itself. In a word, she saw the heaven she could not enter.

To the degree that she had mind, heart, conscience, and an intense desire for true happiness, she was unhappy. Dress, dancing, the passing admiration of society, the pleasures of a merely fashionable life, seemed less and less satisfactory. She was beyond them, as children outgrow their toys, because she had a native superiority to them, and yet they seemed her best resource. She had all her old longing to pursue her art studies, and everything about her stimulated her to this, but her heart and hand appeared paralyzed. She was in just that condition, mental and moral, in which she could do nothing well.

And so the days passed in futile efforts to forget — to drown in almost reckless gayety — the voices of conscience and memory. But she only remembered all the more vividly; she only saw the miserable truth all the more clearly. She suffered more in her torturing consciousness than Dennis in his wild delirium.

After they had been at the hotel about a week, Mr. Ludolph received letters that made his speedy return necessary. On the same day the family of his old New York partner arrived at the house on their return from the Catskills. Mrs.

Von Bräkhiem gladly received Christine under her care, feeling that the addition of such a bright star would make her little constellation one of the most brilliant in the fashionable world.

The ladies of the house were now immersed in the excitement of an amateur concert. Mrs. Von Bräkhiem, bent upon shining among the foremost, though with a borrowed lustre, assigned Christine a most prominent part. She half shrunk from it, for it recalled unpleasant memories; but she could not decline without explanations, and so entered into the affair with a sort of recklessness.

The large parlors were filled with chairs, which were soon occupied, and it was evident that in point of attraction elegant toilets would vie with the music. Christine came down on her father's arm, dressed like a princess, and, though her diamonds were few, such were their size and brilliancy that they seemed on fire. Every eye followed Mrs. Von Bräkhiem's party, and that good lady took half the admiration to herself.

A superior tenor, with an unpronounceable foreign name, had come up from New York to grace the occasion. But personally he lacked every grace himself, his fine voice being the one thing that redeemed him from utter insignificance in mind and appearance. Nevertheless he was vain beyond measure, and made the most of himself on all occasions.

The music was fine, for the amateurs, feeling that they had a critical audience, did their best. Christine chose three brilliant, difficult, but heartless pieces as her contribution to the entertainment (she would not trust herself with anything else); and with something approaching reckless gayety she sought to hide the bitterness at her heart. Her splendid voice and exquisite touch doubled the admiration her beauty and diamonds had excited, and Mrs. Von Bräkhiem basked in still stronger reflected light. She took every opportunity to make it known that she was Miss Ludolph's chaperon.

After her first effort, the "distinguished" tenor from New York opened his eyes widely at her; at her second, he put up his eye-glass in something like astonishment; and the close of her last song found him nervously rummaging a music portfolio in the corner.

But for Christine the law of association had become too strong, and the prolonged applause recalled the evening at Miss Brown's when the same sounds had deafened her, but when turning from it all she had seen Dennis Fleet standing in rapt attention, his lips parted, his eyes glowing with such an honest admiration that even then it was worth more to her than all the clamor. Then, by the same law of association, she again saw that eager, earnest face, changed, pale, dead,—dead!—and she the cause. Regardless of the compliments lavished upon her, she buried her face in her hands and trembled from head to foot.

But the irrepressible tenor had found what he wanted, and now came forward asking that Miss Ludolph would sing a duet with him.

She lifted a wan and startled face. Must the torturing similarity and still more torturing contrast of the two occasions be continued? But she saw her father regarding her sternly,—saw that she was becoming the subject of curious glances and whispered surmises. Her pride was aroused at once, and, goaded on by it, she said, "Oh, certainly; I am not feeling well, but it does not signify."

"And den," put in the tenor, "dis is von grand occazeon to *you*, for it is so unfrequent dat I find any von vorthy to sing dis style of music vith *me*."

"What is the music?" asked Christine, coldly.

To her horror she found it the same selection from Mendelssohn that she had sung with Dennis.

"No," she said, sharply, "I cannot sing that."

"Pardon me, my daughter, you can sing it admirably if you choose," interposed her father.

She turned to him imploringly, but his face was inflexible, and his eyes had an incensed look. For a moment she, too, was angry. Had he no mercy? She was about to decline coldly, but her friends were very urgent and clamorous,— "Please do," "Don't disappoint us," echoing on every side. The tenor was so surprised and puzzled at her insensibility to the honor he had conferred, that, to prevent a scene she could not explain, she went to the piano as if led to the stake.

But the strain was too great upon her in her suffering state. The familiar notes recalled so vividly the one who once before had sung them at her side that she turned almost expecting to see him,—but saw only the vain little animated music-machine, who with many contortions was producing the harmony. "Just this mockery my life will ever be," she thought; "all that I am, the best I can do, will always be connected with something insignificant and commonplace. The rich, impassioned voice of the *man* who sang these words, and who might have taught me to sing the song of a new and happier life, I have silenced forever."

The thought overpowered her. Just then her part recurred, but her voice died away in a miserable quaver, and again she buried her face in her hands. Suddenly she sprung from the piano, darted through the low-cut open window near, and a moment later ordered her startled maid from the room, turned the key, and was alone.

Her father explained coldly to the astonished audience and the half-paralyzed tenor (who still stood with his mouth open) that his daughter was not at all well that evening, and ought not to have appeared at all. This Mrs. Von Bräkhiem took up and repeated with endless variations. But the evidences of sheer mental distress on the part of Christine had been too clear, and countless were the whispered surmises of the fashionable gossips in explanation.

Mrs. Von Bräkhiem herself, burning with curiosity, soon retired, that she might receive from her lovely charge some gushing confidences, which she expected, as a matter of course, would be poured into what she chose to regard as her sympathizing ear. But she knocked in vain at Christine's door.

Later Mr. Ludolph knocked. There was no answer.

"Christine!" he called.

After some delay a broken voice answered, "You cannot enter — I am not well — I have retired."

He turned on his heel and strode away, and that night drank more brandy and water than was good for him.

As for Christine, warped and chilled though her nature had been, she was still a woman, she was still young, and, though she knew it not, she had heard the voice which had spoken her heart into life. Through a chain of circumstances for which she was partly to blame, she had been made to suffer as she had not believed was possible. The terrible words of Mr. Bruder's letter rang continually in her ears, — "Mr. Fleet is not dying a natural death; he has been slain."

For many long, weary days the conviction had been growing upon her that she had indeed slain him and mortally wounded herself. Until to-night she had kept herself outwardly under restraint, but now the long pent-up feeling gave way, and she sobbed as if her heart would break, — sobbed till the power to weep was gone. If now some kind, judicious friend had shown her that she was not so guilty as she deemed herself; that, however frightful the consequences of such acts, she was really not to blame for what she did not intend and could not foresee; more than all, if she could only have known that her worst fears about Dennis were not to be realized, and that he was now recovering, she might at once have entered on a new and happier life. But there was no such friend, no such knowledge, and her wounded spirit was thrown back upon itself.

At last, robed as she had been for the evening, she fell asleep from sheer exhaustion and grief, — for grief induces sleep.

The gems that shone in her dishevelled hair; that rose and fell as at long intervals her bosom heaved with convulsive sobs, like the fitful gusts of a storm that is dying away; the costly fabrics she wore, — made sad mockery in their contrast with the pale, tear-stained, suffering face. The hardest heart might have pitied her, — yes, even the wholly ambitious heart of her father, incensed as he was that a plebeian stranger of this land should have caused such distress.

When Christine awoke, her pride awoke also. With bitterness of spirit she recalled the events of the past evening. But a new phase of feeling now began to manifest itself.

After her passionate outburst she was much calmer. In this respect the unimpeded flow of feeling had done her good, and, as intimated, if kindness and sympathy could now have added their gentle ministrations, she might have been the better for it all her life. But, left to herself, she again yielded to the sway of her old and worst traits. Chief among these was pride; and under the influence of this passion and the acute suffering of her unsoothed, unguided spirit, she began to rebel in impotent anger. She grew hard, cynical, and reckless. Her father's lack of sympathy and consideration alienated her heart even from him. Left literally alone in the world, her naturally reserved nature shut itself up more closely than ever. Even her only friend, Susie

Winthrop, drifted away. One other, who might have been — But she could think of him only with a shudder now. All the rest seemed indifferent, or censorious, or, worse still, to be using her, like Mrs. Von Bräkhiem and even her own father, as a stepping-stone to their personal ambition. Christine could not see that she was to blame for this isolation. She did not understand that cold, selfish natures, like her own and her father's, could not surround themselves with warm, generous friends. She saw only the fact. But with flashing eyes she resolved that her heart's secrets should not be pried into a hair's breadth further; that she would be used only so far as she chose. She would, in short, "face out" the events of the past evening simply and solely on the ground that she had not been well, and permit no questions to be asked.

Cold and self-possessed, she came down to a late breakfast. Mrs. Von Bräkhiem, and others who had been introduced, joined her, but nothing could penetrate through the nice polished armor of her courteous reserve. Her father looked at her keenly, but she coolly returned his gaze.

When alone with her soon afterward, he turned and said, sharply, "What does all this mean?"

She looked around as if some one else were near.

"Were you addressing me?" she asked, coldly.

"Yes, of course I am," said her father, impatiently.

"From your tone and manner, I supposed you must be speaking to some one else."

"Nonsense! I was speaking to you. What does all this mean?"

She turned on him an indescribable look, and after a moment said in a slow, meaning tone, "Have you not heard my explanation, sir?"

Such was her manner, he felt he could as easily strike her as say another word.

Muttering an oath, he turned on his heel and left her to herself.

The next morning her father bade her "Good-by." In parting he said, meaningly, "Christine, beware!"

Again she turned upon him that peculiar look, and replied in a low, firm tone: "That recommendation applies to you, also. Let us both beware, lest we repent at leisure."

The wily man, skilled in character, was now thoroughly convinced that in his daughter he was dealing with a nature very different from his wife's, — that he was now confronted by a spirit as proud and imperious as his own. He clearly saw that force, threatening, sternness would not answer in this case, and that if he carried his points it must be through skill and cunning. By some means he must ever gain her consent and co-operation.

His manner changed. Instinctively she divined the cause; and hers did not. Therefore father and daughter parted as father and daughter ought never to part.

After his departure she was to remain at West Point till the season closed, and then accompany Mrs. Von Bräkhiem to New York, where she was to make as long a visit as she chose; — and she chose to make a long one. In the scenery, and the society of the officers at West Point, and the excitements of the metropolis, she found more to occupy her thoughts than she could have done at Chicago. She went deliberately to work to kill time and snatch from it such fleeting pleasures as she might.

They stayed in the country till the pomp and glory of October began to illumine the mountains, and then (to Christine's regret) went to the city. There she entered into every amusement and dissipation that her tastes permitted, and found much pleasure in frequent visits to the Central Park, although it seemed tame and artificial after the wild grandeur of the mountains. It was well that her nature was so high-toned that she found enjoyment in only what was refined or intellectual. Had it been otherwise she might soon have taken, in her morbid, reckless state, a path to swift and remediless ruin, as many a poor creature all at war with happiness and truth has done. And thus in a giddy whirl of excitement (Mrs. Von Bräkhiem's normal condition) the days and weeks passed, till at last, thoroughly satiated and jaded, she concluded to return home, for the sake of change and quiet, if nothing else. Mrs. Von Bräkhiem parted with her regretfully. Where would she find such another ally in her determined struggle to be talked about and envied a little more than some other pushing, jostling votaries of fashion?

In languor or sleep Christine made the journey, and in the dusk of a winter's day her father drove her to their beautiful home, which from association was now almost hateful to her. Still she was too weary to think or suffer much. They met each other very politely, and their intercourse assumed at once its wonted character of high-bred courtesy, though perhaps it was a little more void of manifested sympathy and affection than before.

Several days elapsed in languid apathy, the natural reaction of past excitement; then an event occurred which most thoroughly aroused her.

CHAPTER XXXVI.

AN APPARITION.

MR. LUDOLPH had hoped to hear on his return that Dennis was dead. That would end all difficulties. Mr. Schwartz did not know; — he was not at last accounts. Ernst was summoned. With a bright, hopeful face he stated that his mother had just received a letter saying Dennis was a little better. He was much surprised at his employer's heavy frown.

"He will live," mused Mr. Ludolph; "and now shall I permit him to return to my employ, or discharge him?"

His brow contracted in lines of thought that suggested shrewdness, cunning, nothing manly, and warily he judged.

"If I do not take him, he will go to Mr. French with certainty. He had better return, for then both he and Christine will be more thoroughly under my surveillance.

"Curses on Christine's waywardness! There may be no resisting her, and my best chance will be in managing him. This I could not do if he were in the store of my rival;" and so for unconscious Dennis this important question was decided.

At last, as we have said, his delirium ceased, and the quiet light of reason came into his eyes. He looked at his mother and smiled, but was too weak even to reach out his hand.

The doctor, coming in soon after, declared danger past, and that all depended now on good nursing. Little fear of his wanting that!

"Ah, mine Gott be praised! mine Gott be praised!" exclaimed Mr. Bruder, who had to leave the room to prevent an explosion of his grateful, happy feelings that might have proved too rude a tempest for Dennis in his weak state. He was next seen striding across the fields to a neighboring grove, ejaculating as he went. When he returned his eyes shone with a great peace and joy, and he had evidently been with Him who had cast out the demon from his heart.

Day after day Dennis rallied. Unlike poor Christine, he had beneath him the two strongest levers, love and prayer, and steadily they lifted him up to health and strength and comparative peace. At last he was able to sit up and walk about feebly, and Mr. Bruder returned rejoicing to his family. As he wrung Dennis's hand at parting, he said, in rather a hoarse voice: "If any von tell me Gott is not goot and heareth not prayer, den I tell him he von grand heathen. Oh! but ve vill velcome you soon. Ve vill haf de grandest supper, de grandest songs, de grandest — " but just here Mr. Bruder thought it prudent to pull his big fur cap over his eyes, and make a rush for the stage.

As if by tacit understanding, Christine's name had not been mentioned during Dennis's recovery. But one evening, after the little girls had been put to bed, and the lamp shaded, he sat in the dimly lighted room, looking fixedly for a long time at the glowing embers. His mother was moving quietly about, putting away the tea-things, clearing up after the children's play; but as she worked she furtively watched him. At last coming to his side she pushed back the hair that seemed so dark in contrast with the thin, white face and said, gently, "You are thinking of Miss Ludolph, Dennis."

He had some blood yet, for that was not the glow of the fire that suffused his cheek; but he only answered, quietly, "Yes, mother."

"Do you think you can forget her?"

"I don't know."

"Prayer is a mighty thing, my son."

"But perhaps it is not God's will that I should ever win her," said Dennis, despondently.

"Then surely it is not yours, my child."

"No, mother," said Dennis, with bowed head and low tone, "but yet I am human and weak."

"You would still wish that it were His will?"

"Yes; I could not help it."

"But you would submit?"

"Yes, with His help I would," firmly.

"That is sufficient, my boy; I have such confidence in God that I know this matter will result in a way to secure you the greatest happiness in the end."

But after a little time he sighed, wearily, "Yet how hard it is to wait till the great plan is worked out!"

Solemnly she quoted, — "God will render to every man according to his deeds. To them who by patient continuance in well-doing seek for glory and honor and immortality, eternal life."

Braced by the stirring words of inspiration, strengthened by his mother's faith, he looked up after a moment and said, earnestly, "At any rate I will try to be a *man in your sense of the word*, and that is saying a great deal."

She beamed at him through her spectacles over her knitting-needles; and he thought, as he gazed fondly at her, that in spite of her quaint, old-fashioned garb, and homely occupation, she appeared more truly a saint than any painted on cathedral windows.

He soon noticed that his mother had grown feeble, and he determined to take her with him on his return, believing that, by his care, and the wise use of tonics, he could restore her to her wonted strength. His increased salary now justified the step.

Early in November his physician said he might return to business if he would be prudent. He gladly availed himself of the permission, for he longed to be employed again.

The clerks all welcomed him warmly, for his good-nature had disarmed jealousy at his rapid rise. But in the greeting of Mr. Ludolph he missed something of the cordiality he expected.

"Perhaps she has told him," thought he; and at once his own manner became tinged with a certain coldness and dignity. He determined that both father and daughter should think of him only with respect.

At the Bruders' the millennium came with Dennis. Metaphorically the fatted calf was killed; their plain little room was trimmed with evergreens, and when he entered he was greeted by such a jubilant, triumphant chorus of welcomes as almost took away his breath. What little he had left was suddenly squeezed out of him; for Mrs. Bruder, dropping her frying-pan and dish-cloth, rushed upon him, exclaiming, "Ah! mine fren! mine fren! De goot Gott be praised;" and she gave him an embrace that made his bones ache.

Mr. Bruder stalked about the room repeating with explosive energy, like minute-guns, "Praise Gott! Praise Gott!" Ernst, his great eyes dimmed with happy tears, clung to Dennis's hand, as if he would make sure, by sense of touch as well as sight, that he had regained his beloved teacher. The little Bruders were equally jubilant, though from rather mixed motives. Dennis's arrival was very well, but they could not keep their round eyes long off the preparations for such a supper as never before had blessed their brief career.

"Truly," thought Dennis, as he looked around upon the happy family, and contrasted its appearance with that which it had presented when he first saw it, "my small investment of kindness and effort in this case has returned large interest. I think it pays to do good."

The evening was one of almost unmingled happiness, even to his sore, disappointed heart, and passed into memory as among the sunniest places of his life.

He found a pleasant little cottage over on the West side, part of which he rented for his mother and sisters.

With Mr. Ludolph's permission he went after them, and installed them in it. Thus he had what he had needed all along, — a home, a resting-place for body and soul, under the watchful eye of love.

About this time Dr. Arten met him, stared a moment, then clapped him on the back in his hearty way, saying, "Well, well, young man! you have cause to be thankful, and not to the doctors, either."

"I think I am," said Dennis, smiling.

Suddenly the doctor looked grave, and asked in a stern voice, "Are you a heathen, or a good Christian?"

"I hope not the former," replied Dennis, a little startled.

"Then don't go and commit suicide again. Don't you know flesh and blood can only stand so much? When an intelligent young fellow like you goes beyond that, he is committing suicide. Bless your soul, my ambitious friend, the ten commandments ain't all the law of God. His laws are also written all over this long body of yours, and you came near paying a pretty penalty for breaking them. You won't get off the second time."

"You are right, doctor; I now see that I acted very wrongly."

"'Bring forth fruits meet for repentance.' I am rich enough to give sound advice," said the brusque old physician, passing on.

"Stop a moment, doctor," cried Dennis, "I want you to see my mother."

"What is the matter with her? She been breaking the commandments, too?"

"Oh, no!" exclaimed Dennis. "She is not a bit of a heathen."

"I am not so sure about that. I know many eminent saints in the church who will eat lobster salad for supper, and then send for the doctor and minister before morning. There is a precious twaddle about 'mysterious Providence.' Providence isn't half so mysterious as people make out. The doctor is expected to look serious and sympathetic, and call their law-breaking and its penalty by some outlandish Latin name that no one can understand. I give 'em the square truth, and tell 'em they've been breaking the commandments."

Dennis could not forbear smiling at the doctor's rough handling of humbug, even in one of its most respectable guises. Then, remembering his mother, he added, gravely: "I am truly anxious about my mother, she has grown so feeble. I want, and yet dread, the truth."

The bantering manner of the good old doctor changed at once, and he said, kindly, "I'll come, my boy, within a few days, though I am nearly run off my feet."

He went off, muttering, "Why don't the people send for some of the youngsters that sit kicking up their heels in their offices all day?"

Dennis soon fell into the routine of work and rapidly grew stronger. But his face had acquired a gravity, a something in expression that only experience gives, which made him appear older by ten years. All trace of the boy had gone, and his countenance was now that of the man, and of one who had suffered.

As soon as he recovered sufficient strength to act with decision, he indignantly tried to banish Christine's image from his memory. But he found this impossible. Though at times his eyes would flash, in view of her treatment, they would soon grow gentle and tender, and he found himself excusing and extenuating, by the most special pleadings, that which he had justly condemned.

One evening his mother startled him out of a long revery, in which he had almost vindicated Christine, by saying, "A very pleasant smile has been gradually dawning on your face, my son."

"Mother," replied he, hesitatingly, "perhaps I have judged Miss Ludolph harshly."

"Your love, not your reason, has evidently been pleading for her."

"Well, mother, I suppose you are right."

"So I suppose the Divine love pleads for the weak and sinful," said Mrs. Fleet, dreamily.

"That is a very pleasant thought, mother, for sometimes it seems that my love could make black white."

"That the Divine love has done, but at infinite cost to itself."

"Oh that my love at any cost to itself could lead her into the new life of the believer!" said Dennis, in a low, earnest tone.

"Your love is like the Divine in being unselfish, but remember the vital differences and take heed. God *can* change the nature of the imperfect creature that He loves. You cannot. His love is infinite in its strength and patience. You are human. The proud, selfish, unbelieving Miss Ludolph (pardon mother's plain words) could not make you happy. To the degree that you were loyal to God, you would be unhappy, and I should surely dread such a union. The whole tone of your moral character would have to be greatly lowered to permit even peace."

"But, mother," said Dennis, almost impatiently, "in view of my unconquerable love, it is nearly the same as if I was married to her now."

"No, my son, I think not. I know your pretty theory on

this subject, but it seems more pretty than true. Marriage makes a vital difference. It is the closest union that we can voluntarily form on earth, and is the emblem of the spiritual oneness of the believer's soul with Christ. We may be led through circumstances, as you have been, to love one with whom we should not form such a union. Indeed, in the true and mystic meaning of the rite, you could not marry Christine Ludolph. The Bible declares that man and wife shall be one. Unless she changes, unless you change (and that God forbid), this could not be. You would be divided, separated in the deepest essentials of your life here, and in every respect hereafter. Again, while God loves every sinful man and woman, He does not take them to His heart till they cry out to Him for strength to abandon the destroying evil He hates. There are no unchanged, unrenewed hearts in heaven."

"O mother, how inexorable is your logic!" said Dennis, breathing heavily.

"Truth in the end is ever more merciful than falsehood," she answered, gently.

After a little, he said, with a heavy sigh, "Mother, you are right, and I am very weak and foolish."

She looked at him with unutterable tenderness. She could not crush out all hope, and so whispered, as before: "Prayer is mighty, my child. It is not wrong for you to love. It is your duty, as well as privilege, to pray for her. Trust your Heavenly Father, do His will, and He will solve this question in the very best way."

Dennis turned to his mother in sudden and passionate earnestness, and said: "Your prayers are mighty, mother, I truly believe. Oh, pray for her, — for my sake as well as hers. Looking from the human side, I am hopeless. It is only God's almighty power that can make us, as you say, truly one. I fear that now she is only a heartless, fashionable girl. Yet, if she is only this, I do not see how I came to love her as I do. But my trust now is in your prayers to God."

"And in your own also: the great Father loves you too, my son. If He chooses that the dross in her character should be burned away, and your two lives fused, there are in His providence just the fiery trials, just the circumstances that will bring it about." (Was she unconsciously uttering a prophecy?) "The crucible of affliction, the test of some great emergency, will often develop a seemingly weak and frivolous girl into noble life, where there is real gold of latent worth to be acted on."

"Christine Ludolph is anything but weak and frivolous," said he. "Her character is strong, and I think most decided in its present bent. But as you say, if the Divine Alchemist wills it, He can change even the dross to gold, and turn unbelief to faith."

Hope, Christine! There is light coming, though as yet you cannot see it. There are angels of mercy flying toward you, though you cannot hear the rustle of their wings. The dark curtain of death and despair can never shut down upon a life linked to heaven by such true, strong prayer. And yet the logical results of wrong-doing will work themselves out, sin must be punished and faith sorely tried.

Dennis heard incidentally that Christine was absent on a visit to New York, but he knew nothing of the time of her return.

He now bent himself steadily and resolutely to the mastering of his business, and under Mr. Bruder's direction resumed his art studies, though now in such moderation as Dr. Arten would commend.

He also entered on an artistic effort that would tax his powers and genius to the very utmost, of which more anon.

By the time Christine returned, he was quite himself

again, though much paler and thinner than when he first entered the store.

After Christine had been at home nearly a week, her father, to rouse her out of her listlessness, said one morning: "We have recently received quite a remarkable painting from Europe. You will find it in the upper show-room, and had better come down to-day to see it, for it may be sold soon. I think you would like to copy one or two figures in it."

The lassitude from her New York dissipation was passing away, and her active nature beginning to assert itself again. She started up and said, "Wait five minutes and I will get sketching materials and go down with you."

By reason of her interdict, made at West Point, so earnestly, and indeed fiercely, and confirmed by her manner, her father had never mentioned the name of Dennis Fleet. The very fact that no one had spoken of him since that dreadful day when tidings came in on every side that he could not live was confirmation in her mind that he was dead.

She dreaded going to the store, especially for the first time, for everything would irresistibly remind her of him whom she could not think of now without a pang. But as the ordeal must come, why, the sooner it was over the better. So a few moments later her hand was on her father's arm, and they were on their way to the Art Building as in happier days.

Mr. Ludolph went to his office, and Christine, looking neither to the right nor to the left, ascended to the upper show-room, and at once sought to engage every faculty in making the sketch her father had suggested. Since Dennis was not, as she believed, either on the earth or elsewhere, she tried to take up life again as it had been before he came, and to act as if he had never been.

Hopeless task! In that familiar place, where they had begun the rearrangement of the store, everything spoke of him. She saw his glowing cheeks; again his dark, eager eyes followed her every movement and interpreted her wishes even before she could speak. Some of the pictures on the walls his hands had handled, and in her strong fancy his lithe form seemed moving the ladder to take them down again, while she, with heart and mind at rest, looked with growing curiosity and interest on her humble helper.

What changes had occurred within a short half-year! She shuddered at the thought that one who was then so instinct with life and happiness could now be dust and nothingness, and she the cause.

Association and conscience were again too powerful. She was becoming nervous and full of a strange unrest, so she concluded to finish her sketch at another time. As she was gathering up her materials she heard some one enter the room.

She was in such a morbid, unstrung state that the least thing startled her. But imagine if you can her wonder and terror as she saw Dennis Fleet—the dead and buried, as she fully believed—enter, carrying a picture as of old, and looking as of old, save that he was paler and thinner. Was it an apparition? or, as she had read, had she dwelt so long on this trouble that her mind and imagination were becoming disordered and able to place their wild creations before her as realities?

Her sketching materials fell clattering to the floor, and after one sharp exclamation of alarm she stood as if transfixed, with parted lips and dilated eyes, panting like a frightened bird.

If a sculptor had wished to portray the form and attitude of one startled by the supernatural, never could he have found a more fitting model than Christine at this moment.

As she had been seated a little on one side Dennis had not seen her at first; but, on recognizing her so unexpectedly, he was scarcely less startled than she, and the valuable picture he was carrying nearly met sudden destruction. But he had no such reason as Christine for the continuance of his surprise, and, at once recovering himself, he set the picture against the wall.

This made the illusion still more strange and terrible to Christine. There was the dead before her, doing just as she had been imagining,—just what he had done at her bidding months before.

Dennis was greatly puzzled by her look of alarm and distress. Then he thought that perhaps she feared he would break out in bitter and angry invectives again, and he advanced toward her to assure her of the contrary.

Slowly and instinctively she retreated and put up her hands with a deprecatory gesture.

"She cannot endure the sight of me," thought he, but at once he said, with dignified courtesy: "Miss Ludolph, you have nothing to fear from me, that you should regard me in that manner. You need not shrink as if from contagion. We can treat each other as courteous strangers, at least."

"I—I—I—thought you were dead!" she gasped, in a loud whisper.

Dennis's cheek grew paler than it had been in all his sickness, and then as suddenly became dark with anger. His eyes were terrible in their indignation as he advanced a few paces almost fiercely. She trembled violently and shrunk farther away.

"You thought I was dead?" he asked, sternly.

"Ye-e-s," in the same unnatural whisper.

"What!" he exclaimed, in short and bitter emphasis, "do you mean to say that you never cared even to ask whether I lived or died in my long, weary illness?—that you were so supremely indifferent to my fate that you could not articulate one sentence of inquiry? Surely this is the very sublimity of heartlessness; this is to be callous beyond one's power of imagination. It seems to me that I would feel as much interest as that in any human being I had once known. If even a dog had licked my hand in good-will, and afterward I had seen it, wounded or sick, creep off into a covert, the next time I passed that way I would step aside to see whether the poor creature had lived or died. But after all the wealth of affection that I lavished upon you, after toiling and almost dying in my vain effort to touch your marble heart, you have not even the humanity to ask if I am above ground!"

The illusion had now passed from Christine's mind, and with it her alarm. The true state of the case was rapidly dawning upon her, and she was about to speak eagerly; but in his strong indignation he continued, impetuously: "You thought I was dead! The wish probably was father to the thought. My presumption deserved no better fate. But permit me to tell you, though all unbidden, I did not die. With God's blessing I expect to live to a good old age, and intend that but few years shall pass before my name is as well known and honored as the ancient one of Ludolph;" and he turned on his heel and strode from the room.

CHAPTER XXXVII.

IF HE KNEW!

FOR a little time after Dennis's angry tread died away, Christine sat almost paralyzed by surprise and deeper emotions. Her mind, though usually clear and rapid in its action, was too confused to realize the truth. Suddenly she sprung up, gathered together her sketching materials, and drawing a thick veil over her face sped through the store, through the streets, to the refuge of her own room. She must be alone.

Hastily throwing aside her wrappings, she began to walk up and down in her excitement. Her listlessness was gone now in very truth, and her eye and cheek glowed as never before. As if it had become the great vivifying principle of her own life, she kept repeating continually in a low, ecstatic tone, "He lives! he lives! he is not dead; his blood is not upon my conscience!"

At last she sat down in her luxurious chair before the window to think it all over, — to commune with herself, — often the habit of the reserved and solitary. From the disjointed sentences she let fall, from the reflection of her excited face in yonder glass, we gather quite correctly the workings of her mind. Her first words were, "Thank heaven! thank something or other, I have not blotted out that true, strong genius."

Again, — "What untold wretchedness I might have saved myself if I had only asked the question, in a casual way,

'How is Mr. Fleet?' Christine Ludolph, with all your pride and imagined superiority, you can be very foolish.

"How he hates and despises me now! little wonder!

"But if he knew!

"Knew what? Why could you not ask after him, as after any other sick man? You have had a score or so of offers, and did not trouble yourself as to the fate of the lovelorn swains. Seems to me your conscience has been very tender in this case. And the fact that he misjudges you, thinks you callous, heartless, and is angry, troubles you beyond measure.

"When before were you so sensitive to the opinion of clerks and trades-people, or even the proudest suitors for your hand? But in this case you must cry out, in a tone of sentimental agony, 'Oh, if he only knew!'

"Knew what?"

Her face in yonder mirror has a strange, introverted expression, as if she were scanning her own soul. Her brow contracts with thought and perplexity.

Gradually a warm, beautiful light steals into her face, transforming it as from the scowl of a winter morning into a dawn of June; her eyes become gentle and tender. A rich color comes out upon her cheeks, spreads up her temples, mantles her brow, and pours a crimson torrent down her snowy neck. Suddenly she drops her burning face into her hands, and hides a vision one would gladly look longer upon. But see, even her little ears have become as red as coral.

The bleakest landscape in the world brightens into something like beauty when the sun shines upon it. So love, the richer, sweeter light of the soul, makes the plainest face almost beautiful; but when it changed Christine Ludolph's faultless, yet too cold and classical, features into those of a loving woman's, it suggested a beauty scarcely human.

A moment later there came a faint whisper: "I fear — I almost fear I love him." Then she lifted a startled, frightened face and looked timidly around as if, in truth, walls had ears.

Reassured by the consciousness of solitude, her head dropped on her wrist and her revery went forward. Her eyes became dreamy, and a half-smile played upon her lips as she recalled proof after proof of his affection, for she knew the cruel words of the last interview were the result of misunderstanding.

But suddenly she darted from her seat and began pacing the room in the strongest perturbation.

"Mocked again!" she cried; "the same cruel fate! my old miserable experience in a new aspect! With everything within my reach, save the one thing I want, I possess the means of all kinds of happiness except that which makes me happy. In every possible way I am pledged to a career and future in which he can take no part. Though my heart is full of the strangest, sweetest chaos, and I do not truly understand myself, yet I am satisfied that this is not a school-girl's fancy. But my father would regard it as the old farce repeated. Already he suspects and frowns upon the matter. I should have to break with him utterly and forever. I should have to give up all my ambitious plans and towering hopes of life abroad. A plain Mrs. in this city of shops is a poor substitute for a countess's coronet and a villa on the Rhine."

Her cheek flushed, and her lip curled.

"That indeed would be the very extravagance of romance, and how could I, least of all, who so long have scoffed at such things, explain my action? These mushroom shopkeepers, who were all nobodies the other day, elevate their eyebrows when a merchant's daughter marries her father's clerk. But when would the wonder cease if a German lady of rank followed suit?

"Then again my word, my honor, every sacred pledge I could give, forbids such folly.

"Would to heaven I had never seen him, for this unfortunate fancy of mine must be crushed in its inception; strangled before it comes to master me as it has mastered him."

After a long and weary sigh she continued: "Well, everything is favorable for a complete and final break between us. He believes me heartless and wicked to the last degree. I cannot undeceive him without showing more than he should know. I have only to avoid him, to say nothing, and we drift apart.

"If we could only have been friends he might have helped me so much! but that now is clearly impossible, — yes, for both of us.

"Truly one of these American poets was right: —

"'For of all sad words of tongue or pen,
The saddest are these, — It might have been.'

"But thanks to the immortal gods, as the pious heathen used to say, his blood is not on my hands, and this has taken a mountain off my heart. Thus relieved I can perhaps forget all the miserable business. Fate forbids that I, as it has forbidden that many another high-born woman, should marry where she might have loved."

If Christine's heart was wronged, her pride was highly gratified by this conclusion. Here was a new and strong resemblance between herself and the great. In mind she recalled the titled unfortunates who had "loved where they could not marry," and with the air and feeling of a martyr to ancestral grandeur she pensively added her name to the list.

With her conscience freed from its burden of remorse, with the knowledge, so sweet to every woman, that she might accept this happiness if she would, in spite of her airs of martyrdom, the world had changed greatly for the better, and with the natural buoyancy of youth she reacted into quite a cheerful and hopeful state.

Her father noticed this on his return to dinner in the evening, and sought to learn its cause. He asked, "How did you make out with your sketch?"

"I made a beginning," she answered, with some little color rising to her cheek.

"Perhaps you were interrupted?"

"Why did you not tell me that Mr. Fleet had recovered?" she asked, abruptly.

"Why, did you think he was dead?"

"Yes."

Mr. Ludolph indulged in a hearty laugh (he knew the power of ridicule).

"Well, that is excellent!" he said. "You thought the callow youth had died on account of your hardness of heart; and this explains your rather peculiar moods and tenses of late. Let me assure you that a Yankee never dies from such a cause."

Mr. Ludolph determined if possible to break down her reserve and let in the garish light, which he knew to be most fatal to all romantic fancies, that ever thrive best in the twilight of secrecy. But she was on the alert now, and in relief of mind had regained her poise and the power to mask her feeling. So she said in a tone tinged with cold indifference, "You may be right, but I had good reason to believe to the contrary, and, as I am not altogether without a conscience, you might have saved much pain by merely mentioning the fact of his recovery."

"But you had adjured me with frightful solemnity never to mention his name again," said her father, still laughing.

Christine colored and bit her lip. She had forgotten for the moment this awkward fact.

"I was nervous, sick, and not myself that day, and every one I met could speak of nothing but Mr. Fleet."

"Well, really," he said, "in the long list of the victims that you have wounded if not slain, I never supposed my clerk and quondam man-of-all-work would prove so serious a case."

"A truce to your bantering, father! Mr. Fleet is humble only in station, not in character, not in ability. You know I have never been very tender with the 'victims,' as you designate them, of the Mellen stamp; but Mr. Fleet is a man, in the best sense of the word, and one that I have wronged. Now that the folly is past I may as well explain to you some things that have appeared strange. I think I can truly say that I have given those gentlemen who have honored, or rather annoyed me, by their unwished-for regard, very little encouragement. Therefore, I was not responsible for any follies they might commit. But for artistic reasons I did encourage Mr. Fleet's infatuation. You remember how I failed in making a copy of that picture. In my determination to succeed, I hit upon the rather novel expedient of inspiring and copying the genuine thing. You know my imitative power is better than my imagination, and I thought that by often witnessing the expression of feeling and passion, I might learn to portray it without the disagreeable necessity of passing through any such experiences myself. But the experiment, as you know, did not work well These living subjects are hard to manage, and, as I have said, I am troubled by a conscience."

Mr. Ludolph's eyes sparkled, and a look of genuine admiration lighted up his features.

"Brava!" he cried; "your plan was worthy of you and of your ancestry. It was a real stroke of genius. You were too tender-hearted, otherwise it would have been perfect. What are the lives of a dozen such young fellows compared with the development and perfection of such a woman as you bid fair to be?"

Christine had displayed in this transaction just the qualities that her father most admired. But even she was shocked at his callousness, and lifted a somewhat startled face to his.

"Your estimate of human life is rather low," she said.

"Not at all. Is not one perfect plant better than a dozen imperfect ones? The gardener often pulls up the crowding and inferior ones to throw them about the roots of the strongest, that in their death and decay they may nourish it to the highest development. The application of this principle is evident. They secure most in this world who have the skill and power to grasp most."

"But how about the rights of others? Conscious men and women are not plants."

"Let them be on their guard then. Every one is for himself in this world. That can be plainly seen through the thin disguises that some try to assume. After all, half the people we meet are little better than summer weeds."

Christine almost shuddered to think that the one bound to her by closest ties cherished such sentiments toward the world, and probably, to a certain extent, toward herself, but she only said, quietly: "I can hardly subscribe to your philosophy as yet, though I fear I act upon it too often. Still it does not apply to Mr. Fleet. He is gifted in no ordinary degree, and doubtless will stand high here in his own land in time. And now, as explanation has been made, with your permission we will drop this subject out of our conversation as before."

"Well," said Mr. Ludolph to himself, between sips of his favorite Rhine wine, "I have gained much light on the subject to-night, and I must confess that, even with my rather wide experience, the whole thing is a decided novelty. If Christine were only less troubled with conscience, over-fastidiousness, or whatever it is, — if she were more moderate in her ambition as an artist, and could be satisfied with power and admiration, as other women are, — what a star she might become in the fashionable world of Europe! But, for some reason, I never feel sure of her. Her spirit is so wilful and obstinate, and she seems so full of vague longing after an ideal, impossible world, that I live in constant dread that she may be led into some folly fatal to my ambition. This Fleet is a most dangerous fellow. I wish I were well rid of him; still, matters are not so bad as I feared — that is, if she told me the whole truth, which I am inclined to doubt. But I had better keep him in my employ during the few months we still remain in this land, as I can watch over him, and guard against his influence better than if he were beyond my control. But no more promotion or encouragement does he get from me."

Janette, Christine's French maid, passed the open door. The thought struck Mr. Ludolph that he might secure an ally in her.

The unscrupulous creature was summoned, and agreed for no very large sum to become a spy upon Christine, and report anything looking toward friendly relations with Dennis Fleet.

"The game is still in my hands," said the wary man. "I will yet steer my richly-freighted argosy up the Rhine. Here's to Christine, the belle of the German court!" and he filled a slender Venetian glass to the brim, drained it, and then retired.

Christine, on reaching her room, muttered to herself: "He now knows all that I mean he ever shall. We are one in our ambition, if nothing else, and therefore our relations must be to a certain degree confidential and amicable.

And now forget you have a conscience, forget you have a heart, and, above all things, forget that you have ever seen or known Dennis Fleet."

Thus the influence of a false education, a proud, selfish, ambitious life, decided her choice. She plunged as resolutely into the whirl of fashionable gayety about her as she had in the dissipations of New York, determined to forget the past, and kill the time that must intervene before she could sail away to her brilliant future in Germany.

But she gradually learned that, if conscience had robbed her of peace before, something else disturbed her now, and rendered her efforts futile. She found that there was a principle at work in her heart stronger even than her resolute will. In spite of her purpose to the contrary, she caught herself continually thinking of Dennis, and indulging in strange, delicious reveries in regard to him.

At last she ceased to shun the store as she had done at first, but with increasing frequency found some necessity for going there.

After the interview in the show-room, Dennis was driven to the bitter conclusion that Christine was utterly heartless, and cared not a jot for him. His impression was confirmed by the fact that she shunned the store, and that he soon heard of her as a belle and leader in the ultra-fashionable world. He, too, bitterly lamented that he had ever seen her, and was struggling with all the power of his will to forget her. He fiercely resolved that, since she wished him dead, she should become dead to him.

Almost immediately after his return he had discovered that the two emblematical pictures had been removed from the loft over the store. He remembered that he had spoken of them to Christine, and from Ernst he gathered that she herself had taken them away. It was possible, he believed, that she had made them the subject of ridicule. At best she must have destroyed them in order to blot out all trace of a disagreeable episode. Whatever may have been their fate, they had, as he thought, failed in their purpose, and were worthless to him, and he was far too proud to make inquiries.

As the weeks passed on, he apparently succeeded better than she. There was nothing in her character, as she then appeared, that appealed to anything gentle or generous. She seemed so proud, so strong and resolute in her choice of evil, so devoid of the true womanly nature, as he had learned to reverence it in his mother, that he could not pity, much less respect her, and even his love could scarcely survive under such circumstances.

When she began coming to the store again, though his heart beat thick and fast at her presence, he turned his back and seemed not to see her, or made some errand to a remote part of the building. At first she thought this might be accident, but she soon found it a resolute purpose to ignore her very existence. By reason of a trait peculiar to Christine, this was only the more stimulating. She craved all the more that which was seemingly denied.

Accustomed to every gratification, to see all yield to her wishes, and especially to find gentlemen almost powerless to resist her beauty, she came to regard this one stern, averted face as infinitely more attractive than all the rest in the world.

"That he so steadily avoids me proves that he is anything but indifferent," she said to herself one day.

She condemned her visits to the store, and often reproached herself with folly in going; but a secret powerful magnetism drew her thither in spite of herself.

Dennis, too, soon noticed that she came often, and the fact awakened a faint hope within him. He learned that his love was not dead, but only chilled and chained by circumstances and his own strong will. True, apart from the fact of her coming, she gave him no encouragement. She was as distant and seemingly oblivious of his existence as he of hers, but love can gather hope from a marvellously little thing.

But one day Christine detected her father watching her movements with the keenest scrutiny, and after that she came more and more rarely. The hope that for a moment had tinged the darkness surrounding Dennis died away like the meteor's transient light.

He went into society very little after his illness, and shunned large companies. He preferred to spend his evenings with his mother and in study. The Winthrops were gone, having removed to their old home in Boston, and he had not formed very intimate acquaintances elsewhere. Moreover, his limited circle, though of the best and most refined, was not one in which Christine often appeared.

But one evening his cheek paled and his heart fluttered as he saw her entering the parlors of a lady by whom he had been invited to meet a few friends. For some little time he studiously avoided her, but at last his hostess, with well-meant zeal, formally presented him.

They bowed very politely and very coldly. The lady surmised that Christine did not care about the acquaintance of her father's clerk, and so brought them no more together. But Christine was pained by Dennis's icy manner, and saw that she was thoroughly misunderstood. When asked to sing, she chose a rather significant ditty: —

> "Ripple, sparkle, rapid stream,
> Let your dancing wavelets gleam
> Quiveringly and bright;
> Children think the surface glow
> Reaches to the depth below,
> Hidden from the light.

"Human faces often seem
Like the sparkle of the stream,
In the social glare;
Some assert, in wisdom's guise,
(Look they not with children's eyes?)
All is surface there."

As she rose from the piano her glance met his with something like meaning in it, he imagined. He started, flushed, and his face became full of eager questioning. But her father was on the watch also, and, placing his daughter's hand within his arm, he led her into the front parlor, and soon after they pleaded another engagement and vanished altogether.

No chance for explanation came, and soon a new and all absorbing anxiety filled Dennis's heart, and the shadow of the greatest sorrow that he had yet experienced daily drew nearer.

CHAPTER XXXVIII.

THE GATES OPEN.

AT Dennis's request, Dr. Arten called and carefully inquired into Mrs. Fleet's symptoms. Her son stood anxiously by awaiting the result of the examination. At last the physician said, cheerily: "There is no immediate occasion for alarm here. I am sorry to say that your mother's lungs are far from strong, but they may carry her through many comfortable years yet. I will prescribe tonics, and you may hope for the best. But mark this well, she must avoid exposure. A severe cold might be most serious in its consequences."

How easy to say, "Do not take cold!" How many whose lives were at stake have sought to obey the warning, but all in vain! Under Dr. Arten's tonics, Mrs. Fleet grew stronger, and Dennis rejoiced over the improvement. But, in one of the sudden changes attendant on the breaking up of winter, the dreaded cold was taken, and it soon developed into acute pneumonia.

For a few days she was very ill, and Dennis never left her side. In the intervals of pain and fever she would smile at him and whisper: "The harbor is near This rough weather cannot last much longer."

"Mother, do not leave us; we cannot spare you," ever pleaded her son.

Contrary to her expectations, however, she rallied, but continued in a very feeble state Dennis was able to resume his duties in the store, and he hoped and tried to believe that the warm spring and summer days soon to come would renew his mother's strength. But every day she grew feebler, and Dr. Arten shook his head.

The Bruders were very kind, and it was astonishing how much Mrs. Bruder, though burdened with her large family, found time to do. If Mrs. Fleet had been her own mother she could not have bestowed upon her more loving solicitude. Mr. Bruder was devotion itself. He removed his easel to an attic-room in Mrs. Fleet's house; and every hour of Dennis's absence heard him say: "Vat I do for you now? I feel no goot unless I do someding."

Some little time after Mrs. Fleet was taken sick a mystery arose. The most exquisite flowers and fruit were left at the house from time to time, marked in a bold, manly hand, "For Mrs. Fleet." But all efforts to discover their source failed.

The reader will guess that Christine was the donor, and Dennis hoped it, — though, he admitted to himself, with little reason.

Mrs. Fleet had not much pain. She seemed gently wafted as by an ebbing tide away from time and earth. Kindly but firmly she sought to prepare Dennis's mind for the change soon to take place. At first he could not endure its mention, but she said, earnestly: "My son, I am not dying. I am just entering on the true, real, eternal life, — a life which is as much beyond this poor feeble existence as the sun is brighter than a glow-worm. I shall soon clasp my dear husband to my heart again, and, oh, ecstasy! I shall soon in reality see the Saviour whom I now see almost continually in vision."

Then again she would turn towards her earthly treasures with unutterable yearning and tenderness.

"Oh that I could gather you up in my arms and take you

all with me!" she would often exclaim. Many times during the day she would call the little girls from their play and kiss their wondering faces.

One evening Dennis came home and found a vase of flowers with a green background of mint, at his mother's bedside. Their delicate fragrance greeted him as soon as he entered. As he sat by her side holding her hand, he said, softly: "Mother, are not these sprays of mint rather unusual in a bouquet? Has the plant any special meaning? I have noticed it before mingled with these mysterious flowers."

She smiled and answered, "When I was a girl its language was, 'Let us be friends again.'"

"Do you think — can it be possible that *she* sends them?" said he, in a low, hesitating tone.

"Prayer is mighty, my son."

"And have you been praying for her all this time, mother?"

"Yes, and will continue to do so to the last."

"O mother! I have lost hope. My heart has been full of bitterness toward her, and I have felt that God was against it all."

"God is not against her learning to know Him, which is life. Jesus has loved her all the time, and she has wronged Him more than she has you."

Dennis bowed his head on his mother's hand, and she felt hot tears fall upon it. At last he murmured: "You are indeed going to heaven soon, dear mother, for your language is not of earth. When will such a spirit dwell within me?"

"Again remember your mother's words," she answered, gently; "prayer is mighty."

"Mother," said he, with a sudden earnestness, "do you think you can pray for us in heaven?"

"I know of no reason to the contrary."

"Then I know you will, and the belief will ever be a source of hope and strength."

Mrs. Fleet was now passing through the land of Beulah. To her strong spiritual vision, the glories of the other shore seemed present, and at times she thought that she really heard music; again it would seem as if her Saviour had entered the plain little room, as He did the humble home at Bethany.

Her thoughts ran much on Christine. One day she wrote, feebly: —

"Would Miss Ludolph be willing to come and see a dying woman? ETHEL FLEET."

Mr. Bruder carried it, but most unfortunately Christine was out, so that her maid, ever on the alert to earn the price of her treachery, received it. It was slightly sealed. She opened it, and saw from its contents that it must be given to Mr. Ludolph. He with a frown committed it to the flames.

"I have written to her," she whispered to her son in the evening, "and think she will come to see me."

Dennis was sleepless that night, through his hope and eager expectation. The following day, and the next passed, and she came not.

"I was right," exclaimed he, bitterly. "She is utterly heartless. It was not she who sent the flowers. Who that is human would have refused such a request! Waste no more thought upon her, for she is unworthy, and it is all in vain."

"No!" said Mrs. Fleet in sudden energy. "It is not in vain. Have I not prayed again and again? and shall I doubt God?"

"Your faith is stronger than mine," he answered, in deep despondency.

"God's time is not always ours," she answered, gently.

But an angry fire lurked in Dennis's eyes, and he muttered to himself as he went to his room: "She has snapped the last slender cord that bound me to her. I could endure almost anything myself, but that she should refuse to visit my dying mother proves her a monster, with all her beauty."

As he was leaving the house in the morning, his mother whispered, gently, "Who was it that said, 'Father, forgive them, they know not what they do'?"

"Ah, but she does know," said he, bitterly. "I can forgive nearly everything against myself, but not slights to you."

"The time will come when you will forgive everything, my son."

"Not till there is acknowledgment and sorrow for the wrong," answered he, sternly. Then with a sudden burst of tenderness he added: "Good-by, darling mother. I will try to do anything you wish, even though it is impossible;" but his love, through Janette's treachery, suffered the deepest wound it had yet received.

Christine of her own accord had almost decided to call upon Mrs. Fleet, but before she could carry out her purpose, while hastily coming downstairs one day, she sprained her ankle, and was confined to her room some little time.

She sent Janette with orders for the flowers, who, at once surmising their destination, said to the florist that she was Miss Ludolph's confidential maid, and would carry them to those for whom they were designed. He, thinking it "all right," gave them to her, and she took them to a Frenchman in the same trade whom she knew, and sold them at half-price, giving him a significant sign to ask no questions. To the same market she brought the fruit; so from that time they ceased as mysteriously as they had appeared at Mrs. Fleet's bedside.

But Dennis was so anxious, and his mother was now failing so rapidly, that he scarcely noted this fact. The warm spring days seemed rather to enervate than to strengthen her. He longed to stay with her constantly, but his daily labor was necessary to secure the comforts needful to an invalid. Every morning he bade her a most tender adieu, and during the day often sent Ernst to inquire how she was.

One evening Christine ventured to send Janette on the same errand and impatiently awaited her return. At last she came, appearing as if flushed and angry.

"Whom did you see?" asked Christine, eagerly.

"I saw Mr. Fleet himself."

"Well, what did he say?"

"He bite his lip, frown, and say, 'Zere is no answer,' and turn on his heel into ze house."

It was now Christine's turn to be angry. "What!" she exclaimed, "does his Bible teach him to forget and forgive nothing? Can it be that he, like the rest of them, believes and acts on only such parts as are to his mood?"

"I don't know nothing about him," said the maid, "only I don't want to go zere again."

"You need not," was the brief reply.

After a long, bitter revery, she sighed: "Ah, well, thus we drift apart. But it is just as well, for apart we must ever be."

One morning early in May Mrs. Fleet was very weak, and Dennis left her with painful misgivings. During the morning he sent Ernst to see how she was, and he soon returned, with wild face, crying, "Come home quick!"

Breaking abruptly from his startled customer, Dennis soon reached his mother's side. Mr. and Mrs. Bruder were sobbing at the foot of the bed, and the girls were pleading piteously on either side,—"O mother! please don't go away!"

"Hush!" said Dennis, solemnly. Awed by his manner,

all became comparatively silent. He bent over the bed, and said, "Mother, you are leaving us."

The voice of her beloved son rallied the dying woman's wandering mind. After a moment she recognized him, smiled faintly, and whispered: "Yes, I think I am — kiss me — good-by. Bring — the children. Jesus — take care — my little — lambs. Good-by — true — honest friends — meet me — heaven. Dennis — these children — your charge — bring them home — to me. Pray for *her*. I don't know — why — she seems very — near to me. Farewell — my good — true — son — mother's blessing — God's blessing — ever rest — on you."

Her eyes closed, and she fell into a gentle sleep.

"She vake no more in dis vorld," said Mrs. Bruder, in an awed tone.

Mr. Bruder, unable to control his feelings any longer, hurried from the room. His wife, with streaming eyes, silently dressed the little girls, and took them home with her, crying piteously all the way for mamma.

Pale, tearless, motionless, Dennis sat, hour after hour holding his mother's hand. He noted that her pulse grew more and more feeble. At last the sun in setting broke through the clouds that had obscured it all day, and filled the room with a sudden glory.

To Dennis's great surprise, his mother's eyes opened wide, with the strange, far-off look they ever had when she was picturing to herself the unknown world.

Her lips moved. He bent over her and caught the words: "Hark! hear! — It never was so sweet before. See the angels — thronging toward me — they never came so near before."

Then a smile of joy and welcome lighted up her wan features, and she whispered, "O Dennis, husband, — are we once more united?"

Suddenly there was a look of ecstasy such as her son had never seen on any human face, and she cried almost aloud, "Jesus — my Saviour!" and received, as it were, directly into His arms, she passed from earth.

We touch briefly on the scenes that followed. Dennis took the body of his mother to her old home, and buried it under the wide-spreading elm in the village churchyard, where as a happy child and blooming maiden she had often sat between the services. It was his purpose to remove the remains of his father and place them by her side as soon as he could afford it.

His little sisters accompanied him east, and he found a home for them with a sister of his mother, who was a good, kind, Christian lady. Dennis's salary was not large, but sufficient to insure that his sisters would be no burden to his aunt, who was in rather straitened circumstances. He also arranged that the small annuity should be paid for their benefit.

It was hard parting from his sisters, whose little hearts seemed breaking at what appeared to them to be a new bereavement.

"How can I leave them!" he exclaimed, with tears falling fast from his eyes.

"They are children," said his aunt, soothingly, "and will forget their troubles in a few days."

And so it proved; but Dennis, with a sore heart, and feeling very lonely, returned to Chicago.

When at last Christine got out again, she learned from Ernst at the store that Dennis's mother had died, and that he had taken the remains and his sisters east. In his sorrow he seemed doubly interesting to her.

"How I wish it were in my power to cheer and comfort him!" she sighed, "and yet I fear my ability to do this is less than that of any one else. In very truth he seems to despise and hate me now. The barriers between us grow stronger and higher every day. How different it all might have been if — But what is the use of these wretched 'ifs'? What is the use of resisting this blind, remorseless fate that brings happiness to one and crushes another?"

Wearily and despondingly she rode back to the elegant home in which she found so little enjoyment.

Whom should she meet there but Mrs. Von Bräkhiem from New York? bound westward with a gay party on a trip to the Rocky Mountains and California. They had stopped to spend a few days in Chicago, and were determined to take Christine on with them. Her father strongly seconded the plan. Though Christine surmised his motive, she did not care to resist. Since she would soon be separated from Dennis forever, the less she saw of him the less would be the pain. Moreover, her sore and heavy heart welcomed any change that would cause forgetfulness; and so it was speedily arranged.

Mrs. Von Bräkhiem and her party quite took possession of the Ludolph mansion, and often made it echo with gayety.

On the evening of the day that Dennis buried his mother, Ernst went over at Mr. Ludolph's request to carry a message. He found the house the scene of a fashionable revel. There were music and dancing in the parlors, and from the dining-room the clink of glasses and loud peals of laughter proved that this was not Christine's ideal of an entertainment as she had portrayed it to her father on a former occasion. In truth, she had little to do with the affair; it was quite impromptu, and Mr. Ludolph and Mrs. Von Bräkhiem were responsible for it.

But Ernst could not know this, and to him it seemed shocking. The simple funeral service taking place on that day in the distant New-England village had never been absent from his thoughts a moment. Since early morning he had gone about with his little face composed to funereal gravity.

His simple, warm-hearted parents felt that they could only show proper respect for the occasion by the deepest gloom. Their rooms were arranged in stiff and formal manner, with crape here and there. All unnecessary work ceased, and the children, forbidden to play, were dressed in mourning as far as possible, and made to sit in solemn and dreadful state all day. It would not have surprised Ernst if the whole city had gone into mourning. Therefore the revelry at the Ludolph mansion seemed to him heartless and awful beyond measure, and nearly the first thing he told Dennis on the latter's return was that they had had "a great dancing and drinking party, the night of the funeral, at Mr. Ludolph's." Then, trying to find some explanation for what seemed to him such a strange and wicked thing, he suggested, "Perhaps they meant it for a wake."

Poor little Ernst's ideas of the world, outside of his home, had been gathered from a very low neighborhood.

He also handed Dennis a letter that Mr. Ludolph requested should be given him on his return. It read as follows:—

"CHICAGO, May 6th, 1871.

"I have been compelled to supply your place in your absence: therefore your services will be no longer needed at this store. Enclosed you will find a check for the small balance still due you.

"AUGUST LUDOLPH."

Dennis's brow grew very dark, and in bitter soliloquy he said, half aloud, as he strode up and down his little room in great agitation: "And so it all ends! The girl at whose side my mother would have watched in the most dangerous and loathsome of diseases; the woman of ice whom I sought to melt and render human by as warm, true love as ever man lavished on one who rewarded his affection, — this beautiful monster will not even visit my mother when dying; she holds a revel on the day of the funeral; and now, through her influence no doubt, I am robbed of the chance of winning honest bread. She cannot even endure the sight of the man who once told her the unvarnished truth. Poor as you deem me, Christine Ludolph, with God's help not many years shall pass before it will be condescension on my part to recognize you."

He would not even go to the store again. The Bruders, having heard what had occurred, took Ernst away also; but Dennis soon found him a better situation elsewhere.

The day on which Dennis returned, Christine was speeding in a palace-car toward the Rocky Mountains, outwardly gay, determined to enjoy herself and carry out her reckless purpose to get the most possible out of life, cost what it might.

If she had been a shallow girl, thoughtless and vain, with only mind enough to take in the events of the passing moment, she might have bought many fleeting pleasures with her abundant wealth. But this she was not, with all her faults, and wherever she went, in the midst of gayest scenes, and in the presence of the grandest and most inspiring scenery, thought and memory, like two spectres that no spell could lay, haunted her and robbed her of peace and any approach to happiness. Though possessing the means of gratifying every whim, though restrained by no scruples from doing what she chose, she felt that all around were getting more from life than she.

During her absence she experienced a sudden and severe attack of illness. Her friends were much alarmed about her, and she far more about herself. All her old terror returned. In one respect she was like her mother; she had no physical courage, but shrunk with inexpressible dread from danger, pain, and death. Again the blackness of darkness gathered round her, and not one in the gay pleasure party could say a word to comfort her.

She recovered, and soon regained her usual health, but her self-confidence was more thoroughly shaken. She felt like one in a little cockle-shell boat out upon a shoreless ocean. While the treacherous sea remained calm, all might be well, but she knew that a storm would soon arise, and that she must go down, beyond remedy. Again she had been taught how suddenly, how unexpectedly, that storm might rise.

Dennis resolved at once to enter on the career of an artist. He sold to Mr. French, at a moderate price, some paintings and sketches he had made. He rented a small room that became his studio, sleeping-apartment,—in brief, his home, and then went to work with all the ordinary incentives to success intensified by his purpose to reach a social height that would compel Christine to look upward if their acquaintance was renewed.

Disappointment in love is one of the severest tests of character in man or woman. Some sink into weak sentimentality, and mope and languish; some become listless, apathetic, and float down the current of existence like driftwood. Men are often harsh and cynical, and rail at the sex to which their mothers and sisters belong. Sometimes a man inflicts a well-nigh fatal wound and leaves his victim to cure it as best she may. From that time forth she may be like the wronged Indian, who slays as many white men as he can. Not a few, on finding they cannot enter the beautiful paradise of happy love, plunge into imbruting vice and drown not only their disappointment but themselves in dissipation. Their course is like that of some who deem that the best way to cure a wound or end a disease is to kill the patient as soon as possible. If women have true metal in them (and they usually have) they become unselfishly devoted to others, and by gentle, self-denying ways seek to impart to those about them the happiness denied to themselves.

But with all manly young men the instinct of Dennis is perhaps the most common. They will rise, shine, and dazzle the eyes that once looked scornfully or indifferently at them.

As he worked patiently at his noble calling this smaller ambition was gradually lost in the nobler, broader one, to be a true artist and a good man.

During his illness some gentlemen of large wealth and liberality, who wished to stimulate and develop the native artistic talent of their city, offered a prize of two thousand dollars for the finest picture painted during the year, the artist also having the privilege of selling his work.

On his return after his illness Dennis heard of this, and determined to be one of the competitors. He applied to Mr. Cornell, who had the matter in charge, for permission to enter the lists, which that gentleman granted rather doubtfully. He had known Dennis only as a critic, not as an artist. But having gained his point, Dennis went earnestly to work on the emblematic painting he had resolved upon, and with what success the following chapters will show.

His mother's sickness and death, of course, put a complete stop to his artistic labors for a time, but when entering on his new career, he gave himself wholly to this effort.

The time for exhibition and decision was fixed, — Saturday morning, October 7th, 1871.

CHAPTER XXXIX.

SUSIE WINTHROP APPEARS AGAIN.

OUR story passes rapidly over the scenes and events of the summer and fall of '71. Another heavy blow fell upon Dennis in the loss of his old friend and instructor, Mr. Bruder.

By prayer and effort, his own and others, he was saved morally and spiritually, but he had been greatly shattered by past excess. He was attacked by typhoid fever, and after a few days' illness died. Recovery from this disease depends largely upon strength and purity of constitution. But every one of the innumerable glasses of liquor that poor Bruder had swallowed had helped to rob him of these, and so there was no power to resist.

Under her husband's improved finances, Mrs. Bruder had removed to comfortable lodgings in Harrison Street, and these she determined to keep if possible, dreading for the sake of her children the influences of a crowded tenement house. Dennis stood by her, a staunch and helpful friend; Ernst was earning a good little sum weekly, and by her needle and wash-tub the patient woman continued the hard battle of life with fair prospects of success.

Dennis's studio was on the south side, at the top of a tall building overlooking the lake. Even before the early summer sun rose above the shining waves he was at his easel, and so accomplished what is a fair day's work before many of his profession had left their beds. Though he worked hard and long, he still worked judiciously. Bent upon accomplishing what was almost impossible within the limited time remaining, he determined that, with all his labor, Dr. Arten should never charge him with suicidal tendencies again. Therefore he trained himself mentally and morally for his struggle as the athlete trains himself physically.

He believed in the truth, too little recognized among brain-workers, that men can develop themselves into splendid mental conditions, wherein they can accomplish almost double their ordinary amount of labor.

The year allotted to the competitors for the prize to be given in October was all too short for such a work as he had attempted, and through his own, his mother's, and Mr. Bruder's illness, he had lost a third of the time, but in the careful and skilful manner indicated he was trying to make it up. He had a long conversation with shrewd old Dr. Arten, who began to take a decided interest in him. He also read several books on hygiene. Thus he worked under the guidance of reason, science, Christian principle, instead of mere impulse, as is too often the case with genius.

In the absorption of his task he withdrew utterly from society, and, with the exception of his mission class, Christian worship on the Sabbath, and attendance on a little prayer-meeting in a neglected quarter during the week, he permitted no other demands upon his time and thoughts.

His pictures had sold for sufficient to provide for his sisters and enable him to live, with close economy, till after the prize was given, and then, if he did not gain it (of which he was not at all sure), his painting would sell for enough to meet future needs.

And so we leave him for a time earnestly at work. He was like a ship that had been driven hither and thither, tempest-tossed and in danger. At last, under a clear sky and in smooth water, it finds its true bearings, and steadily pursues its homeward voyage.

The Christine whom he had first learned to love in happy unconsciousness, while they arranged the store together, became a glorified, artistic ideal. The Christine whom he had learned to know as false and heartless was now to him a strange, fascinating, unwomanly creature, beautiful only as the sirens were beautiful, that he might wreck himself body and soul before her unpitying eyes. He sought to banish all thought of her.

Christine returned about midsummer. She was compelled to note, as she neared her native city, that of all the objects it contained Dennis Fleet was uppermost in her thoughts. She longed to go to the store and see him once more, even though it should be only at a distance, with not even the shadow of recognition between them. She condemned it all as folly, and worse than vain, but that made no difference to her heart, which would have its way.

Almost trembling with excitement she entered the Art Building the next day, and glanced around with a timidity that was in marked contrast to her usual cold and critical regard. But, as the reader knows, Dennis Fleet was not to be seen. From time to time she went again, but neither he nor Ernst appeared. She feared that for some reason he had gone, and determined to learn the truth. Throwing off the strange timidity and restraint that ever embarrassed her where he was concerned, she said to Mr. Schwartz one day: "I don't like the way that picture is hung. Where is Mr. Fleet? I believe he has charge of that department."

"Why, bless you! Miss Ludolph," replied Mr. Schwartz, with a look of surprise, "Mr. Ludolph discharged him over two months ago."

"Discharged him! what for?"

"For being away too much, I heard," said old Schwartz, with a shrug indicating that that might be the reason and might not.

Christine came to the store but rarely thereafter, for it had lost its chief element of interest. That evening she said to her father, "You have discharged Mr. Fleet?"

"Yes," was the brief answer.

"May I ask the reason?"

"He was away too much."

"That is not the real reason," she said, turning suddenly upon him. "Father, what is the use of treating me as a child? What is the use of trying to lock things up and keep them from me? I intend to go to Germany with you this fall, and that is sufficient."

With a courtly smile Mr. Ludolph replied, "And I have lived long enough, my daughter, to know that what people *intend* and what they *do* are two very different things."

She flushed angrily and said: "It was most unjust to discharge him as you did. Do you not remember that he offered his mother's services as nurse when I was dreading the small-pox?"

"You are astonishingly grateful in this case," said her father, with a meaning that Christine understood too well; "but, if you will read the records of the Ludolph race, you will find that its representatives have often been compelled to do things somewhat arbitrarily. Since you have been gone, I have received letters announcing the death of my brother and his wife. I am now Baron Ludolph!"

But Christine was too angry and too deeply wounded to note this information, which at one time would have elated her beyond measure. She coldly said, "It is a pity that noblemen are compelled to aught but noble deeds;" and, with this parting arrow, she left him.

Even her father winced, and then with a heavy frown said, "It is well that this Yankee youth has vanished; still, the utmost vigilance is required."

Again he saw the treacherous maid and promised increased

reward if she would be watchful, and inform him of every movement of Christine.

In the unobtrusive ways that her sensitive pride permitted, Christine tried to find out what had become of Dennis, but vainly. She offered her maid a large reward if she would discover him, but she had been promised a larger sum not to find him, and so did not. The impression was given that he had left the city, and Christine feared, with a sickening dread, that she would never see him again. But one evening Mr. Cornell stated a fact in a casual way that startled both Mr. and Miss Ludolph.

He was calling at their house, and they were discussing the coming exhibition of the pictures which would compete for the prize.

"By the way, your former clerk and porter is among the competitors; at least he entered the lists last spring, but I have lost sight of him since. I imagine he has given it up, and betaken himself to tasks more within the range of his ability."

The eyes of father and daughter met, but she turned to Mr. Cornell, and said, coolly, though with a face somewhat flushed, "And has Chicago so much artistic talent that a real genius has no chance here?"

"I was not aware that Mr. Fleet was a genius," answered Mr. Cornell.

"I think that he will satisfy you on that point, and that you will hear from him before the exhibition takes place."

Mr. Ludolph hastily changed the subject, but he had forebodings as to the future.

Christine went to her room, and thought for a long time; suddenly she arose, exclaiming, "He told me his story once on canvas; I will now tell him mine."

She at once stretched the canvas on a frame for a small picture, and placed it on an easel, that she might commence with dawn of day.

During the following weeks she worked scarcely less earnestly and patiently than Dennis. The door was locked when she painted, and before she left the studio the picture was hidden.

She meant to send it anonymously, so that not even her father should know its authorship. She hoped that Dennis would recognize it.

When she was in the street her eyes began to have an eager, wistful look, as if she was seeking some one. She often went to galleries, and other resorts of artists, but in vain, for she never met him, though at times the distance between them was less than between Evangeline and her lover, when she heard the dip of his oar in her dream. Though she knew that if she met him she would probably give not one encouraging glance, yet the instinct of her heart was just as strong.

Mr. Ludolph told the maid that she must find out what Christine was painting, and she tried to that degree that she wakened suspicion.

On one occasion Christine turned suddenly on her, and said: "What do you mean? If I find you false — if I have even good reason to suspect you —I will turn you into the street, though it be at midnight!"

And the maid learned, as did Mr. Ludolph, that she was not dealing with a child.

During Monday, October 2d, Dennis was employed all the long day in giving the finishing touches to his picture. It was not worked up as finely as he could have wished; time did not permit this. But he had brought out his thought vividly, and his drawings were full of power. On the following Saturday the prize would be given.

In the evening he walked out for air and exercise. As he was passing one of the large hotels, he heard his name called. Turning, he saw on the steps, radiant with welcome, his old friend, Susie Winthrop. Her hand was on the arm of a tall gentleman, who seemed to have eyes for her only. But in her old impulsive way she ran down the steps, and gave Dennis a grasp of the hand that did his lonely heart good. Then, leading him to the scholarly-looking gentleman, who was gazing through his glasses in mild surprise, she said: "Professor Leonard, my husband, Mr. Fleet. This is the Dennis Fleet I have told you about so often."

"Oh—h," said the professor, in prolonged accents, while a genial light shone through his gold spectacles. "Mr. Fleet, we are old acquaintances, though we have never met before. If I were a jealous man, you are the only one I should fear."

"And we mean to make you wofully jealous to-night, for I intend to have Mr. Fleet dine with us and spend the evening. No, I will take no excuse, no denial. This infatuated man will do whatever I bid him, and he is a sort of Greek athlete. If you do not come right along I shall command him to lay violent hands on you and drag you ignominiously in."

Dennis was only too glad to accept, but merely wished to make a better toilet.

"I have just come from my studio," he said.

"And you wish to go and divest yourself of all artistic flavor and become commonplace. Do you imagine I will permit it? No! so march in as my captive. Who ever heard of disputing the will of a bride? This man" (pointing up to the tall professor) "never dreams of it."

Dennis learned that she was on her wedding trip, and saw that she was happily married, and proud of her professor, as he of her.

With feminine tact she drew his story from him, and yet it was but a meagre, partial story, like the play of Hamlet with Hamlet left out, for he tried to be wholly silent on his love and disappointment. But in no respect did he deceive

Mrs. Leonard. Her husband went away for a little time. In his absence she asked, abruptly, "Have you seen Miss Ludolph lately?"

"No!" said Dennis, with a telltale flush. Seeing her look of sympathy, and knowing her to be such a true friend, the impulsive young man gave his confidence almost before he knew it. She was just the one to inspire trust, and he was very lonely, having had no one to whom he could speak his deeper feelings since his mother died.

"Miss Ludolph wronged me in a way that a man finds it hard to forget or forgive," he said, in a low, bitter tone; "but I should have tried to do both had she not treated my mother most inhumanly;" and he told his story over again with Hamlet in.

Mrs. Leonard listened with breathless interest, and then said: "She is a strange girl, and that plan of making you her unconscious model is just like her, though it was both cruel and wicked. And yet, Mr. Fleet, with shame for my sex I admit it, how many would have flirted with you to the same degree from mere vanity and love of excitement! I have seen Miss Ludolph, and I cannot understand her. We are no longer the friends we once were, but I cannot think her utterly heartless. She is bent upon becoming a great artist at any cost, and I sometimes think she would sacrifice herself as readily as any one else for this purpose. She looks to me as if she had suffered, and she has lost much of her old haughty, cold manner, save when something calls it out. Even in the drawing-room she was abstracted, as if her thoughts were far away. You are a man of honor, and it is due that you should know the following facts. Indeed I do not think that they are a secret any longer, and at any rate they will soon be known. If Mr. Ludolph were in Germany he would be a noble. It is his intention to go there this fall, and take his wealth and Christine with him, and assert his ancestral titles and position. Christine could not marry in this land without incurring her father's curse, and I think she has no disposition to do that, — her ambition is fully in accord with his."

"Yes," said Dennis, bitterly, "and where other women have hearts, she has ambition only."

The professor returned and the subject was dropped.

Dennis said, on taking his leave: "I did not expect to show any one my picture till it was placed on exhibition with the others, but, if you care to see it, you may to-morrow. Perhaps you can make some suggestions that will help me."

They eagerly accepted the invitation, and came the following morning. Dennis watched them with much solicitude. When once they understood his thought, their delight and admiration knew no bounds. The professor turned and stared at him as if he were an entirely different person from the unpretending youth who had been introduced on the preceding evening.

"If you do not get the prize," he said, sententiously, "you have a great deal of artistic talent in Chicago."

"'A Daniel come to judgment!'" cried his wife.

CHAPTER XL.

SUGGESTIVE PICTURES AND A PRIZE.

AT last the day of the exhibition dawned. Dennis had sent his picture, directed to Mr. Cornell, with his own name in an envelope nailed to its back. No one was to know who the artists were till after the decision was given. Christine had sent hers also, but no name whatever was in the envelope attached to it.

At an early hour, the doors were thrown open for all who chose to come. The committee of critics had ample time given them for their decision, and at one o'clock this was to be announced.

Although Dennis went rather early, he found that Christine was there before him. She stood with Professor and Mrs. Leonard, Mr. Cornell, and her father, before his picture. He could only see her side face, and she was glancing from the printed explanation in the catalogue to the painting. Mrs. Leonard was also at her side, seeing to it that no point was unnoted. Christine's manner betrayed intense interest and excitement, and with cause, for again Dennis had spoken to her deepest soul in the language she best loved and understood.

As before she saw two emblematic pictures within one frame merely separated by a plain band of gold.

The first presented a chateau of almost palatial proportions, heavy, ornate, but stiff and quite devoid of beauty. It appeared to be the abode of wealth and ancestral greatness.

Everything about the place indicated lavish expenditure The walks and trees were straight and formal, the flowers that bloomed here and there, large and gaudy. A parrot hung in a gilded cage against a column of the piazza. No wild songsters fluttered in the trees, or were on the wing. Hills shut the place in and gave it a narrow, restricted appearance, and the sky overhead was hard and brazen. On the lawn stood a graceful mountain ash, and beneath it were two figures. The first was that of a man, and evidently the master of the place. His appearance and manner chiefly indicated pride, haughtiness, and also sensuality. He had broken a spray from the ash-tree, and with a condescending air was in the act of handing it to a lady, in the portraiture of whom Dennis had truly displayed great skill. She was very beautiful, and yet there was nothing good or noble in her face. Her proud features showed mingled shame and reluctance to receive the gift in the manner it was bestowed, and yet she was receiving it. The significance of the mountain ash is "Grandeur." The whole scene was the portrayal, in the beautiful language of art, of a worldly, ambitious marriage, where the man seeks mere beauty, and the woman wealth and position, love having no existence.

It possessed an eloquence that Christine could not resist, and she fairly loathed the alliance she knew her father would expect her to make after their arrival in Germany, though once she had looked forward to it with eagerness as the stepping-stone to her highest ambition.

The second picture was a beautiful contrast. Instead of the brazen glare of the first, the air was full of glimmering lights and shades, and the sky of a deep transparent blue. Far up a mountain side, on an overhanging cliff, grew the same graceful ash-tree, but its branches were entwined with vines of the passion-flower that hung around in slender streamers. On a jutting rock, with precarious footing, stood a young man reaching up to grasp a branch, his glance bold and hopeful, and his whole manner full of daring and power. He had evidently had a hard climb to reach his present position; his hat was gone; his dress was light and simple and adapted to the severest effort.

But the chief figure in this picture also was that of a young girl who stood near, her right hand clasping his left, and steadying and sustaining him in his perilous footing. The wind was in her golden hair, and swept to one side her light, airy costume. Her pure, noble face was lifted up toward *him*, rather than toward the spray he sought to grasp, and an eager, happy light shone from her eyes. She had evidently climbed *with* him to their present vantage-point, and now her little hand secured and strengthened him as he sought to grasp, for her, success and prosperity joined with unselfish love. The graceful wind-flowers tossed tneir delicate blossoms around their feet, and above them an eagle wheeled in its majestic flight.

Below and opposite them on a breezy hillside stood a modern villa, as tasteful in its architecture as the former had been stiff and heavy. A fountain played upon the lawn, and behind it a cascade broke into silver spray and mist. High above this beautiful earthly home, in the clear, pure air rose a palace-like structure in shadowy, golden outline, indicating that after the dwelling-place of time came the grander, the perfect mansion above.

Christine looked till her eyes were blinded with tears, and then dropped her veil. In the features of the lady in each case she had not failed to trace a faint likeness, sufficient to make it clear to herself. She said in a low, plaintive tone, with quivering lips, "Mr. Fleet painted that picture."

"Yes," said Mrs. Leonard, looking at her with no little wonder and perplexity.

By a great effort Christine recovered herself and said, "You know how deeply fine paintings always affect me."

Dennis of course knew nothing of Christine's feelings. He could only see that his picture had produced a profound effect on her, and that she had eyes for nothing else. But he overheard Mr. Cornell say, "It is indeed a remarkable painting."

"Do you know its author?" asked Mr. Ludolph, with a heavy frown.

"No, I do not. It is still a mystery."

"Will it take the prize, do you think?"

"I am not at liberty to give an opinion as yet," replied Mr. Cornell, with a smile. "There is another picture here, almost if not quite as fine, though much smaller and simpler;" and he took Mr. Ludolph off to show him that.

Dennis was now recognized by Mrs. Leonard and her husband, who came forward and greeted him cordially, and they started on a tour of the gallery together. Though his heart beat fast, he completely ignored Christine's presence, and responded coldly to Mr. Ludolph's slight bow.

Christine, on being aware of his presence, furtively devoured him with her eyes. The refining influences of his life were evident in his face and bearing, and she realized her ideal of what a man ought to be. Eagerly she watched till he should discover her painting where it hung opposite his own, and at last she was amply rewarded for all her toil. He stopped suddenly and stood as if spell-bound.

The picture was very simple, and few accessories entered into it. Upon a barren rock of an island stood a woman gazing far out at sea, where in the distance a ship was sailing *away*. Though every part had been worked up with exquisite finish, the whole force and power of the painting lay in the expression of the woman's face, which was an indescribable mingling of longing and despair. Here also Christine had traced a faint resemblance to herself, though the woman was middle-aged and haggard, with famine in her cheeks.

As Dennis looked and wondered, the thought flashed into his mind, "Could *she* have painted that?" He turned suddenly toward her and was convinced that she had done so; for she was looking at him with something of the same expression, or at least he fancied so. She blushed deeply and turned hastily away. He was greatly agitated, but in view of the eyes that were upon him controlled himself and remained outwardly calm.

Mr. Ludolph also was convinced that his daughter had painted the picture, and he frowned more heavily than before. He turned a dark look on her, and found her regarding Dennis in a manner that caused him to grind his teeth with rage. But he could only sit down and watch the course of events.

The people were now thronging in. The gentlemen who made up the prize, with their committee of award, of which Mr. Cornell was chairman, were also present. Most critically they examined each picture till at last their choice narrowed down to the two paintings above described. But it soon became evident that their choice would fall upon the larger one, and Dennis saw that he was to be the victor. To his surprise Christine seemed utterly indifferent as to the result of their decision. He could not know that the prize had no place in her thoughts when she painted her picture. She had found her reward in its effect on him.

At one o'clock Mr. Cornell came forward and said: "Ladies and gentlemen, and especially do I address that group of liberal citizens who are so generously seeking to encourage art in our great and prosperous city, it gives me pleasure to inform you that your munificence has brought forth rich fruit, for here are many paintings that would do credit to any gallery. We hesitated a little time between two very superior pictures, but at last we have decided that the larger one is worthy of the prize. The smaller picture is one of great merit; its treatment is unusually fine, though the subject is not new.

"The two emblematic pictures in some parts show crude and hasty work; indeed some minor parts are quite unfinished. The artist evidently has not had sufficient time. But the leading features are well wrought out, and the power and originality of the entire effort so impress us that, as I have said, we render our decision in its favor. That all may know our verdict to be fair, we state on our honor that we do not know by whom a single painting present was executed. Dr. Arten, as the largest contributor towards the prize, you are appointed to bestow it. On the back of the picture you will find an envelope containing the name of the artist, whom we all shall delight to honor."

Amid breathless expectation, Dr. Arten stepped forward, took down the envelope, and read in a loud, trumpet-like voice, —

"DENNIS FLEET."

CHAPTER XLI.

FIRE! FIRE!

"WILL Dennis Fleet come forward?" cried Dr. Arten. Very pale, and trembling with excitement, Dennis stepped out before them all.

"Take heart, my young friend; I am not about to read your death-warrant," said the doctor, cheerily. "Permit me to present you with this check for two thousand dollars, and express to you what is of more value to the true artist, our esteem and appreciation of your merit. May your brush ever continue to be employed in the presentation of such noble, elevating thoughts."

And the good doctor, quite overcome by this unusual flight of eloquence, blew his nose vigorously and wiped from his spectacles the moisture with which his own eyes had bedewed them.

Dennis responded with a low bow, and was about to retire; but his few friends, and indeed all who knew him, pressed forward with their congratulations.

Foremost among these were the professor and his wife. Tears of delight fairly shone in Mrs. Leonard's eyes as she shook his hand again and again. Many others also trooped up for an introduction, till he was quite bewildered by strange names, and compliments that seemed stranger still.

Suddenly a low, well-known voice at his side sent a thrill to his heart and a rush of crimson to his face.

"Will Mr. Fleet deign to receive my congratulations also?"

He turned and met the deep blue eyes of Christine Ludolph lifted timidly to his. But at once the association that had long been uppermost in regard to her — the memory of her supposed treatment of his mother — flashed across him, and he replied, with cold and almost stately courtesy, "The least praise or notice from Miss Ludolph would be a most unexpected favor."

She thought from his manner that he might as well have said "unwelcome favor," and with a sad, disappointed look she turned away.

Even in the excitement and triumph of the moment, Dennis was oppressed by the thought that he had not spoken as wisely as he might. Almost abruptly he broke away and escaped to the solitude of his own room.

He did not think about his success. The prize lay forgotten in his pocketbook. He sat in his arm-chair and stared apparently at vacancy, but in reality at the picture that he was sure Christine had painted. He went over and over again with the nicest scrutiny all her actions in the gallery, and now reproached himself bitterly for the repelling answer he had given when she spoke to him. He tried to regain his old anger and hardness in view of her wrongs to him and his, but could not. The telltale picture, and traces of sorrow and suffering in her face in accord with it, had disarmed him. He said to himself, and half believed, that he was letting his imagination run away with his reason, but could not help it. At last he seized his hat and hastened to the hotel where Mrs. Leonard was staying. She at once launched out into a eulogistic strain descriptive of her enjoyment of the affair.

"I never was so proud of Chicago," she exclaimed. "It is the greatest city in the world. Only the other day her streets were prairies. I believe my husband expected to find buffalo and Indians just outside the town. But see!

already, by its liberality and attention to art, it begins to vie with some of our oldest cities. But what is the matter? You look so worried."

"Oh, nothing," said Dennis, coming out of his troubled, abstracted manner.

With her quick intuition, Mrs. Leonard at once divined his thoughts, and said soon after, when her husband's back was turned: "All I can say is, that she was deeply, most deeply affected by your picture, but she said nothing to me, more than to express her admiration. My friend, you had better forget her. They sail for Europe very soon; and, besides, she is not worthy of you."

"I only wish I could forget her, and am angry with myself that I cannot," he replied, and soon after said "good-night."

Wandering aimlessly through the streets, he almost unconsciously made his way to the north side, where the Ludolph mansion was situated. Then a strong impulse to go to it came over him, and for the first time since the far-off day when, stunned and wounded by his bitter disappointment, he had gone away apparently to die, he found himself at the familiar place. The gas was burning in Mr. Ludolph's library. He went around on the side street (for the house was on a corner), and a light shone from what he knew to be Christine's studio. She undoubtedly was there. Even such proximity excited him strangely, and in his morbid state he felt that he could almost kiss the feeble rays that shimmered out into the darkened street. In his secret soul he utterly condemned his folly, but promised himself that he would be weak no longer after that one night. The excitements of the day had thrown him off his balance.

Suddenly he heard, sweet and clear, though softened by distance and intervening obstacles, the same weird, pathetic ballad that had so moved him when Christine sung it at Le

Grand Hotel, on the evening after he had pointed out the fatal defect in her picture. At short intervals, kindred and plaintive songs followed.

"There is nothing exultant or hopeful about those strains," he said to himself. "For some reason she is not happy. Oh that I might have one frank conversation with her and find out the whole truth! But it seems that I might just as well ask for a near look at yonder star that glimmers so distantly. For some reason I cannot believe her so utterly heartless as she has seemed; and then mother has prayed. Can it all end as a miserable dream?"

Late at night the music ceased, and the room was darkened.

Little dreamed Christine that her plaintive minstrelsy had fallen on so sympathetic an ear, and that the man who seemingly had repelled her slightest acquaintance had shivered long hours in the cold, dark street.

So the Divine Friend waits and watches, while we, in ignorance and unbelief, pay no heed. Stranger far, He waits and watches when we know, but yet, unrelenting, ignore His presence.

With heavy steps, Dennis wearily plodded homeward. He was oppressed by that deep despondency which follows great fatigue and excitement.

In the southwest he saw a brilliant light. He heard the alarm-bells, and knew there was a fire, but to have aroused him that night it must have come scorchingly close. He reached his dark little room, threw himself dressed on the couch, and slept till nearly noon of the next day.

When he awoke, and realized how the first hours of the Sabbath had passed, he started up much vexed with himself, and after a brief retrospect said: "Such excitements as those of yesterday are little better than a debauch, and I must shun them hereafter. God has blessed and succeeded me, and it is but a poor return I am making. However my unfortunate attachment may end, nothing is gained by moping around in the hours of night. Henceforth let there be an end of such folly."

He made a careful toilet and sat down to his Sabbath-school lesson.

To his delight he again met Mrs. Leonard, who came to visit her old mission class. She smiled most approvingly, and quoted, "'He that is faithful in that which is least is faithful also in much.'"

He went home with her, and in the evening they all went to church together.

He cried unto the Lord for strength and help, and almost lost consciousness of the service in his earnest prayer for true manhood and courage to go forward to what he feared would be a sad and lonely life. And the answer came; for a sense of power and readiness to do God's will, and withal a strange hopefulness, inspired him. Trusting in the Divine strength, he felt that he could meet his future now, whatever it might be.

Again the alarm-bells were ringing, and there was a light in the southwest.

"There seems to be a fire over there in the direction of my poor German friend's house. You remember Mrs. Bruder. I will go and call on them, I think. At any rate I should call, for it is owing to her husband that I won the prize;" and they parted at the church-door.

Christine had left the picture-gallery soon after Dennis's abrupt departure. Her gay friends had tried in vain to rally her, and rather wondered at her manner, but said, "She is so full of moods of late, you can never know what to expect."

Her father, with a few indifferent words, left her for his place of business. His hope still was to prevent her meeting Dennis, and to keep up the estrangement that existed

Christine went home and spent the long hours in bitter revery, which at last she summed up by saying, "I have stamped out his love by my folly, and now his words, 'I despise you,' express the whole wretched truth." Then clenching her little hands she added, with livid lips and a look of scorn: "Since I can never help him (and therefore no one) win earthly greatness, I will never be the humble recipient of it from another. Since his second picture cannot be true of my experience, neither shall the first."

And she was one to keep such a resolve. The evening was spent, as we know, in singing alone in her studio, this being her favorite, indeed her only way, of giving expression to her feelings. Very late she sought her bed to find but little sleep.

The day of rest brought no rest to her, suggested no hope, no sacred privilege of seeking Divine help to bear up under life's burdens. To her it was a relic of superstition, at which she chafed as interfering with the usual routine of affairs. She awoke with a headache, and a long miserable day she found it. Sabbath night she determined to have sleep, and therefore took an opiate and retired early.

Mr. Ludolph sat in his library trying to construct some plan by which Christine could be sent to Germany at once.

When Dennis reached the neighborhood of the fire he found it much larger than he supposed, and when he entered Harrison Street, near Mrs. Bruder's home, he discovered that only prompt action could save the family. The streets were fast becoming choked with fugitives and teams, and the confusion threatened to develop into panic and wide-spread danger. The fire was but a block away when he rushed upstairs to the floor which the Bruders occupied. From the way in which blazing brands were flying he knew that there was not a moment to spare.

He found Mrs. Bruder startled, anxious, but in no way comprehending the situation.

"Quick!" cried Dennis. "Wake and dress the children, — pack up what you can lay your hands on and carry, — you have no time to do anything more."

"Ah! mine Gott! vat you mean?"

"Do as I say, — there's no time to explain. Here, Ernst, help me;" and Dennis snatched up one child and commenced dressing it before it could fairly wake. Ernst took up another and followed his example. Mrs. Bruder, recovering from her bewilderment, hastily gathered a few things together, saying in the mean time, "Surely you don't dink our home burn up?"

"Yes, my poor friend, in five minutes more we must all be out of this building."

"Oh, den come dis minute! Let me save de schilder;" and, throwing a blanket around the youngest, the frightened woman rushed downstairs, followed by Ernst and his little brother, while Dennis hastened with the last child and the bundle.

Their escape was none too prompt, for the blazing embers were falling to such a degree in the direct line of the fire as to render their position very perilous. But though their progress was necessarily slow, from the condition of the streets, the breadth of the fire was not great at this spot, and they soon reached a point to the west and windward that was safe. Putting the family in charge of Ernst, and telling them to continue westward, Dennis rushed back, feeling that many lives might depend upon stout hands and brave hearts that night. Moreover he was in that state of mind which made him court rather than shun danger.

He had hardly left his humble friends before Mrs. Bruder stopped, put her hand on her heart and cried: "O Ernst! O Gott forgive me! dot I should forget him — your fader's picture. I must go back."

"O moder, no! you are more to us than the picture." The woman's eyes were wild and excited, and she cried, vehemently: "Dot picture saved mine Berthold life — yes, more, more, him brought back his artist soul. Vithout him ve vould all be vorse dan dead. I can no live vithout him. Stay here;" and with the speed of the wind the devoted wife rushed back to the burning street, up the stairs, already crackling and blazing, to where the lovely landscape smiled peacefully in the dreadful glare, with its last rich glow of beauty. She tore it from its fastenings, pressed her lips fervently against it, regained the street, but with dress on fire. She staggered forward a few steps in the hot stifling air and smoke, and then fell upon her burden. Spreading her arms over it, to protect it even in death, the mother's heart went out in agony toward her children.

"Ah merciful Gott! take care of dem," she sighed, and the prayer and the spirit that breathed it went up to heaven together.

CHAPTER XLII.

BARON LUDOLPH LEARNS THE TRUTH.

WITH eyes ablaze with excitement, Dennis plunged into the region just before the main line of fire, knowing that there the danger would be greatest. None realized the rapidity of its advance. At the door of a tenement house he found a pale, thin, half-clad woman tugging at a sewing-machine.

"Madam," cried Dennis, "you have no time to waste over that burden if you wish to escape."

"What is the use of escaping without it?" she answered, sullenly. "It is the only way I have of making a living."

"Give it to me then, and follow as fast as you can." Shouldering what meant to the poor creature shelter, clothing, and bread, he led the way to the southeast, out of the line of fire. It was a long, hard struggle, but they got through safely.

"How can I ever pay you?" cried the grateful woman.

But he did not stay to answer, and now determined to make his way to the west and windward of the fire, as he could then judge better of the chances of its spreading. He thought it safer to go around and back of the flames, as they now seemed much wider, and nearer the south branch of the Chicago River.

He found that he could cross the burnt district a little to the southwest, for the small wooden houses were swept so utterly away that there were no heated, blazing ruins to contend with. He also saw that he could do better by making quite a wide circuit, as he thus avoided streets choked by fugitives. Reaching a point near the river on the west side of the fire, he climbed a high pile of lumber, and then discovered to his horror that the fire had caught in several places on the south side, and that the nearest bridges were burning.

To those not familiar with the topography of the city, it should be stated that it is separated by the Chicago River, a slow, narrow stream, into three main divisions, known as the south, the north, and the west side.

By a triumph of engineering, the former mouth of this river at the lake is now its source, the main stream being turned back upon itself, and dividing into two branches at a point a little over half a mile from the lake, one flowing to the southwest into the Illinois, and the other from the northwest into the main stream.

The south division includes all the territory bounded on the east by the lake, on the north by the main river and on the west by the south branch. The north division includes the area bounded on the east by the lake, on the south by the main river, and on the west by the north branch, while the west division embraces all that part of the city west of the two branches. The fire originated in De Koven Street, the southeastern part of the west side, and it was carried steadily to the north and east by an increasing gale. The south side, with all its magnificent buildings, was soon directly in the line of the fire.

When Dennis saw that the flames had crossed the south branch, and were burning furiously beyond, he knew that the best part of the city was threatened with destruction. He hastened to the Washington Street tunnel, where he found a vast throng, carrying all sorts of burdens, rushing either way. He plunged in with the rest, and soon found himself hustled hither and thither by a surging mass of humanity. A little piping voice that seemed under his feet cried; "O mamma! mamma! Where are you? I'm gettin' lost."

"Here I am, my child," answered a voice some steps in advance, and Dennis saw a lady carrying another child; but the rushing tide would not let her wait, — all, in the place where they were wedged, being carried right along. Stooping down, he put the little girl on his shoulder where she could see her mother, and so they pressed on. Suddenly, in the very midst of the tunnel, the gas ceased, by reason of the destruction of the works, and utter darkness filled the place.

There was a loud cry of consternation, and then a momentary and dreadful silence, which would have been the preface of a fatal panic, had not Dennis cried out, in a ringing voice, "All keep to the right!"

This cry was taken up and repeated on every hand, and side by side, to right and left, the two living streams of humanity, with steady tramp! tramp! rushed past each other.

When they emerged into the glare of the south side Dennis gave the child to its mother and said, "Madam, your only chance is to escape in that direction," pointing northwest.

He then tried to make his way to the hotel where Professor and Mrs. Leonard were staying, but it was in the midst of an unapproachable sea of fire. If they had not escaped some little time before, they had already perished. He then tried to make his way to the windward toward his own room. His two thousand dollars and all his possessions were there, and the instinct of self-preservation caused him to think it was time to look after his own. But progress was now very difficult. The streets were choked by drays, carriages, furniture, trunks, and every degree and condition of humanity. Besides, his steps were often stayed by thrilling scenes and the need of a helping hand. In order to make his way faster he took a street nearer the fire, from which the people had mostly been driven. As he was hurrying along with his hat drawn over his eyes to avoid the sparks that were driven about like fiery hail, he suddenly heard a piercing shriek. Looking up he saw the figure of a woman at the third story window of a fine mansion that was already burning, though not so rapidly as those in the direct line of the fire. He with a number of others stopped at the sound.

"Who will volunteer with me to save that woman?" cried he.

"Wal, stranger, you can reckon on this old stager for one," answered a familiar voice.

Dennis turned and recognized his old friend, the Good Samaritan.

"Why, Cronk," he cried, "don't you know me? Don't you remember the young man you saved from starving by suggesting the snow-shovel business?"

"Hollo! my young colt. How are you? give us yer hand. But come, don't let's stop to talk about snow in this hell of a place with that young filly whinnying up there."

"Right!" cried Dennis. "Let us find a ladder and rope; quick —"

At a paint-shop around the corner a ladder was found that reached to the second story, and some one procured a rope.

"A thousand dollars," cried another familiar voice, "to the man who saves that woman!"

Looking round, Dennis saw the burly form of Mr. Brown, the brewer, his features distorted by agony and fear; then glancing up he discovered in the red glare upon her face that the woman was no other than his daughter. She had come to spend the night with a friend, and, being a sound sleeper, had not escaped with the family.

"Who wants yer thousand dollars?" replied Bill Cronk's gruff voice. "D'ye s'pose we'd hang out here over the bottomless pit for any such trifle as that? We want to save the gal."

Before Cronk had ended his characteristic speech, Dennis was half-way up the ladder. He entered the second story, only to be driven back by fire and smoke.

"A pole of some kind!" he cried.

The thills of a broken-down buggy supplied this, but the flames had already reached Miss Brown. Being a girl of a good deal of nerve and physical courage, however, she tore off her outer clothing with her own hands. Dennis now passed her the rope on the end of the buggy-thill and told her to fasten it to something in the room that would support her weight, and lower herself to the second story. She fastened it, but did not seem to know how to lower herself. Dennis tried the rope, found it would sustain his weight; then, bringing into use an art learned in his college gymnasium, he over-handed rapidly till he stood at Miss Brown's side. Drawing up the rope he fastened her to it and lowered her to the ladder, where Bill Cronk caught her, and in a moment more she was in her father's arms, who at once shielded her from exposure with his overcoat. Dennis followed the rope down, and had hardly got away before the building fell in.

"Is not this Mr. Fleet?" asked Miss Brown.

"Yes."

"How can we ever repay you?"

"By learning to respect honest men, even though they are not rich, Miss Brown."

"Did you know who it was when you saved me?"

"Yes."

"Mr. Fleet, I sincerely ask your pardon."

But before Dennis could reply they were compelled to fly for their lives.

Mr. Brown shouted as he ran, "Call at the house or place of business of Thomas Brown, and the money will be ready."

But Thomas Brown would have found it hard work to rake a thousand dollars out of the ashes of either place the following day. The riches in which he trusted had taken wings.

Cronk and Dennis kept together for a short distance, and the latter saw that his friend had been drinking. Their steps led them near a large liquor-store which a party of men and boys were sacking. One of these, half intoxicated, handed Bill a bottle of whiskey, but as the drover was lifting it to his lips Dennis struck it to the ground. Cronk was in a rage instantly.

"What the —— did you do that for?" he growled.

"I would do that and more too to save your life. If you get drunk to-night you are a lost man," answered Dennis, earnestly.

"Who's a-goin' ter get drunk, I'd like ter know? You feel yer oats too much to-night. No man or horse can kick over the traces with me;" and he went off in the unreasoning anger of a half-drunken man. But he carried all his generous impulses with him, for a few minutes after, seeing a man lying in a most dangerous position, he ran up and shook him, crying, "I say, stranger, get up, or yer ribs will soon be roasted."

"Lemme 'lone," was the maudlin answer. "I've had drink 'nuff. 'Tain't mornin' yet."

"Hi, there!" cried a warning voice, and Cronk started back just in time to escape a blazing wall that fell across the street. The stupefied man he had sought to arouse was hopelessly buried. Cronk, having got out of danger, stood and scratched his head, his favorite way of assisting reflection.

"That's just what that young critter Fleet meant. What a cussed ole mule I was to kick up so! Ten chances to one but it will happen to me afore mornin'. Look here, Bill Cronk, you jist p'int out of this fiery furnace. You know yer failin', and there's too long and black a score agin you in t'other world for you to go to-night;" and Bill made a bee line for the west side.

Struggling off to windward through the choked streets for a little distance, Dennis ascended the side stairs of a tall building, in order to get more accurately the bearings of the fire. He now for the first time realized its magnitude, and was appalled. It appeared as if the whole south side must go. At certain points the very heavens seemed on fire. The sparks filled the air like flakes of fiery snow, and great blazing fragments of roofs, and boards from lumber-yards, sailed over his head, with the ill-omened glare of meteors. The rush and roar of the wind and flames were like the thunder of Niagara, and to this awful monotone accompaniment was added a Babel of sounds, — shrieks, and shouts of human voices, the sharp crash of falling buildings, and ever and anon heavy detonations, as the fire reached explosive material. As he looked down into the white upturned faces in the thronged streets, it seemed to him as if the people might be gathering for the last great day. Above all the uproar, the court-house bell could be heard, with its heavy, solemn clangor, no longer ringing alarm, but the city's knell.

But he saw that if he reached his own little room in time to save anything he must hasten. His course lay near the Art Building, the place so thronged with associations to him. An irresistible impulse drew him to it. It was evident that it must soon go, for an immense building to the southwest, on the same block was burning, and the walls were already swaying.

Suddenly a man rushed past him, and Mr. Ludolph put his pass key in the side door.

"Mr. Ludolph, it is not safe to enter," said Dennis.

"What are you doing here with your ill-omened face?" retorted his old employer, turning toward him a countenance terrible in its expression. As we have seen, anything that threatened Mr. Ludolph's interests, even that which most men bow before, as sickness and disaster, only awakened his anger; and his face was black with passion and distorted with rage.

The door yielded, and he passed in.

"Come back, quick, Mr. Ludolph, or you are lost!" cried Dennis at the door.

"I will get certain papers, though the heavens fall!" yelled back the infuriated man, with an oath.

Dennis heard an awful rushing sound in the air. He drew his hat over his face as he ran, crouching. Hot bricks rained around him, but fortunately he escaped.

When he turned to look, the Art Building was a crushed and blazing ruin. Sweet girlish faces that had smiled upon him from the walls, beautiful classical faces that had inspired his artist soul, stern Roman faces, that had made the past seem real, the human faces of gods and goddesses that made mythology seem not wholly a myth, and the white marble faces of the statuary, that ever reminded him of Christine, were now all blackened and defaced forever. But not of these he thought, as he shudderingly covered his eyes with his hands to shut out the vision; but of that terrible face that in the darkness had yelled defiance to heaven.

CHAPTER XLIII.

"CHRISTINE, AWAKE! FOR YOUR LIFE!"

DENNIS was too much stunned and bewildered to do more than instinctively work his way to the windward as the only point of safety, but the fire was now becoming so broad in its sweep that to do this was difficult. The awful event he had witnessed seemed partially to paralyze him; for he knew that the oath, hot as the scorching flames, was scarcely uttered before Mr. Ludolph's lips were closed forever. He and his ambitious dream perished in a moment, and he was summoned to the other world to learn what his proud reason scoffed at in this.

For a block or more Dennis was passively borne along by the rushing mob. Suddenly a voice seemed to shout almost in his ear, "The north side is burning!" and he started as from a dream. The thought of Christine flashed upon him, perishing perhaps in the flames. He remembered that now she had no protector, and that he for the moment had forgotten her; though in truth he had never imagined that she could be imperilled by the burning of the north side.

In an agony of fear and anxiety he put forth every effort of which he was capable, and tore through the crowd as if mad. There was no way of getting across the river now save by the La Salle Street tunnel. Into this dark passage he plunged with multitudes of others. It was indeed as near Pandemonium as any earthly condition could be. Driven forward by the swiftly pursuing flames, hemmed in on every side, a shrieking, frenzied, terror-stricken throng rushed into the black cavern. Every moral grade was represented there. Those who led abandoned lives were plainly recognizable, their guilty consciences finding expression in their livid faces. These jostled the refined and delicate lady, who, in the awful democracy of the hour, brushed against thief and harlot. Little children wailed for their lost parents, and many were trampled underfoot. Parents cried for their children, women shrieked for their husbands, some praying, many cursing with oaths as hot as the flames that crackled near. Multitudes were in no other costumes than those in which they had sprung from their beds. Altogether it was a strange, incongruous, writhing mass of humanity, such as the world had never looked upon, pouring into what might seem, in its horrors, the mouth of hell.

As Dennis entered the utter darkness, a confused roar smote his ear that might have appalled the stoutest heart, but he was now oblivious to everything save Christine's danger. With set teeth he put his shoulder against the living mass and pushed with the strongest till he emerged into the glare of the north side. Here, escaping somewhat from the throng, he made his way rapidly to the Ludolph mansion, which to his joy he found was still considerably to the windward of the fire. But he saw that from the southwest another line of flame was bearing down upon it.

The front door was locked, and the house utterly dark. He rang the bell furiously, but there was no response. He walked around under the window and shouted, but the place remained as dark and silent as a tomb. He pounded on the door, but its massive thickness scarcely admitted of a reverberation.

"They must have escaped," he said; "but, merciful heaven! there must be no uncertainty in this case. What shall I do?"

The windows of the lower story were all strongly guarded and hopeless, but one opening on the balcony of Christine's studio seemed practicable if it could be reached. A half-grown elm swayed its graceful branches over the balcony, and Dennis knew the tough and fibrous nature of this tree. In the New-England woods of his early home he had learned to climb for nuts like a squirrel, and so with no great difficulty he mounted the trunk and dropped from an overhanging branch to the point he sought. The window was down at the top, but the lower sash was fastened. He could see the catch by the light of the fire. He broke the pane of glass nearest it, hoping that the crash might awaken Christine, if she were still there. But after the clatter died away there was no sound. He then noisily raised the sash and stepped in.

What a rush of memories came over him as he looked around the familiar place! There was the spot on which he had stood and asked for the love that he had valued more than life. There stood the easel on which, through Christine's gifted touch, his painted face had pleaded with scarcely less eloquence, till he blotted it out with his own hand. In memory of it all his heart again failed him, and he sighed, "She will never love me."

But there was no time for sentiment. He called loudly: "Miss Ludolph, awake! awake! for your life!"

There was no answer. "She must be gone," he said. The front room, facing toward the west, he knew to be her sleeping-apartment. Going through the passage, he knocked loudly, and called again; but in the silence that followed he heard his own watch tick, and his heart beat. He pushed the door open with the feeling of one profaning a shrine, and looked timidly in. Even in that thrilling hour of peril and anxiety, his eye was enraptured by the beauty of the room. Not only was it furnished with the utmost luxuriance, but everything spoke of a quaint and cultured taste, from the curious marble clock and bronze on the mantel, even to the pattern of the Turkey carpet on which the glare of the fire, as it glinted through the shutters, played faintly. One of the most marked features, however, was an exquisite life-size statue of Diana at the foot of the bed, grasping her bow with one hand, and in the act of seizing an arrow with the other, as if aroused to self-defence. When Dennis first saw it, he was so startled by its lifelike attitude that he stepped back into the passage. But, with all the beauty of the room, it was utterly pagan; not a single thing suggested Christian faith or a knowledge of the true God. With the exception of its modern air, it might just as well have been the resting-place of a Greek or Roman maiden of rank.

Reassured, he timidly advanced again, and then for the first time, between the two marble statuettes holding back the curtains of the bed, saw Christine, but looking more white and deathlike than the marble itself.

She lay with her face toward him. Her hair of gold, unconfined, streamed over the pillow; one fair round arm, from which her night-robe had slipped back, was clasped around her head, and a flickering ray of light, finding access at the window, played upon her face and neck with the strangest and most weird effect.

So deep was her slumber that she seemed dead, and Dennis, in his overwrought state, thought that she was. For a moment his heart stood still, and his tongue was paralyzed. A distant explosion aroused him. Approaching softly he said, in an awed whisper (he seemed powerless to speak louder), "Miss Ludolph! — Christine!"

But the light of the coming fire played and flickered over the still, white face, that never before had seemed so strangely beautiful.

"Miss Ludolph! — O Christine, awake!" cried Dennis, louder.

To his wonder and unbounded perplexity, he saw the hitherto motionless lips wreathe themselves into a lovely smile, but otherwise there was no response, and the ghostly light played and flickered on, dancing on temple, brow, and snowy throat, and clasping the white arm in wavy circlets of gold. It was all so weird and strange that he was growing superstitious, and losing faith in his own senses. He could not know that she was under the influence of an opiate, and that his voice of all others could, like a faint echo, find access to her mind so deeply sunk in lethargy.

But a louder and nearer explosion, like a warning voice, made him wholly desperate; and he roughly seized her hand, determining to dispel the illusion, and learn the truth at once.

Christine's blue eyes opened wide with a bewildered stare; a look of the wildest terror came into them, and she started up and shrieked, "Father! father!"

Then turning toward the as yet unknown invader, she cried, piteously: "Oh, spare my life! Take everything; I will give you anything you ask, only spare my life."

She evidently thought herself addressing a ruthless robber.

Dennis retreated toward the door the moment she awakened; and this somewhat reassured her.

In the firm, quiet tone that always calms excitement he replied, "I only ask you to give me your confidence, Miss Ludolph, and to join with me, Dennis Fleet, in my effort to save your life."

"Dennis Fleet! Dennis Fleet! save my life! O ye gods, what does it all mean?" and she passed her hand in bewilderment across her brow, as if to brush away the wild fancies of a dream.

"Miss Ludolph, as you love your life, arouse yourself and escape! The city is burning!"

"I don't believe it!" she cried, in an agony of terror

and anger. "Leave the room! How dare you! You are not Dennis Fleet; he is a white man, and you are black! You are an impostor! Leave quick, or my father will come and take your life! Father! father!"

Dennis without a word stepped to the window, tore aside the curtain, threw open the shutters, and the fire filled the room with the glare of noonday. At that moment an explosion occurred which shook the very earth. Everything rattled, and a beautiful porcelain vase fell crashing to the floor.

Christine shrieked and covered her face with her hands.

Dennis approached the bedside, and said in a gentle, firm tone that she knew to be his: "Miss Ludolph, I *am* Mr. Fleet. My face is blackened through smoke and dust, as is every one's out in the streets to-night. You know something of me, and I think you know nothing dishonorable. Can you not trust me? Indeed you must; your life depends upon it!"

"Oh, pardon me, Mr. Fleet!" she cried, eagerly. "I am not worthy of this, but now that I know you, I do trust you from the depth of my soul!"

"Prove it then by doing just as I bid you," he replied, in a voice so firm and prompt that it seemed almost stern. Retreating to the door, he continued: "I give you just five minutes in which to make your toilet and gather a light bundle of your choicest valuables. Dress in woollen throughout, and dress warmly. I will see that the servants are aroused. Your father is on the south side, and cannot reach you. You must trust in God and what I can do for you."

"I must trust to you *alone*," she said. "Please send my maid to me."

Mr. Ludolph had sipped his wine during the evening, and his servants had sipped, in no dainty way, something stronger, and therefore had not awakened readily. But the uproar in the streets had aroused them, and Dennis found them scuttling down the upper stairs in a half-clad state, each bearing a large bundle, which had been made up without regard to *meum* and *tuum*.

"Och, murther! is the wourld burning up?" cried the cook.

"Be still, ye howlin' fool," said the cool and travelled maid. "It's only von big fire!"

"Go to your mistress and help her, quick!" cried Dennis.

"Go to my meestress! I go to de street and save my life."

"O Janette!" cried Christine. "Come and help me!"

"I am meeserable zat I cannot. I must bid mademoiselle quick adieu," said the heartless creature, still keeping up the veneer of French politeness.

Dennis looked through the upper rooms and was satisfied that they were empty. Suddenly a piercing shriek from Christine sent him flying to her room. As he ran he heard her cry, "O Mr. Fleet! come! help!"

To go back a little (for on that awful night events marched as rapidly as the flames, and the experience of years was crowded into hours, and that of hours into moments), Christine had sought as best she could to obey Dennis's directions, but she was sadly helpless, having been trained to a foolish dependence on her maid. She had accomplished but little when she heard a heavy step in the room. Looking up, she saw a strange man regarding her with an evil eye.

"What do you want?" she faltered.

"You, for one thing, and all you have got, for another," was the brutal reply.

"Leave this room!" she cried, in a voice she vainly tried to render firm.

"Not just yet," he answered, with a satanic grin. She sought to escape by him with the loud cry that Dennis heard, but the ruffian planted his big grimy hand in the delicate frill of her night-robe where it clasped her throat, and with a coarse laugh said: "Not so fast, my dainty!"

Trembling and half fainting (for she had no physical courage), she cried for Dennis, and never did knightly heart respond with more brave and loving throb to the cry of helpless woman than his. He came with almost the impetus of a thunderbolt, and the man, startled, looked around, and catching a glimpse of Dennis's blazing eyes, dropped his hold on Christine, and shrunk and cowered from the blow he could not avert. Before his hand could instinctively reach the pistol it sought, there was a thud, and he fell like a log to the floor. Then, springing upon him, Dennis took away his weapons, and, seizing him by the collar of his coat, dragged him backward downstairs and thrust him into the street. Pointing his own pistol at him, he said, "If you trouble us again, I will shoot you like a dog!"

The villain slunk off, and finding some kindred spirits sacking a liquor-store not far off, he joined the orgy, seeking to drown his rage in rum, and he succeeded so effectually that he lay in the gutter soon after. The escaping multitude trampled over him, and soon the fire blotted out his miserable existence, as it did that of so many who rendered themselves powerless by drink.

When Dennis returned he found Christine panting helplessly on a chair.

"Oh, dress! dress!" he cried. "We have not a moment to spare."

The sparks and cinders were falling about the house, a perfect storm of fire. The roof was already blazing, and smoke was pouring down the stairs.

At his suggestion she had at first laid out a heavy woollen

dress and Scotch plaid shawl. She nervously sought to put on the dress, but her trembling fingers could not fasten it over her wildly throbbing bosom. Dennis saw that in the terrible emergency he must act the part of a brother or husband, and springing forward he assisted her with the dexterity he had learned in childhood.

Just then a blazing piece of roof, borne on the wings of the gale, crashed through the window, and in a moment the apartment, that had seemed like a beautiful casket for a still more exquisite jewel, was in flames.

Hastily wrapping Christine in the blanket shawl, he snatched her, crying and wringing her hands, into the street.

Holding his hand she ran two or three blocks with all the speed her wild terror prompted; then her strength began to fail, and she pantingly cried that she could run no longer. But this rapid rush carried them out of immediate peril, and brought them into the flying throng pressing their way northward and westward. Wedged into the multitude they could only move on with it in the desperate struggle forward. But fire was falling about them like a meteoric shower.

Suddenly Christine uttered a sharp cry of pain. She had stepped on a burning cinder, and then realized for the first time, in her excitement, that her feet were bare.

"Oh, what shall I do?" she cried piteously, limping and leaning heavily on Dennis's arm.

"Indeed, Miss Ludolph, from my heart I pity you."

"Can you save me? Oh, do you think you can save me?" she moaned, in an agony of fear.

"Yes, I feel sure I can. At any rate I shall not leave you;" and taking her a little out of the jostling crowd he knelt and bound up the burned foot with his handkerchief. A little farther on they came to a shoe-store with doors open and owners gone. Almost carrying Christine into it, for her other foot was cut and bleeding, he snatched down a pair of boy's stout gaiters, and wiping with another handkerchief the blood and dust from her tender little feet, he made the handkerchiefs answer for stockings, and drew the shoes on over them.

In the brief moment so occupied, Christine said, with tears in her eyes: "Mr. Fleet, how kind you are! How little I deserve all this!"

He looked up with a happy smile, and she little knew that her few words amply repaid him.

There was a crash in the direction of the fire. With a cry of fear, Christine put out her hands and clung to him.

"Oh, we shall perish! Are you not afraid?"

"I tremble for you, Miss Ludolph."

"Not for yourself?"

"No! why should I? I am safe. Heaven and mother are just beyond this tempest."

"I would give worlds for your belief."

"Come quick!" cried he, and they joined the fugitives, and for a half-hour pressed forward as fast as was possible through the choked streets, Dennis merely saying an encouraging word now and then. Suddenly she felt herself carried to one side, and falling to the ground with him. In a moment he lifted her up, and she saw with sickening terror an infuriated dray-horse plunging through the crowd, striking down men, women, and children.

"Are you hurt?" he asked, gently, passing his arm around her and helping her forward, that they might not lose a single step.

"Awful! Awful!" she said, in a low, shuddering tone.

The dreadful scenes and the danger were beginning to overpower her.

A little farther on they reached an avenue to the north-west through which Dennis hoped to escape. But they could make but little headway through the dense masses of drays, carriages, and human beings, and at last everything came to a dead lock. Their only hope was to stand in their place till the living mass moved on again.

Strange, grotesque, and sad beyond measure were the scenes by which they were surrounded. By the side of the aristocratic Christine, now Baroness Ludolph, stood a stout Irishwoman, hugging a grunting, squealing pig to her breast. A little in advance a hook-nosed spinster carried in a cage a hook-nosed parrot that kept discordantly crying, "Polly want a cracker." At Dennis's left a delicate lady of the highest social standing clasped to her bare bosom a babe that slept as peacefully as in the luxurious nursery at home. At her side was a little girl carrying as tenderly a large wax doll. A diamond necklace sparkled like a circlet of fire around the lady's neck. Her husband had gone to the south side, and she had had but time to snatch this and her children. A crowd of obscene and profane rowdies stood just behind them, and with brutal jest and coarse laughter they passed around a whiskey-bottle. One of these roughs caught a glimpse of the diamond necklace, and was putting forth his blackened hand to grasp it, when Dennis pointed the captured pistol at him and said, "This is law now!"

The fellow slunk back.

Just before them was a dray with a corpse half covered with a blanket. The family sat around crying and wringing their hands, and the driver stood in his seat, cursing and gesticulating for those in advance to move on. Some moments passed, but there was no progress. Dennis became very anxious, for the fire was rapidly approaching, and the sparks were falling like hail. Every few moments some woman's dress was ablaze, or some one was struck by the flying brands, and shrieks for help were heard on every side. Christine, being clad in woollen, escaped this peril in part. She stood at Dennis's side trembling like a leaf, with her hands over her face to shut out the terrible sights.

At last the driver, fearing for his life, jumped off his dray and left all to their fate. But a figure took his place that thrilled Dennis's heart with horror.

There on the high seat stood Susie Winthrop, — rather Mrs. Leonard. The light of insanity glowed in her eyes; her long hair swept away to the north, and turning toward the fiery tempest she bent forward as if looking for some one. But after a moment she sadly shook her head, as if she had sought in vain. Suddenly she reached out her white arms toward the fire, and sung, clear and sweet above the horrid din: —

> "O burning flakes of fiery snow,
> Bury me too, bury me deep;
> My lover sleeps thy banks below;
> Fall on me, that I may sleep!"

At this moment a blazing brand fell upon the horses' heads; they started forward, and the crazed lady fell over on the corpse below. The animals being thoroughly terrified turned sharp around on the sidewalk, and tore their way right toward the fire, trampling down those in their track, and so vanished with their strangely assorted load.

Dennis, fearing to stay any longer where he was, determined to follow in their wake and find a street leading to the north less choked, even though it might be nearer the fire, and so with his trembling companion he pressed forward again.

Two blocks below he found one comparatively clear, but in terrible proximity to the conflagration. Indeed, the houses were burning on each side, but the street seemed clear of flame. He thought that by swiftly running they could get through. But Christine's strength was fast failing her, and just as they reached the middle of the block a tall brick building fell across the street before them! Thus their only path of escape was blocked by a blazing mass of ruins that it would have been death to cross.

They seemed hemmed in on every side, and Dennis groaned in agony.

Christine looked for a moment at the impassable fiery barrier, then at Dennis, in whose face and manner she read unutterable sympathy for herself, and the truth flashed upon her.

With a piercing shriek she fainted dead away in his arms.

CHAPTER XLIV.

ON THE BEACH.

IN the situation of supreme peril described in the last chapter, Dennis stood a second helpless and hopeless. Christine rested a heavy burden in his arms, happily unconscious. Breathing an agonized prayer to heaven, he looked around for any possibility of escape. Just then an express-wagon was driven furiously toward them, its driver seeking his way out by the same path that Dennis had chosen. As he reached them the man saw the hopeless obstruction, and wheeled his horses. As he did so, quick as thought, Dennis threw Christine into the bottom of the wagon, and, clinging to it, climbed into it himself. He turned her face downward from the fire, and, covering his own, he crouched beside her, trusting all now to God.

The driver urged his horses toward the lake, believing that his only chance. They tore away through the blazing streets. The poor man was soon swept from his seat and perished, but his horses rushed madly on till they plunged into the lake.

At the sound of water Dennis lifted his head and gave a cry of joy. It seemed that the hand of God had snatched them from death. Gently he lifted Christine out upon the sands and commenced bathing her face from the water that broke in spray at his feet. She soon revived and looked around. In a voice full of awe and wonder she whispered, "Ah! there is another world and another life, after all."

"Indeed there is, Miss Ludolph," said Dennis, supporting her on his arm and bending over her, "but, thanks to a merciful Providence, you are still in this one."

"How is it?" she said, with a bewildered air. "I do not understand. The last I remember, we were surrounded by fire, you were despairing, and it seemed that I died."

"You fainted, Miss Ludolph. But God as by a miracle brought us out of the furnace, and for the present we are safe." After she had sufficiently rallied from her excessive exhaustion and terror, he told her how they escaped.

"I see no God in it all," she said; "only a most fortunate opportunity, of which you, with great nerve and presence of mind, availed yourself. To you alone, again and again this dreadful night, I owe my life."

"God uses us as His instruments to do His will. The light will come to you by and by, and you will learn a better wisdom."

"In this awful conflagration the light has come. On every side I see as in letters of fire, 'There is no God.' If it were otherwise these scenes would be impossible. And any being permitting or causing the evils and crimes this dreadful night has witnessed, I shall fear and hate beyond the power of language to express."

She uttered these words sitting on the sands with multitudes of others, her face (from which Dennis had washed the dust and smoke) looking in the glare so wan and white that he feared, with a sickening dread, that through exposure, terror, or some of the many dangers by which they were surrounded, she might pass into the future world with all her unbelief and spiritual darkness. He yearned over her with a solicitude and pity that he could not express. She seemed so near, — indeed he could feel her form tremble, as he knelt beside her, and supported her by his arm, —and yet, in view of her faithless state, how widely were they separated! Should any one of the many perils about them quench the little candle of her life, which even now flickered faintly, where in the wide universe could he hope to meet her again? God can no doubt console His children and make up to them every loss, but the passionate heart, with its intense human love, clings to its idol none the less.

Dennis saw that the fire would probably hem them in on the beach for the remainder of the night and the following day. He determined therefore in every way possible to beguile the weary, perilous hours, and, if she would permit it, to lead her thoughts heavenward. Hence arose from time to time conversations, to which, with joy, he found Christine no longer averse. Indeed, she often introduced them.

Chafing her hands, he said in accents of the deepest sympathy, "How I pity you, Miss Ludolph! It must indeed be terrible to possess your thoughtful mind, to realize these scenes so keenly, and yet have no faith in a Divine Friend. I cannot explain to you the mystery of evil, — why it came, or why it exists. Who can? I am but one of God's little children, and only know with certainty that my Heavenly Father loves and will take care of me."

"How do you know it?" she asked, eagerly.

"In several ways. Mainly because I feel it."

"It all seems so vague and unreal," she sighed, dreamily. "There is nothing certain, assured. There is no test by which I can at once know the truth."

"That does not prevent the truth from existing. That some are blind is no proof that color does not exist."

"But how can you be sure there is a God? You never saw Him."

"I do not see the heat that scorches us, but I feel it, and know it exists."

"But I feel the heat the same as yourself, and I have no consciousness of a Divine Being."

"That does not take away my consciousness that He is my Saviour and Friend. As yet you are spiritually dead. If you were physically dead, you would not feel the heat of this fire."

"Oh, it is all mystery, — darkness," she cried, piteously.

The sun had now risen quite above the waters of the lake, but seen through the lurid smoke which swept over its face, it seemed like one of the great red cinders that were continually sailing over their heads. In the frightful glare, the transition from night to day had scarcely been noted. The long, narrow beach was occupied by thousands of fugitives, who were hemmed in on every side. On the south was the river, skirted with fire, while opposite, on the west, the heat was almost intolerable; on the east were the cold waves of the lake, and on the north a burning pier that they could not cross. Their only hope was to cling to that narrow line where fire and water mingled, and with one element to fight the other. Here again was seen the mingling of all classes which the streets and every place of refuge witnessed. Judges, physicians, statesmen, clergymen, bankers, were jostled by roughs and thieves. The laborer sat on the sand with his family, side by side with the millionnaire and his household. The poor debauched woman of the town moaned and shivered in her scant clothing, at a slight remove from the most refined Christian lady. In the unparalleled disaster, all social distinctions were lost, levelled like the beach on which the fugitives cowered. From some groups was heard the voice of prayer; from others, bitter wailings and passionate cries for lost members of the family; others had saved quantities of vile whiskey, if nothing else, and made the scene more ghastly by orgies that seemed not of earth. Added to the liquor, were the mad excitement and recklessness which often seize the depraved classes on such occasions. They committed excesses that cannot be mentioned, — these drunken, howling, fighting wretches. Obscene epitnets and words fell around like blows. And yet all were so occupied with their own misfortunes, sufferings, and danger, as scarcely to heed their neighbors, unless these became very violent.

Upon this heterogeneous mass of humanity the fire rained down almost as we imagine it to have fallen upon the doomed cities of the plain, and the hot breath of the flames scorched the exposed cheek and crisped even eyebrows and hair. Sparks, flakes, cinders, pieces of roof, and fiery pebbles seemed to fill the air, and often cries and shrieks announced that furniture and bedding which had been dragged thither, and even the clothing of women and children, were burning. Added to all the other terrors of the scene was the presence of large numbers of horses and cattle, snorting and plunging in their fright and pain.

But the sound that smote Dennis's heart with the deepest commiseration was the continuous wail of helpless little children, many of them utterly separated from parents and friends, and in the very agony of fear.

He greatly dreaded the effect of these upon Christine, knowing how, in the luxurious past, she had been shielded from every rough experience. But she at length rallied into something like composure. Her constitution was elastic and full of vitality, and after escaping from immediate danger she again began to hope. Moreover, to a degree that even she could not understand, his presence was a source of strength and courage, and her heart clung to him with desperate earnestness, believing him the sole barrier against immediate death, and (what she dreaded scarcely less) a lonely, wretched existence, should her life be spared.

Though he never lost sight of her for a moment, and kept

continually wetting her hair and person, he found time to render assistance to others, and, by carrying his hat full of water here and there, extinguished many a dangerous spark. He also, again and again, snatched up little children from under the trampling hoofs of frightened horses.

As she watched him, so self-forgetful and fearless, she realized more and more vividly that he was sustained and animated by some mighty principle that she knew nothing of, and could not understand. The impression grew upon her that he was right and she wrong. Though it all remained in mystery and doubt, she could not resist the logic of true Christian action.

But as the day advanced the flames grew hotter, and their breath more withering. About noon Dennis noticed that some shanties on the sand near them were in danger of catching fire and perilling all in that vicinity. Therefore he said, "Miss Ludolph, stay here where I leave you for a little time, so that I may know just where to find you."

"Oh, do not leave me!" she pleaded; "I have no one in the wide world to help me except you."

"I shall not be beyond call. You see those shanties there; if possible we must keep them from burning, or the fire will come too near for safety." Then, starting forward, he cried, "Who will volunteer to keep the fire back? All must see that if those buildings burn we shall be in danger."

Several men stepped forward, and with hats and anything that would hold water they began to wet the old rookeries. But the fiery storm swooped steadily down on them, and their efforts were as futile as if they had tried to beat back the wind. Suddenly a mass of flame leaped upon the buildings, and in a moment they were all ablaze.

"Into the lake, quick!" cried Dennis, and all rushed for the cool waters.

Lifting Christine from the sand, and passing his arm

around her trembling, shivering form, he plunged through the breakers, and the crowd pressed after him. Indeed they pushed him so far out in the cold waves that he nearly lost his footing, and for a few moments Christine lost hers altogether, and added her cries to those of the terror-stricken multitude. But pushing in a little nearer the shore, he held her firmly and said, with the confidence that again inspired hope: "Courage, Miss Ludolph. With God's help I will save you yet."

Even as she clung to him in the water, she looked into his face. He was regarding her so kindly, so pitifully, that a great and generous impulse, the richest, ripest fruit of her human love, throbbed at her heart, and faltered from her lips,—"Mr. Fleet, I am not worthy of this risk on your part. If you will leave me you can save your own life, and your life is worth so much more than mine!"

True and deep must have been the affection that could lead Christine Ludolph to say such words to any human being. There was a time when, in her creed, all the world existed but to minister to her. But she was not sorry to see the look of pained surprise which came into Dennis's face and to hear him say, very sadly: "Miss Ludolph, I did not imagine that you could think me capable of that. I had the good fortune to rescue Miss Brown last night, at greater peril than this, and do you think I would leave you?"

"You are a true knight, Mr. Fleet," she said, humbly, "and the need or danger of every defenceless woman is alike a sacred claim upon you."

Dennis was about to intimate that, though this was true in knightly creed, still among all the women in the world there might be a preference, when a score of horses, driven before the fire, and goaded by the burning cinders, rushed down the beach, into the water, right among the human fugitives.

Again went up the cry of agony and terror. Some were

no doubt stricken down not to rise again. In the *mêlée* Dennis pushed out into deeper water, where the frantic animals could not plunge upon him. A child floated near, and he snatched it up. As soon as the poor brutes became quiet, clasping Christine with his right arm and holding up the child with the other, he waded into shallow water.

The peril was now perhaps at its height, and all were obliged to wet their heads, to keep even their hair from singeing. Those on the beach threw water on each other without cessation. Many a choice bit of property — it might be a piano, or an express-wagon loaded with the richest furs and driven to the beach as a place of fancied security — now caught fire, and added to the heat and consternation.

When this hour of extreme danger had passed, standing with the cold billows of the lake breaking round him, and the billows of fire still rolling overhead, Dennis began to sing in his loud, clear voice: —

> "Jesus, lover of my soul,
> Let me to thy bosom fly,
> While the billows near me roll,
> While the tempest still is high."

Voice after voice joined in, some loud and strong, but others weak and trembling, — the pitiful cry of poor terror-stricken women to the only One who it seemed could help them in their bitter extremity. Never before were those beautiful words sung in such accents of clinging, touching faith. Its sweet cadence was heard above the roar of the flames and the breakers.

Christine could only cling weeping to Dennis.

When the hymn ceased, in harshest discord the voice of a half-drunken man grated on their ears.

"An' what in bloody blazes does yer Jasus burn us all up

for, I'd like to know. Sure an' he's no right to send us to hell before our time."

"Oh, hush! hush!" cried a dozen voices, shocked and pained.

"Divil a bit will I hush, sure; an' haven't I as good a right to have me say as that singin' parson!"

"You are an Irishman, are you not?" said Dennis, now venturing out of the water.

"Yis! what have ye got to say agin it?" asked the man, belligerent at once.

"Did you ever know an Irishman refuse to do what a lady asked of him?"

"Faith no, and I niver will."

"Then this lady, who is sick and suffering, asks you to please keep still, and I will be still also; so that's fair."

The Irishman scratched his head a moment, and said in a quieter tone, "Since ye spake so civil and dacent, I'll do as ye sez; and here's to the leddy's health;" and he finished a bottle of whiskey, which soon laid him out on the beach.

"Thank you! Thank you!" said grateful voices on every side.

Dennis found the mother of the child and gave it to her; and then causing Christine to sit down near the water, where he could easily throw it on her, he stood at her side, vigilant and almost tender in his solicitude. Her tears were falling very fast, and he presently stooped down and said, gently, "Miss Ludolph, I think the worst of the danger is over."

"O Mr. Fleet!" she whispered, "dreadful as it may seem to you, the words of that drunken brute there are nearer the language of my heart than those of your sweet hymn. How can a good God permit such creatures and evils to exist?"

"Again I must say to you," said Dennis, "that I cannot explain the mystery of evil. But I know this, God is superior to it; He will at last triumph over it. The Bible reveals Him to us as able and as seeking to deliver all who will trust Him and work with Him, and those who venture out upon His promises find them true. Miss Ludolph, this is not merely a matter of theory, argument, and belief. It is more truly a matter of experience. The Bible invites, 'Oh, taste and see that the Lord is good.' I have tasted and know He is. I have trusted Him for years, and He never failed me."

"You certainly have been sustained throughout this dreadful scene by a principle that I cannot understand, but I would give all the world to possess it."

"You may possess it, Miss Ludolph."

"How? how?" she asked, eagerly.

"Do you wish to believe as I do?"

"Yes, indeed; and yet my heart rebels against a God who permits, even if He does not cause, all this evil."

"Does it rebel against a Being who from first to last tries to save men from evil?"

"Tries! tries! what an expression to apply to a God! Why does He not do it in every case?"

"Because multitudes will not let Him."

"Oh, that is worse still! Surely, Mr. Fleet, you let your reason have nothing to do with your faith. How can a poor and weak being like myself prevent an Almighty one from doing what He pleases?"

"I am stronger than you, Miss Ludolph, and yet I could not have saved you to-night unless you had first trusted me, and then done everything in your power to further my efforts."

"But your power is human and limited, and you say God is all-powerful."

"Yes, but it is His plan and purpose never to save us against our will. He has made us in His own image and endowed us with reason, conscience, and a will to choose between good and evil. He appeals to these noble faculties from first to last. He has given us hearts, and seeks to win them by revealing His love to us. More than all, His Spirit, present in the world, uses every form of truth in persuading and making us willing to become His true children. So you see that neither on the one hand does God gather us up like drift-wood, nor does He on the other drag us at His chariot wheels, unwilling captives, as did those who, at various times, have sought to overrun the world by force. God seeks to conquer the world by the might of the truth, by the might of love."

Christine was hanging with the most eager interest on his words. Suddenly his eyes, which had expressed such a kindly and almost tender interest in her, blazed with indignation, and he darted up the beach. Turning around she saw, at some little distance, a young woman most scantily clad, clinging desperately to a bundle which a large, coarse man was trying to wrench from her. The wretch, finding that he could not loosen her hold, struck her in the face with such force that she fell stunned upon the ground, and the bundle flew out of her hand. He eagerly snatched it up, believing it to contain jewelry. Before he could escape he was confronted by an unexpected enemy. But Dennis was in a passion, and withal weak and exhausted, while his adversary was cool, and an adept in the pugilistic art. The two men fought savagely, and Christine, forgetting herself in her instinctive desire to help Dennis, was rushing to his side, crying, "If there is a man here worthy of the name, let him strike for the right!" but before she and others could reach the combatants the thief had planted his fist on Dennis's temple. Though the latter partially parried the blow, it fell with such force as to extend him senseless on the earth. The villain, with a shout of derision, snatched up the bundle and dashed off apparently toward the fire. There was but a feeble attempt made to follow him. Few understood the case, and indeed scenes of violence and terror had become so common that the majority had grown apathetic, save in respect to their personal well-being.

Christine lifted the pale face, down which the blood was trickling, into her lap, and cried, in a tone of indescribable anguish, "Oh, he is dead! he is dead!"

"Oh, no, miss; he is not dead, I guess," said a good-natured voice near. "Let me bring a hatful of water from the lake, and that'll bring him to."

And so it did. Dennis opened his eyes, put his hand to his head, and then looked around. But when he saw Christine bending over him with tearful eyes, and realized how tenderly she had pillowed his aching head, he started up with a deep flush of pleasure, and said: "Do not be alarmed, Miss Ludolph; I was only stunned for a moment. Where is the thief?"

"Oh, they let him escape," said Christine, indignantly.

"Shame!" cried Dennis, regaining his feet rather unsteadily.

"Wal, stranger, a good many wrongs to-night must go unrighted."

The poor girl who had been robbed sat on the sands swaying back and forth, wringing her hands, and crying that she had lost everything.

"Well, my poor friend, that is about the case with the most of us. We may be thankful that we have our lives. Here is my coat,' for her shoulders and neck were bare; "and if you will come down to the lake this lady," pointing to Christine, "will bathe the place where the brute struck you."

"Shall I not give up my shawl to some of these poor creatures?" asked Christine.

"No, Miss Ludolph, I do not know how long we may be

kept here; but I fear we shall suffer as much from cold as from heat, and your life might depend upon keeping warm."

"I will do whatever you bid me," she said, looking gratefully at him.

"That is the way to feel and act toward God," he said, gently.

But with sudden impetuosity she answered: "I cannot. See what He has just permitted to happen before my eyes. Right has not triumphed, but the foulest wrong."

"You do not see the end, Miss Ludolph."

"But I must judge from what I see."

After she had bathed the poor girl's face, comforted and reassured her, Dennis took up the conversation again and found Christine eager to listen. Pausing every few moments to throw water over his companion, he said: "Faith is beyond reason, beyond knowledge, though not contrary to them. You are judging as we do not judge about the commonest affairs, — from a few isolated, mysterious facts, instead of carefully looking the subject all over. You pass by what is plain and well understood to what is obscure, and from that point seek to understand Christianity. Every science has its obscure points and mysteries, but who begins with those to learn the science? Can you ignore the fact that millions of highly intelligent people, with every motive to know the truth, have satisfied themselves as to the reality of our faith? Our Bible system of truth may contain much that is obscure, even as the starry vault has distances that no eye or telescope can penetrate, and as this little earth has mysteries that science cannot solve, but there is enough known and understood to satisfy us perfectly. Let me assure you, Miss Ludolph, that Christianity rests on broad truths, and is sustained by arguments that no candid mind can resist after patiently considering them."

She shook her head, silenced perhaps, but not satisfied.

CHAPTER XLV.

"PRAYER IS MIGHTY." CHRISTINE A CHRISTIAN.

THE day was now declining, and the fire in that part of the city opposite them had so spent itself that they were beginning to have a little respite from immediate danger. The fiery storm of sparks and cinders was falling mostly to the northward.

Dennis now ventured to sit down almost for the first time, for he was wearied beyond endurance. The tremendous danger and excitements, and the consciousness of peril to the one most dear to him, had kept him alert long after he ought to have had rest, but over-taxed nature now asserted its rights, and the moment the sharp spur of danger was removed he was overpowered by sleep.

Christine spoke to him as he sat near, but even to her (a thing he could not have imagined possible) he returned an incoherent reply.

"My poor friend, you do indeed need rest," said she, in kindest accents.

He heard her voice like a sweet and distant harmony in a dream, swayed a moment, and would have fallen over in utter unconsciousness on the sands, had she not glided to his side and caught his head upon her lap.

In the heavy stupor that follows the utmost exhaustion, Dennis slept hour after hour. The rest of the day was a perfect blank to him. But Christine, partially covering and shading his face with the edge of her shawl, bent over him as patient in watching as he had been brave in her deliverance. It was beautiful to see the features once so cold and haughty, now sweet with more than womanly tenderness. There upon that desolate beach, cold, hungry, homeless, shelterless, she was happier than she had been for months. But she trembled as she thought of the future; everything was so uncertain. She seemed involved in a labyrinth of dangers and difficulties from which she could see no escape. She knew that both store and home had gone, and probably most, if not all, of her father's fortune. She felt that these losses might greatly modify his plans, and really hoped that they would lead him to remain in this country. She felt almost sure that he would not go back to Germany a poor man, and to remain in America was to give her a chance of happiness, and happiness now meant life with him over whom she bent. For a long time she had felt that she could give up all the world for him, but now existence would scarcely be endurable without him. In proportion to the slowness with which her love had been kindled was its intensity,— the steady, concentrated passion of a strong, resolute nature, for the first time fully aroused. All indecision passed from her mind, and she was ready to respond whenever he should speak; but woman's silence sealed her lips, and more than maiden delicacy masked her heart. While she bent over him with an expression that, had he opened his eyes, might have caused him to imagine for a moment that his sleep had been death, and he had wakened in heaven, yet he must needs awake to find that the look and manner of earth had returned. Her sensitive pride made her guarded even in expressing her gratitude, and she purposed to slip his head off upon her shawl whenever he showed signs of awakening, so that he might believe that the earth only had been his resting-place.

But now in his unconsciousness, and unnoted by all

around, indeed more completely isolated by the universal misery and apathy about her than she could have been in her own home, with a delicious sense of security, she bent her eyes upon him, and toyed daintily with the curling locks on his brow. Whatever the future might be, nothing should rob her of the strange, unexpected happiness of this opportunity to be near him, purchased at such cost.

As she sat there and saw the fire rush and roar away to the northward, and the sun decline over the ruins of her earthly fortune, she thought more deeply and earnestly of life than ever before. The long, heavy sleep induced by the opiate had now taken away all sense of drowsiness, and never had her mind been clearer. In the light of the terrible conflagration many things stood out with a distinctness that impressed her as nothing had ever done before. Wealth and rank had shrivelled to their true proportions, and she said, half aloud: —

"That which can vanish in a night in flame and smoke cannot belong to us, is not a part of us. All that has come out of the crucible of this fire is my character, myself. It is the same with Mr. Fleet; but, comparing his character with mine, how much richer he is! What if there is a future life, and we enter into it with no other possession than our character? and that which is called soul or spirit is driven forth from earth and the body as we have just been from our wealth and homes? I can no longer coolly and contemptuously ignore as superstition what he believes. He is not superstitious, but calm, fearless, and seemingly assured of something that as yet I cannot understand. One would think that there must be reality in his belief, for it sustains him and others in the greatest of trials. The hymn he sang was like a magnet introduced among steel filings mingled with this sand. The mere earth cannot move, but the steel is instinct with life. So, while many of us could not respond, others seemed inspired at the name of Jesus with new hope and courage, and cried to the Nazarene as if He could hear them. Why don't people cry for help to other good men who lived in the dim past, and whose lives and deeds are half myth and half truth? why to this one man only? for educated Catholics no longer pray to the saints."

Then her thoughts reverted to Mr. Ludolph.

"Poor father!" said she; "how will he endure these changes? We have not felt and acted toward each other as we ought. He is now probably anxious beyond measure, fearing that I perished in my sleep, and so I should have done, had it not been for this more than friend that I have so wronged. Oh, that I could make amends! I wonder, —oh, I wonder if he has any spark of love left for me? He seems kind, even tender, but he is so to every one, — he saved Miss Brown —"

But here a most violent interruption took place. Christine, in the complete absorption of her thoughts, had not noticed that a group of rough men and women near by, who had been drinking all day, had now become intoxicated and violent. They were pushing and staggering, howling and fighting, in reckless disregard of the comfort of others, and before she knew it she was in the midst of a drunken brawl. One rough fellow struck against her, and another trod on Dennis, who started up with a cry of pain. In a moment he comprehended the situation, and, snatching up Christine and the shawl, he pushed his way out of the *mêlée* with his right arm, the wretches striking at him and one another aimlessly in their fury; while both men and women used language that was worse than their blows. After a brief struggle, Dennis and Christine extricated themselves, and made their way northward up the beach till they found a place where the people seemed quiet.

Dennis's sudden awakening had revealed to him that his head had been pillowed, and it seemed such a kind and thoughtful act on Christine's part that he could scarcely believe it; at the same time he was full of shame and self-reproach that by his sleep he had left her unguarded, and he said: "Miss Ludolph, I hope you will pardon your recreant knight, who slept while you were in danger; but really I could not help it."

"It is I who must ask pardon," replied Christine, warmly. "After your superhuman exertions, your very life depended on rest. But I made a wretched watcher, — indeed I have lost confidence in myself every way. To tell the truth, Mr. Fleet, I was lost in thought, and with your permission I would like to ask you further about two things you said this morning. You asserted that you knew God loved you, and that Christianity was sustained by arguments that no candid mind could resist. What are those arguments? and how can you know such a comforting thing as the love of God?"

His eyes lighted up in his intense delight that she should again voluntarily recur to this subject, and he hoped that God was leading her to a knowledge of Him, and that he, in answer to his own and his mother's prayers, might be partially instrumental in bringing the light. Therefore he said, earnestly: "Miss Ludolph, this is scarcely the time and place to go over the evidences of Christianity. When in happy security I hope you may do this at your leisure, and am sure you will be convinced, for I believe that you honestly wish the truth. But there is no need that you should wait and look forward into the uncertain future for this priceless knowledge. The father will not keep his child waiting who tries to find him. God is not far from any one of us. When our Lord was on earth, He never repulsed those who sought Him in sincerity, and He is the true manifestation of God.

"Moreover," he continued, reverently, "God is now on earth as truly as when Christ walked the waves of Galilee, or stood with the life-giving word upon His lips at the grave of His friend Lazarus. The mighty Spirit of God now dwells among men to persuade, help, and lead them into all truth, and I believe He is guiding you. This Divine Spirit can act as directly on your mind as did Christ's healing hand when He touched blind eyes and they saw, and palsied bodies and they sprung into joyous activity."

Under his eager, earnest words, Christine's eyes also lighted up with hope, but after a moment her face became very sad, and she said, wearily, "Mystery! mystery! you are speaking a language that I do not understand."

"Can you not understand this: 'For God so loved the world, that He gave His only begotten Son, that whosoever believeth in Him should not perish, but have everlasting life'? and that the Bible tells us that His Son did, in very truth, die that we might live?"

"Yes, yes, I know that the Bible seems to teach all that, but there must be some mistake about it. Why should an all-powerful God take such a costly, indirect way of accomplishing His purpose when a word would suffice?"

"We will not discuss God's reasons; I think they are beyond us. But imagining the Bible story to be true, even though you do not believe it, is not the love of God revealed to us through His son, Jesus Christ?"

"Yes, it is the very extravagance of disinterested love. So much so that my reason revolts at it. It is contrary to all my ideas of Deity and power."

"Pardon me, Miss Ludolph, for saying it, but I think your ideas of Deity are borrowed more from mythology and human greatness than from the Bible. Let your reason stand aside a moment; this is not contrary to it, but beyond it. Imagining the Bible story true, can you not wish it true?

If the man who died on Calvary out of love for you and for us all is also God, would you fear to trust yourself to Him? Could you distrust One who loved you well enough to die for you?"

"No! no, indeed! if I only could believe it, no! But how can I ever be sure it is true? I am sure of nothing. I am not sure there is a God. I am not sure the Bible is more than human in its character. I feel as if my feet stood out upon those shifting waves, and as if there were nothing certain or stable."

"But in part you know the truth, Miss Ludolph, though you do not believe it, and I believe that the God of whom we have spoken *can directly reveal Himself to you* and make His truth as real to you as it is to me."

"Mr. Fleet," cried Christine, "if I could believe as you do, I should be the happiest of the happy, for I should feel that, however much I suffered in this brief life, in the existence beyond I should be more than compensated;" and covering her tearful face with her hands she moaned, as if it were wrung from her, "I have suffered so much, and there seemed no remedy!"

Dennis's feelings were also deeply touched, and the dew of sympathy gathered in his own eyes. In the gentlest accents he said, "Oh that you could trust that merciful, mighty One who invites all the heavy laden to come to Him for rest!"

She looked up and saw his sympathy, and was greatly moved. In faltering tones she said: "You feel for me, Mr. Fleet. You do not condemn me in my blindness and unbelief. I cannot trust Him, because I am not sure He exists. If there was such a God I would gladly devote my whole being to Him; but I trust *you*, and will do anything you say."

"Will you kneel on these sands with me in prayer to Him?" he asked, earnestly.

She hesitated, trembled, but at last said, "Yes."

He took her hand as if they were brother and sister, and they knelt together on the desolate beach. The glow of sunset was lost in the redder glow of the fire that smouldered all over the ruins, and still raged in the northwest, and the smoke and gathering gloom involved them in obscurity.

Though the weary, apathetic fugitives regarded them not, we believe that angelic forms gathered round, and that the heart of the Divine Father yearned toward His children.

When they rose, after a simple prayer from Dennis, in which he pleaded almost as a child might with an earthly father, Christine trembled like a leaf, and was very pale, but her face grew tearless, quiet, and very sad. Dennis still held her hand in the warm, strong grasp of sympathy. Gently she withdrew it, and said, in a low, despairing tone: "It is all in vain. There is no answer. Your voice has been lost in the winds and waves."

"Wait the King's time," said he, reverently.

"You addressed him as Father. Would a good father keep his child waiting?"

"Yes, sometimes He does; He is also King."

After a moment she turned to him the saddest face he ever looked upon, and said, gently, again giving him her hand, "Mr. Fleet, you have done your best for me, and I thank you all the same."

He was obliged to turn away to hide his feelings. Silently they again sat down on the beach together. Weariness and something like despair began to tell on Christine, and Dennis trembled when he thought of the long night of exposure before her. He bent his face into his hands and prayed as he had never prayed before. She looked at him wistfully, and knew he was pleading for her; but she now believed it was all in vain. The feeling grew upon her that belief or unbelief was a matter of education and temperment, and that the feelings of which Dennis spoke were but the deceptive emotions of our agitated hearts. To that degree that the Divine love seemed visionary and hopeless, she longed for him to speak of his own, if in truth it still existed, that she could understand and believe in. If during what remained of life she could only drink the sweetness of that, she felt it was the best she could hope for — and then the blank of nothingness.

But he prayed on, and with something of his mother's faith seemed at last, as it were, in the personal presence of Christ. With an importunity that would not be denied, he entreated for her who despaired at his side.

At last, putting her hand lightly on his arm, she said: "Mr. Fleet, waste no more time on me. From the groans I hear, some poor woman is sick or hurt. Perhaps you can do some real good by seeing to her needs."

He rose quietly, feeling that in some way God would answer, and that he must patiently wait.

Going up the beach a short distance he found a German woman lying just on the edge of the water. In answer to his questions, he learned from her broken English that she was sick and in pain. A sudden thought struck him. In seeking to help another, might not Christine find help herself, and in the performance of a good deed, might not the Author of all good reveal Himself? Returning to her, he said: "Miss Ludolph, the poor woman you have heard is sick and alone. She is German, and you can speak to her and comfort her as only a woman can."

Christine went at once, though with little confidence in her powers. Indeed it was, perhaps, the first visit of charity and mercy she had ever made. But she would have done anything he asked, and determined to do her best. She helped the poor creature farther up from the water, and then, taking her hands, spoke to her soothingly and gently in her native tongue.

"Heaven and all the angels bless your sweet face for taking pity on a poor lone body, and so they will too," is the free rendering of her grateful German.

"Would you please say a little prayer for a lone, sick body?" she asked, after a little while.

Christine hesitated a moment, and then thought: "Why not? if it will be of any comfort to the poor thing. It can do neither of us harm."

Dennis saw her kneel at the woman's side, lift her white face to heaven, and her lips move. Her attitude was unmistakably that of prayer. He could scarcely believe his eyes.

Her petition was brief and characteristic: "O God, — if there is a God, — help this poor creature!"

Then Dennis saw her start up and glance around in a strange, bewildered manner. Suddenly she clasped her hands and looked up with an ecstatic, thrilling cry: "There is! there is! God lives and loves me, I feel, I know, and therefore I may hope and live." Turning to the still raging flames, she exclaimed: "Burn on with your fiery billows, I do not fear you now! I am safe, safe forever! Oh, how can I ever love and praise Thee enough!"

Then, springing to Dennis's side, she took both his hands in hers, and said: "Mr. Fleet, you have saved my life again and again, and I am, oh, how grateful! but in leading me to this knowledge you have made me your debtor for evermore. God does live, and I believe now He loves even me."

As the glare of the fire fell on her face, he was awed and speechless at its expression. From its ecstatic joy and purity it seemed that the light of heaven, instead of her burning home, was illumining it.

At last he said, brokenly, "Thank God! thank God! my many, many prayers are answered!"

The look of love and gratitude she gave him will only find its counterpart in heaven, when the saved beam upon those who led them to the Saviour. The whole of her strong womanly soul, thoroughly aroused, was in her face, and it shone like that of an angel.

To Dennis, with the force of fulfilled prophecy, recurred his mother's words, and unconsciously he spoke them aloud:

"PRAYER IS MIGHTY."

CHAPTER XLVI.

CHRISTINE'S GRAVE.

AFTER a moment Christine returned to her charge and said, gently, "I think I can take better care of you now."

The poor woman looked at her in a bewildered way, half fearing she had lost her senses. But there was that in Christine's tone and manner now that went like sunlight and warmth to the heart, and in broadest German the grateful creature was soon blessing her again and again, and Christine felt that she was blessed beyond even her wildest dreams.

Dennis now felt that she must have food and rest. She appeared, in the ghostly light of the distant flames, so pale and spirit-like, that he almost feared she would slip away to heaven at once, and he began looking for some one stronger, older, and more suitable, to take her place. At a little distance farther north he at last found a stout German woman sitting with her two children on a large feather bed, the sole relic of her household goods. Dennis acquainted her with the case, and she soon took the matter out of his and Christine's hands in a very satisfactory way.

To the south and west opportunity of escape was utterly cut off; eastward were the waters of the lake, so that their only chance was to push northward. After making their way slowly for a short distance among the thickly scattered groups and the varied articles that had been dragged to the shore for safety, Dennis thought he heard a familiar voice.

"Dr. Arten!" he cried.

"Hallo! who wants me?" answered the good old physician, bustling up in rather incongruous costume, consisting of a dress coat, white vest, red flannel drawers, and a very soiled pair of slippers.

"O doctor! the very sight of you inspires hope and courage."

"Surely a young fellow like you can be in no want of those articles?"

"If he is lacking," cried Christine, "it must be for the reason that he has given hope and courage to every one he has met, and so has robbed himself."

"Heigho!" exclaimed the doctor, "you here?"

"Yes, thanks to the heroism of Mr. Fleet."

"Fleet, is that all you have saved from the fire?" asked the doctor, with a humorous twinkle, pointing to Christine.

"I am well satisfied," said Dennis, quietly, but with rising color.

"I should have perished, had not Mr. Fleet come to my rescue," continued Christine, warmly, glad of an opportunity to express a little of her gratitude.

The doctor turned his genial, humorous eye on her and said: "Don't be too grateful, Miss Ludolph; he is a young man, and only did his duty. Now if I had been so fortunate you might have been as grateful as you pleased."

It was Christine's turn to grow rather rosier than even the red fire warranted, but she said, "You would have your joke, doctor, if the world were burning up."

"Yes, and after it burned up," he replied. "What do you think of that, Miss Ludolph, with your German scepticism?"

Tears came in Christine's eyes, and she said, in a low tone, "I am glad to say that I have lost my German scepticism in the fire also."

"What!" cried the doctor, seizing both her hands in his hearty way. "Will you accept of our Christian superstition?"

"I think I have accepted your glorious Christian truth, and the thought makes me very happy."

"Well, now I can almost say, Praise God for the fire, though old Dr. Arten must commence again where the youngsters are who kick up their heels in their office all day."

With professional instinct he slipped his finger on Christine's pulse, then rummaged in his pocket and soon drew out some powders, and in his brusque way made her take one.

"Oh, how bitter!" she exclaimed.

"That is the way the ladies treat me," began the merry bachelor: "not an ounce of gratitude when I save their lives. But let a young fellow like Fleet come along and get them out of danger by mere brute strength, instead of my delicate, skilful way, and language breaks down with their thanks. Very well, I shall have compensation,—I shall present my bill before long. And now, young man, since you have set out to rescue my little friend here, you had better carry the matter through, for several reasons which I need not urge. Your best chance is to make your way northward, and then continue around to the west, where you can find food and shelter;" and with a hearty grasp of the hand, the brave, genial old man wished them "God speed!"

Dennis told him of the poor German woman, and then pushed on in the direction indicated. But Christine was growing weak and exhausted. At last they reached the Catholic cemetery. It was crowded with fugitives, and the fire to the northwest still cut off all escape, even if Christine's strength had permitted further exertion. It was now approaching midnight, and she said, wearily: "Mr. Fleet, I am very sorry, but I fear I cannot take another step. The powder Dr. Arten gave me strengthened me for a time, but its effect is passing away, and I feel almost paralyzed with fatigue. I am not afraid to stay here, or indeed anywhere now."

"It seems a very hard necessity that you should have to remain in such a place, Miss Ludolph, but I see no help for it. We are certainly as well off as thousands of others, and so I suppose ought not to complain."

"I feel as if I could never complain again, Mr. Fleet. I only hope my father is as safe and as well as we are. I cannot tell you how my heart goes out toward him now that I see everything in a different light. I have not been a true daughter, and I do long to make amends. He surely has escaped, don't you think?"

"Mr. Ludolph was possessed of unusual sagacity and prudence," said Dennis, evasively. "What any man could do, he could. And now, Miss Ludolph, I will try to find you a resting-place. There are such crowds here that I think we had better go nearer that side, where early in the evening the fire drove people away."

The cemetery had not been used of late years, and many of the bodies had been removed. This caused excavations here and there, and one of these from which the gathered leaves and grass had been burned, Dennis thought might answer for Christine's couch, as in the hollow of this vacant and nearly filled grave she would be quite sheltered from the wind, and the sand was still warm from the effects of the fire. To his surprise she made no objection.

"I am so weary that I can rest anywhere," she said, "and a grave is not to me what it was once."

He arranged her shawl so that it might be mattress, pillow, and covering, and wrapped her up.

"And how will you endure the long cold hours, my friend?" she asked, looking up most sympathetically.

"Thanks to your kindness, I had such a good sleep this afternoon that I feel strong and rested," he replied, with a smile.

"I fear you say so to put my mind at rest;" but even as she spoke her eyes closed and she went to sleep like a tired and trusting child. As with Dennis a few hours before, the limit of nature's endurance had been reached, and the wealthy, high-born Miss Ludolph, who on Sabbath night had slept in the midst of artistic elegance and luxury, now, on Monday night, rested in a vacant grave under the open and storm-gathering sky. Soon — to be accurate, at two o'clock on the morning of Tuesday — rain began to fall. But, with all the discomfort it brought, never had rain been more welcome.

Christine shivered in her sleep, and Dennis looked around vainly for some additional covering. The thronging fugitives were all in a similar plight, and their only course was simply to endure till some path of escape opened.

The night was indeed a long one to him. At first excitement and happiness kept him awake and unconscious of time and discomfort. But he soon felt how weary and hungry he was, for he had eaten nothing since his slight supper on Sabbath evening. The heat of the fire perceptibly lessened as the rain began falling, and without his coat Dennis was soon chilled to the bone. On every side he heard moans of discomfort, and he knew that he had far more reason to endure patiently than many near him. He tried to keep himself warm by walking around, but at last he grew too weary for that, and sat, a patient, cowering watcher, at the head of Christine's weird couch, listening sadly at times to the pitiful crying of little children and the sighs and groans of older sufferers.

At last the light of welcome day streaked the eastern horizon, and Christine opened her eyes in a bewildered way, but, on seeing him swaying backward and forward with half-closed eyes, sprung up and said, "And have you sat and watched there all the long night?"

"I hope you feel rested and better, Miss Ludolph," he replied, startled from drowsiness by her voice.

"It has been raining, too. I fear you are wet through. Oh, how much you must have suffered on my account!"

"I imagine you are as wet as I am, Miss Ludolph. This has been a very democratic experience for you. We are all about alike in this strange camping-ground."

"No; your kindness made me quite comfortable. Indeed, I never slept better. And you, without any coat or shelter, have watched patiently hour after hour."

"Well, you did as much for me yesterday afternoon, so we are quits."

"I think there is a great difference," she said. "And remember what a watcher I made; I let those drunken creatures run over you."

"I don't see how you could have helped it," said he, laughing. "That you should have cared for me as you did was a favor that I never expected," he added, blushing.

She blushed too, but made no reply; at the same time she was vexed with herself that she did not. Dennis, with a lover's blindness, misunderstood her silence, and thought that, as a friend, she was more grateful than he could wish, but he must speak in no other character.

Then he remembered that it would be dishonorable to urge his suit under the circumstances; it would be a source of inexpressible pain to her, with her strong sense of obligation, to put aside expressions of his deeper regard, and he resolved to avoid if possible any manifestations of his feelings. While she was dependent upon him he would act the part of a brother toward her, and if his human love could never find its consummation, he would bear his loss as patiently as possible. But in spite of himself a tinge of sadness and restraint came into his manner, and Christine sighed to herself, "If *he* only knew, and *I* only knew, just the truth, how much happier we might be!"

There was a general movement now in the strangely assorted multitude. The fire had swept everything away so completely on the north side that there were not hot blazing ruins to prevent crossing. Accordingly men came pouring over, looking for their families. On every side were cries of joy on recognition of those whom fear and terrible forebodings had buried under the blackened remains of once happy homes. But mingled with exclamations of joy were sobs and wails of anguish, as some now realized in the lapsing hours that absent members of the household were lost.

Christine looked in vain for her father; at last Dennis said: "Miss Ludolph, do you feel equal to the effort of crossing to the west side? You must be faint with hunger, and there only can we hope for help."

"Oh, yes! let us go at once, for your sake as well as mine;" for she saw that his long fasting and great fatigue had made him very haggard.

They urged their way across the burned district as fast as their exhausted state would permit, carefully avoiding burning brands that still lay in the street.

"I hope you will have patience with me in my slow progress," said Christine, "for I feel as I imagine Rip Van Winkle must have done, after his twenty years' nap."

"I think you have borne up heroically, Miss Ludolph," said Dennis, warmly.

"Oh, no! I am not in the least heroic, but I confess that I am very hungry. I never knew what hunger was before. Well, I can now appreciate what must often be the condition of the poor, and hope not to be so forgetful of them hereafter."

"I am glad to hear you say that you are hungry, Miss Ludolph, for it proves that with care you will rally after this dreadful exposure, and be your former self."

"Ah! Mr. Fleet, I hope I shall never be my old self again. I shudder when I think what I was when you awakened me that dreadful night."

"But I have feared," said he, ever avoiding any reference to his own services, "that, though you might escape the fire, the exposure would be greater than you could endure. I trembled for you last night when it began to rain, but could find no additional covering."

"No brother could be kinder or more thoughtful of me," she said, turning upon him a glad, grateful face.

"That is it," thought Dennis. "She hints to me what must be our relationship. She is the Baroness Ludolph, and is pledged to a future that I cannot share."

But as he saw her gratitude, he resolved all the more resolutely not to put it to the hard test of refusing his love. A little later he unconsciously sighed wearily, and she looked at him wistfully.

"Oh that I *knew* if he felt toward me as he once did!" she said to herself.

They now reached the unscathed streets of the west side, which were already thronged with fugitives as hungry and gaunt as themselves. Mingling with this great strange tide of weak, begrimed, hollow-eyed humanity, they at last reached Dr. Goodwin's beautiful church. Here already had begun the noble charity dispensed from that place during the days of want and suffering that followed.

CHAPTER XLVII.

SUSIE WINTHROP.

WAITING with multitudes of others, Christine and Dennis at last received an army biscuit (hard-tack in the soldier's vernacular) and a tin-cup of what resembled coffee. To him it was very touching to see how eagerly she received this coarse fare, proving that she was indeed almost famished. Too weak to stand, they sat down near the door on the sidewalk. A kind lady presently came and said, "If you have no place to go you will find it more comfortable in the church."

They gladly availed themselves of her permission, as the thronged street was anything but pleasant.

"Mr. Fleet," said Christine, "I am now going to take care of you in return for your care last night," and she led him up to a secluded part of the church by the organ, arranged some cushions on a seat, and then continued: "As I have obeyed you, so you must now be equally docile. Don't you dare move from that place till I call you;" and she left him.

He was indeed wearied beyond expression, and most grateful for a chance to rest. This refuge and the way it was secured seemed almost a heavenly experience, and he thought with deepest longing, "If we could always take care of each other, I should be perhaps too well satisfied with this earthly life."

When after a little time Christine returned he was sleeping as heavily as he had done before upon the beach, but the smile his last thought occasioned still rested on his face. For some little time she also sat near and rested, and her eyes sought his face as if a story were written there that she never could finish. Then she went to make inquiries after her father. But no one to whom she spoke knew anything about him.

Bread and other provisions were constantly arriving, but not fast enough to meet the needs of famishing thousands. Though not feeling very strong she offered her services, and was soon busily engaged. All present were strangers to her, but, when they learned from the inquiries for her father that she was Miss Ludolph, she was treated with deference and sympathy. But she assumed nothing, and as her strength permitted, during the day, she was ready for any task, even the humblest. She handed food around among the hungry, eager applicants, with such a sweet and pitying face that she heard many a murmured blessing. Her efforts were all the more appreciated as all saw that she too had passed through the fire and had suffered deeply. At last a kind, motherly lady said: "My dear, you look ready to drop. Here, take this," and she poured out a glass of wine and gave her a sandwich; "now, go and find some quiet nook and rest. It's your duty."

"I have a friend who has suffered almost everything in saving me. He is asleep now, but he has had scarcely anything to eat for nearly three days, and I know he will be very hungry when he wakes."

"Nothing to eat for three days! Why, you must take him a whole loaf, and this, and this," cried the good lady, about to provision Dennis for a month.

"Oh, no," said Christine, with a smile, "so much would not be good for him. If you will give me three or four sandwiches, and let me come for some coffee when he wakes, it will be sufficient;" and she carried what now seemed treasures to where Dennis was sleeping, and sat down with a happy look in her face.

The day had been full of sweet, trustful thoughts. She was conscious of a presence within her heart and all around that she knew was Divine, and in spite of her anxiety about her father and the uncertainty of the future, she had a rest and contentment of mind that she had never experienced before. Then she felt such a genuine sympathy for the sufferers about her, and found them so grateful when she spoke to them gently and kindly, that she wondered she had never before discovered the joy of ministering to others. She was entering a new world, and, though there might be suffering in it, the antidote was ever near, and the pleasures promised to grow richer, fuller, more satisfying, till they developed into the perfect happiness of heaven. But every Christian joy that was like a sweet surprise, — every thrilling hope that pointed to endless progress in all that is best and noblest in life, instead of the sudden blank and nothingness that threatened but yesterday, — and, above all, the animating consciousness of the Divine love which kept her murmuring, "My Saviour, my good, kind Heavenly Father," all reminded her of him who had been instrumental in bringing about the wondrous change. Often during the day she would go and look at him, and could Dennis only have opened his eyes at such a moment, and caught her expression, no words would have been needed to assure him of his happiness.

The low afternoon sun shone in gold and crimson on his brow and face through the stained windows before he gave signs of waking, and then she hurried away to get the coffee hot from the urn.

She had hardly gone before he arose greatly refreshed and strengthened, but so famished that a roast ox would have seemed but a comfortable meal. His eye at once caught the sandwiches placed temptingly near

"That is Miss Ludolph's work," he said; "I wonder if she has saved any for herself." He was about to go and seek her when she met him with the coffee.

"Go back," she said; "how dare you disobey orders?"

"I was coming to find you."

"Well, that is the best excuse you could have made, but I am here; so sit down and drink this coffee and devour these sandwiches."

"Not unless you share them with me."

"Insubordinate! See here," and she took out her more dainty provision from behind a seat and sat down opposite, in such a pretty, companionable way that he in his admiration and pleasure forgot his sandwiches.

"What is the matter?" she asked. "You are to eat the sandwiches, not me."

"A very proper hint, Miss Ludolph; one might well be inclined to make the mistake."

"Now that is a compliment worthy of the king of the Cannibal Islands."

"Miss Ludolph," said Dennis, looking at her earnestly, "you do indeed seem happy."

A ray of light slanting through a yellow diamond of glass fell with a sudden glory upon her face, and in a tone of almost ecstasy she said: "Oh, I am so glad and grateful, when I realize what might have been, and what is! It seems that I have lost so little in this fire in comparison with what I have gained. And but for you I might have lost everything. How rich this first day of life, real, true life, has been! My Heavenly Father has been so kind to me that I cannot express it. And then to think how I have wronged Him all these years!"

"You have indeed learned the secret of true eternal happiness, Miss Ludolph."

"I believe it, — I feel sure of it. All trouble, all pain will one day pass away forever; and sometimes I feel as if I must sing for joy. I do so long to see my father and tell him. I fear he won't believe it at first, but I can pray as you did, and it seems as if my Saviour would not deny me anything. And now, Mr. Fleet, when you have finished your lunch, I am going to ask one more favor, and then will dub you truest knight that ever served defenceless woman. You will find my father for me, for I believe you can do anything."

Even in the shadow where he sat she caught the pained expression of his face.

She started up and grasped his arm.

"You know something," she said; then added: "Do not be afraid to find my father now. When he knows what services you have rendered me, all estrangement, if any existed, will pass away."

But he averted his face, and she saw tears gathering in his eyes.

"Mr. Fleet," she gasped, "do you know anything I do not?"

He could hide the truth no longer. Indeed it was time she should learn it. Turning and taking her trembling hand, he looked at her so sadly and kindly that she at once knew her father was dead.

"Oh, my father!" she cried, in a tone of anguish that he could never forget, "you will never, never know. All day I have been longing to prove to you the truth of Christianity by my loving, patient tenderness, but you have died, and will never know," she moaned, shudderingly.

He still held her hand,—indeed she clung to his as to something that might help sustain her in the dark, bitter hour.

"Poor, poor father!" she cried; "I never treated him as I ought, and now he will never know the wealth of love I was hoping to lavish on him." Then, looking at Dennis almost reproachfully, she said: "Could you not save him? You saved so many others."

"Indeed I could not, Miss Ludolph; I tried, and nearly lost my life in the effort. The great hotel behind the store fell and crushed all in a moment."

She shuddered, but at last whispered, "Why have you kept this so long from me?"

"How could I tell you when the blow would have been death? Even now you can scarcely bear it."

"My little beginning of faith is sorely tried. Heavenly Spirit," she cried, "guide me through this darkness, and let not doubt and unbelief cloud my mind again."

"Such prayer will be answered," said Dennis, in a deep, low tone.

They sat in the twilight in silence. He still held her hand, and she was sobbing more gently and quietly. Suddenly she asked, "Is it wrong thus to grieve over the breaking of an earthly tie?"

"No, not if you will say as did your Lord in His agony, 'O my Father, Thy will be done.'"

"I will try," she said, softly, "but it is hard."

"He is a merciful and faithful High Priest. For in that He Himself hath suffered, being tempted, He is able to succor them that are tempted."

"Do you know that I think my change in feeling makes me grieve all the more deeply? Until to-day I never loved my father as I ought. It is the curse of unbelief to deaden everything good in the heart. Oh, I do feel such a great, unspeakable pity for him!"

"Like as a father pitieth his children, so the Lord pitieth them that fear Him."

"Is that in the Bible?" she asked.

"Yes."

"It is very sweet. He indeed must be my refuge now, for I am alone in the world."

"He has said, 'I will never leave thee nor forsake thee.' I have passed through this sorrow so recently myself that I can sympathize with you as a fellow-sufferer."

"True, true, you have," she answered. "Is that the reason that Christ suffered with us, — that we might know He sympathized with us?"

"Yes."

"How unspeakably comforting is such sympathy, both human and divine! Tell me about your mother."

"I fear I cannot without being unmanned. She was one of heaven's favorites, and I owe everything to her. I can tell you one thing though, she prayed for you continually, — even with her dying lips, when my faith had broken down."

This touched Christine very deeply. At last she said, "I shall see her some day."

"I wish you had seen her," he continued very sadly, looking as if at a scene far away.

"You cannot wish it more than I. Indeed I would have called on her, had it not been for an unfortunate accident."

He looked at her with some surprise, as if not understanding her remark, but said, "She greatly wished to see you before she died."

"Oh, I wish I had known it!"

"Did you not know it?" he asked, in a startled manner.

"No, but I felt grateful to her, for I understood that she offered to take care of me in case I had the small-pox. I wanted to visit her very much, and at last thought I would venture to do so, but just then I sprained my ankle. I sent my maid to inquire, but fear she didn't do my errand very well," added Christine, looking down.

"She never came, Miss Ludolph." Then he continued, eagerly: "I fear I have done you a great wrong. A little time before my mother died, she wrote you a line saying that she was dying and would like to see you. I did not know you could not come, — I thought you would not."

Crimson with shame and humiliation, Christine buried her burning cheeks in her hands and murmured, "I never received it."

"And did you send the exquisite flowers and fruit?" he asked. "Ah, I see that you did. I am so glad, — so very glad that I was mistaken! I sincerely ask your pardon for my unjust thoughts."

"It is I who should ask pardon, and for a long time I have earnestly wished that I might find opportunity to do so. My conduct has been simply monstrous, but of late it has seemed worse than the reality. Everything has been against me. If you only knew — but — " (and her head bowed lower). Then she added, hastily, "My maid has been false, and I must have appeared more heartless than ever." But, with bitter shame and sorrow, she remembered who must have been the inspirer of the treachery, and, though she never spoke of it again, she feared that Dennis suspected it also. It was one of those painful things that must be buried, even as the grave closes over the frail, perishing body.

Let those who are tempted to a wicked, dishonorable deed remember that, even after they are gone, the knowledge of it may come to those who loved them, like an incurable wound.

Dennis's resolution not to speak till Christine should be no longer dependent on him was fast melting away, as he learned that she had not been so callous and forgetful as she had seemed. But before he could add another word, a wild, sweet, mournful voice was heard singing: —

"O fiery storm, wilt never cease?
Thy burning hail falls on my heart;
Bury me deep, that I in peace
May rest where death no more can part."

In awed, startled tones they both exclaimed, "SUSIE WINTHROP!"

CHAPTER XLVIII.

DR. ARTEN STRUCK BY LIGHTNING.

HASTENING down into the body of the church, Dennis and Christine found Mrs. Leonard lying on some cushions in a pew. She was scantily clad, her sweet face scorched and blackened, and her beautiful hair almost crisped away.

Her husband was bending over her in an agony of mingled grief and joy. She had just been brought in from wandering aimlessly and alone quite out upon the prairie, singing in a low, plaintive way to herself words suggested by the sudden disaster that had temporarily robbed her of husband, of reason, and almost of life.

Dennis afterward learned from Professor Leonard that when first aroused they had escaped from the hotel, but, not realizing the danger, he had stepped back a moment at her request to get something she valued very much, and they had become separated.

"And thus at last I find the poor child," he cried, with a look of agony.

Mrs. Leonard did not know any of them, but continued her low, plaintive singing.

Dr. Arten, who had found his way to the church as one of the centres, was soon in attendance, his benevolent face becoming the very embodiment of pity. The crowd were pushed back, and with other kind ladies Christine took charge of her poor unconscious friend, and all was done that skill and tender love could suggest. At last, under the doctor's opiates, her low, weird singing ceased, and she slept, her husband holding her hand. The thronging fugitives were kept a little away, and Dr. Arten slept near, to be within call.

A lady asked Christine to go home with her, but she thanked her and said, "No, I would rather remain in the church near my friends."

Dennis saw that she was greatly wearied. Taking her hand, he said: "Miss Ludolph, it is my turn to take care of you again. See, our friends are preparing a place there for the ladies to sleep. Please go to rest at once, for you do indeed need it."

"I am very tired, but I know I could not sleep. How strange this life is! All day, the world, in spite of what has happened, seemed growing brighter. Now with the night has come the deeper darkness of sorrow. On every side pain and suffering seem to predominate, and to me there will ever be so much mystery in events like my father's death and my friend Susie's experience, that I know it will be hard to maintain a childlike faith."

"God will help you to trust; you will not be left to struggle alone. Then remember you are His child, and earthly parents do much that little children cannot understand."

With a faint smile she answered: "I fear I shall be one of those troublesome children that are ever asking why. All day it has seemed so easy to be a Christian, but already I learn that there will be times when I shall have to cling to my Saviour, instead of being carried forward in His arms. Indeed, I almost fear that I shall lose Him in the darkness."

"But He will not lose you," replied Dennis. "Since you are not sleepy, let me tell you a short Bible story."

"Oh, do, please do, just as if I were a little child."

"It is in the New Testament. Jesus had sent His disciples in a boat across the sea of Galilee, while He should go up alone on a mountain to pray. The night came, and with it a storm swept down against the disciples. The smooth sea was lashed into great foam-crested waves which broke over their little ship. They tugged hour after hour at the oars, but in vain. The night grew darker, the wind more contrary, the waves higher and more threatening, their arms wearied, and they may have feared that they would perish alone and without remedy in the black midnight. But we read that 'He saw them toiling in rowing,' though they knew it not. From the distant mountain side 'He saw them'—marked every weary stroke of the oar, and every throb of fear. But at last, when they were most ready to welcome Him, when none could say, 'We should have rowed through the storm alone,' He came to them walking safely on the dark waves that threatened them with death, and said, 'Be of good cheer, it is I; be not afraid.' Then they gladly received Him into the ship, and immediately the rough waves were hushed, and the keel of the boat grated on the beach toward which they had vainly rowed. Then they that were in the ship came and worshipped Him, saying, 'Of a truth thou art the Son of God.'

"Now it was on the evening of that very night that these same disciples had engaged in a scene of festivity. They had stood in the sunset on the mountain slope, and seen their Lord feed many thousand. Then all was peace, safety, and good cheer. Life changed as quickly for them as for you, but did not their Divine Master see them as truly in the stormy night as in the sunlight? Did He leave them to perish?

"He is watching you, Miss Ludolph, for He is ever the same; and before this stormy night of your sorrow passes away you will hear His voice, saying, 'Be of good cheer, it is I; be not afraid.'"

"Already I hear it," she said, in a low, glad voice, smiling through her tears. "I can, I do trust Him, and the conflicting winds of doubt and fear are becoming still. Among all these homeless people there must be many sad, discouraged hearts. You have helped me so much; can you not say a word or sing something that will help them?"

Dennis thought a moment, and then, in a sweet, clear voice that penetrated every part of the large building, sung:—

"Father in Heaven, the night is around us,
Terror and danger our portion have been;
We cry unto Thee, oh, save and defend us,
Comfort the trembling, and pardon our sin.

"Hearts that are heavy, look onward and upward;
Though wild was the storm that wrecked your loved homes,
Faith lifts your sad glances hopefully heavenward,
To mansions prepared with glory-crowned domes.

"Hearts that are breaking, whose lov'd ones have vanished,
Swept down in the seething ocean of fire,
E'en now they may rest where pain is all banished,
And join their glad songs with the heavenly choir.

"Hearts that are groaning with life's weary burden,
Who fear to go forward, to sorrow a prey;
Jesus invites you—'Oh, come, heavy laden;'
Leave sin at His feet, bear mercy away."

After the first line there was a breathless hush; but, when he closed, low sobbings might be heard from many of the women, and in the dim light not a few tears shone in the eyes of manhood. Dennis's voice was sympathetic in its character, and he had the power of throwing into it much feeling.

Christine was weeping quietly, but her tears now were like the warm spring rain as it falls on the precious seed. At last she said, "You have done these people much good."

"To you belongs all the credit, for it was at your suggestion I sang."

She shook her head, and then said, "Good-night, my friend, I shall never forget this day with its mingled experience; but I think, I hope, I shall never doubt God again;" and she went to her rest.

The light of the next day brought to view many hard realities, and chief among these was the bread question. Dennis was up with the dawn, and by eager inquiries sought to comprehend the situation. Some were gloomy and discouraged, some apathetic, and some determined, courageous, and hopeful; and to this last class he belonged.

Most thankful that he had come out of the fiery ordeal unscathed, he resolved to contribute his quota toward a new and better Chicago. Young, and sanguine in temperament, he already saw the city rise from its ashes in statelier proportions and richer prosperity. With a thrill of exultation he heard the report that some Napoleonic business men had already telegraphed for building material, and were even now excavating the hot ruins.

Christine had hardly joined him as he stood at the door when a gentleman entered and asked, "Who here are willing and able to work for fair wages?"

"I am at your service," said Dennis, stepping forward promptly.

"You are a gentleman, sir," said the speaker, impressed with the fact by Dennis's bearing, though his hat and coat were gone; "I need laborers who can handle the pick and shovel."

"I will work for less, then, till I can handle these tools as well as a laborer. There is no reason why I should eat the bread of charity a day longer. especially when so many need it more than I."

"I said you were a gentleman; I now say you are a man, and that to me means a great deal more," said the energetic stranger. "You shall have two dollars a day with the rest."

He turned to Christine and said, almost proudly, "The supper you have to-night shall be yours also."

"That is," she replied, with a smile, "I shall live on your charity instead of that of some one else."

His face grew sad at once, but he answered, as he went away, "I could not give you charity, Miss Ludolph."

Christine saw that she had pained him, and was much vexed with herself. But his remark added to the hope and almost belief that she still held her old place in his heart, and she resolved to make amends in the evening for her unlucky speech.

With a smile she said to herself: "If he only knew that I would prefer the coarsest, scantiest fare provided by him to the most costly banquet, he would not have gone away with that long face. How rich life would be if I could commence it with him, and we struggle up together! O Heaven, grant," she sighed, looking earnestly upward, "that through these wonderful, terrible changes, I may climb the mountain at his side, as he so graphically portrayed it in his picture!"

Mrs. Leonard still slept, and her husband in an agony of anxiety watched at her side. At last, a little before midday, she opened her eyes and said, in her natural tone: "Why. John, I must have greatly overslept. Where am I?" and then, as her husband fairly sobbed for joy, she started up and said, hurriedly: "What is the matter? What has happened?"

"Oh, be calm!" whispered Christine to the professor. "Everything depends on keeping her quiet." Then she bent over her friend, and said: "Do not be alarmed, Susie;

you are now safe and well, and so is your husband. But you have been ill, and for his sake and your own you must keep quiet."

She turned inquiringly to her husband, who said, more calmly, "It is all true, and if you can only be careful we can go back to Boston as well as ever."

"I will do anything you say, John; but why am I in a church?"

"You were taken sick in the street, and this was the nearest place to bring you."

"O dear! I have had such strange, dreadful dreams. I am so glad they were only dreams, and you are here with me;" and she lay quietly holding her husband's hands and looking contentedly in his face. It was evident she was herself again, and much better.

Dr. Arten soon after came and said, cheerily, "All right! all right! will have you out in a day or two as good as new, and then, Miss Ludolph, you will see how much more grateful she is to the old doctor than you were."

"You must present your bill," replied Christine, with a smile.

"May I?" retorted the doctor, wiping his lips.

"O, I don't know about that," cried Christine; adding, quickly, "when I welcome you to my own home you may."

"An old maid's hall, I suppose."

"It will be an orphan's home, at least," said Christine, softly and sadly.

Tears filled the old man's eyes, and putting his arm around her he drew her to him, saying, as he stroked her drooping head: "Poor child! poor child! I did not know. But you shall never want a protector while the old doctor is above ground. As far as possible I will be a father to you;" and Christine knew she had found a friend as true and strong as steel, and she buried her face on his shoulder and cried as trustingly as his own child might have done.

"O Christine!" cried Mrs. Leonard, "I am so sorry for you!"

At the voice of her old friend she at once rallied, and, trying to smile through her tears, said, "God has been so much better to me than I deserved that I have only gratitude when I think of myself; but my poor father —" and again she covered her face and wept.

"Christine, come here," said Mrs. Leonard, softly, and she put her arms around the weeping girl. "You spoke of God's being good to you. Have you in truth found and learned to trust Him?"

"Yes," she replied, eagerly, joy and peace coming out in her face like the sun shining through clouds and rain. Then with bowed head she whispered low: "The one I wronged on earth led me to the One I wronged in heaven, and both have forgiven me. Oh, I am so glad, so happy!"

"Then you have seen Mr. Fleet."

"Yes, he saved my life again and again; but in teaching me how to find my Saviour, he has done far more for me."

"And you will not wrong him any more, will you, Christine? He has loved you so long and faithfully."

In reply she lifted an eager face to her friend and said, "Do you think he can love me still after my treatment of him?"

"Give him a chance to tell you," said Mrs. Leonard, with a half-mischievous smile. "Has he not shown his feelings?"

"He has treated me more as a brother might have done, and yet he is so very respectful and deferential — I hope — but I am not perfectly sure — and then he seems under some restraint."

Mrs. Leonard said, musingly: "He knows that you are Baroness Ludolph. I told him last week, for I thought he ought to know, and the fact of your approaching departure for Europe has been no secret of late. He thinks you are pledged to a future in which he cannot share; and in your grateful, dependent condition he would not cause you the pain of refusing him. I think that is just where he stands," she concluded, with a woman's mastery of the science of love, and taking almost as much interest in her friend's affair as she had felt in her own. To most ladies this subject has a peculiar fascination, and, having settled their own matters, they enter with scarcely less zest on the task of helping others arrange theirs. Mrs. Leonard rallied faster under the excitement of this new interest than from the doctor's remedies.

After a few moments' thought Christine said, decidedly: "All that nonsense about the Baroness Ludolph is passed forever, — burned up in the fire with many things of more value. I have been fed too long on the husks of human greatness and ambition to want any more of them. They never did satisfy me, and in the light and heat of the terrific ordeal through which I have just passed they shrivelled into utter nothingness. I want something that I cannot lose in a whiff of smoke and flame, and I think I have found it. Henceforth I claim no other character than that of a simple Christian girl." Then bowing her head on her friend's shoulder she added, in a whisper, "If I could climb to true greatness by Mr. Fleet's side, as he portrayed it in his picture, it seems to me heaven would begin at once."

The doctor, who had taken the professor aside, now joined them, and said: "Mrs. Leonard, you have only to take reasonable care of yourself, and you will soon recover from this shock and exposure. I wish all my patients were doing as well."

She replied with a smile, taking her husband's hand: "Since I have found my old Greek here, with his learned spectacles, I am quite myself, and I feel as if I were only playing invalid."

"You may have slept in a church before," said the doctor, with a twinkle in his eye, "and you must do so again. But no one will thunder at you from the pulpit this time, so I leave you in peace and security, and to-night will be within call."

Christine followed him to the lobby of the church, when the irrepressible joker could not forbear saying: "Now let me give you a little paternal advice. Don't be too grateful to that young Fleet. He only did his duty, and of course doesn't deserve any special — "

Christine, with flushing cheeks, interrupted him as if she had not heard: "Doctor, how good and kind you are! Here you are off without any rest to look after the sick and suffering, and you seem to bring health and hope wherever you go."

"Yes, yes; but I send my bill in too — mind that." (Some of his poorer patients never received any, and he, when twitted of the fact, would mutter, roughly, "Business oversight — can't attend to everything.")

Christine looked for a moment at the face so inspiring in its hearty benevolence, and with an impulse, so unlike the cold, haughty girl of old, sprung forward, threw her arms around his neck, and gave him a kiss which he declared afterward was like a mild stroke of lightning, and said, "And there is the first instalment of what I owe you."

The old gentleman looked as if he decidedly liked the currency, and with moistened eyes that he vainly tried to render humorous, he raised his finger impressively in parting, and said, "Don't you ever get out of debt to me."

CHAPTER XLIX.

BILL CRONK'S TOAST.

AFTER all, it was a long day to Christine. Tears would start from her eyes at the thought of her father, but she realized that the only thing for her to do was to shroud his memory in a great, forgiving pity, and put it away forever. She could only turn from the mystery of his life and death — the mystery of evil — to Him who taketh away the sin of the world. There was no darkness in that direction. She busied herself with Mrs. Leonard, and the distribution of food to others, till six o'clock, and then she stood near the door to watch till her true knight should appear in his shirt-sleeves, with a shovel on his shoulder, and an old burnt, tattered felt hat on his head, instead of jewelled crest and heron plume.

Dennis had gone to his work not very hopeful. He knew Christine would be his grateful friend while she lived, and would perhaps even regard him as a brother, but all this might be and still she be unable to respond to his deeper feelings. Moreover, he knew she was Baroness Ludolph, and might be heiress of such titles and estates in Germany as would require that she should go at once to secure them; and so she seemed clearly to pass beyond his sphere.

As he shovelled the hot bricks and cinders hour after hour among other laborers, the distance between himself and the Baroness Ludolph seemed to increase: and when, begrimed and weary, he sat down to eat his dinner of a single sandwich saved from breakfast (for as yet he had no money), the ruins around him were quite in keeping with his feelings. He thought most regretfully of his two thousand dollars and burned picture. The brave, resolute spirit of the morning had deserted him. He did not realize that few men have lived who could be brave and hopeful when weary and hungry, and fewer still, when, in addition, they doubted the favor of the lady of their love.

The work of the afternoon seemed desperately hard and long, but with dogged persistency Dennis held his own with the others till six, and in common with them received his two dollars. Whether Christine would accept the supper he brought or not, he determined to fulfil his promise and bring one. Wearily he trudged off to the west side, in order to find a store. No one who met him would have imagined that this plodding laborer was the artist who the week before had won the prize and title of genius.

If he had been purchasing a supper for himself, he would doubtless have been sensible about it; but one that the Baroness Ludolph might share was a different matter. He bought some very rich cake, a can of peaches, a box of sardines, some fruit, and then his money gave out! But, with these incongruous and indigestible articles made up into one large bundle, he started for the church. He had gone but a little way when some one rushed upon him, and little Ernst clasped him round the neck and fairly cried for joy. Sitting on the sidewalk near were the other little Bruders, looking as forlorn and dirty as three motherless children could. Dennis stopped and sat down beside them (for he was too tired to stand), while Ernst told his story — how their mother had left them, and how she had been found so burned that she was recognized only by a ring (which he had) and a bit of the picture preserved under her body. They had been looking ever since to find him, and had slept where they could.

As Ernst sobbingly told his story the other children cried in doleful chorus, and Dennis's tears fell fast too, as he realized how his humble friend had perished. He remembered her kindness to his mother and little sisters, and his heart acknowledged the claim of these poor little orphans. Prudence whispered, "You cannot afford to burden yourself with all these children," and pride added, "What a figure you will make in presenting yourself before the Baroness Ludolph with all these children at your heels!" But he put such thoughts resolutely aside, and spoke like a brother; and when one of the children sobbed, "We so hungry!" out came the Baroness Ludolph's fruit and cake, and nothing remained for Christine but the sardines and peaches, since these could not well be opened in the street. The little Bruders having devoured what seemed to them the ambrosia of the gods, he took the youngest in his arms, Ernst following with the others; and so they slowly made their way to the church where Christine was now anxiously waiting, with many surmises and forebodings at Dennis's delay.

At last, in the dusk, the little group appeared at the church-door, and she exclaimed, "What has kept you so, Mr. Fleet?"

He determined to put the best face on the situation, and indulge in no heroics, so he said, "You could not expect such a body of infantry as this to march rapidly."

"What!" she exclaimed, "have you brought all the lost children in the city back with you?"

"No, only those that fell properly to my care;" and in a few words he told their story.

"And do you, without a cent in the world, mean to assume the burden of these four children?" she asked, in accents of surprise.

He could not see her face, but his heart sunk within him, for he thought that to her it would seem quixotic and become another barrier between them; but he answered, firmly: "Yes, till God, who has imposed the burden, removes it, and enables me to place them among friends in a good home. Mrs. Bruder, before she died, wrote to her family in Germany, telling her whole story. Relatives may take the children; if not, some way will be provided."

"Mr. Fleet, I wonder at you," was her answer. "Give me that child, and you bring the others."

He wondered at her as he saw her take the child and imprint a kiss on the sleepy, dirty face; and Ernst, who had been eying her askance, crept timidly nearer when he saw the kiss, and whispered, "Perhaps her old outside heart has been burnt away."

They followed to a lobby of the lecture-room, and here she procured a damp towel and proceeded to remove the tear and dust stains from the round and wondering faces of the children. Having restored them to something of their original color, she took them away to supper, saying to Dennis, with a decided nod, "You stay here till I come for you."

Something in her manner reminded him of the same little autocrat who had ordered him about when they arranged the store together. She soon returned with a basin of water and a towel, saying: "See what a luxury you secure by obeying orders. Now give an account of yourself, as every lady's knight should on his return. How have you spent the day?"

He could not forbear laughing as he said: "My employment has been almost ludicrously incongruous with the title by which you honor me. I have been shovelling brick and mortar with other laborers."

"All day?"

"All day."

Her glance became so tender and wistful that he forgot

to wash his hands in looking at her, and felt for the moment as if he could shovel rubbish forever, if such could be his reward.

Seemingly by an effort, she regained her brusque manner, which he did not know was but the mask she was trying to wear, and said, quickly: "What is the matter? Why don't you wash your face?"

"You told me to give an account of myself," he retorted, at the same time showing rising color in his dust-begrimed face.

"Well, one of your ability can do two things at once. What have you got in that bundle?"

"You may have forgotten, but I promised to bring you home something that you chose to regard as charity."

"If I was so ungracious, you ought to have rewarded me by bringing me a broken brick. Will you let me see what you brought?" but without waiting for permission she pounced upon the bundle and dragged out the peaches and sardines.

He, having washed and partially wiped his face, was now able to display more of his embarrassment, and added, apologetically: "That is not all I had. I also bought some cake and fruit, and then my money gave out."

"And do you mean to say that you have no money left?"

"Not a penny," he answered, desperately.

"But where are the cake and fruit?"

"Well," he said, laughingly, "I found the little Bruders famishing on the sidewalk, and they got the best part of your supper."

"What an escape I have had!" she exclaimed. "Do you think I should have survived the night if I had eaten those strangely assorted dainties, as in honor bound I would have done, since you brought them?" Then with a face of comical severity she turned upon him and said: "Mr.

Fleet, you need some one to take care of you. What kind of economy do you call this, sir, especially on the part of one who has burdened himself with four helpless children?"

There was a mingling of sense and seriousness in her raillery, which he recognized, and he said, with a half-vexed laugh at himself: "Well, really, Miss Ludolph, I suppose that I have not wholly regained my wits since the fire. I throw myself on your mercy." (The same expression he had used once before. She remembered it, and her face changed instantly.) Turning hastily away to hide her feelings, she said, in a rather husky voice, "When I was a wicked fool, I told you I had none; but I think I am a little changed now." Then she added, sharply, "Please don't stand there keeping our friends waiting;" and she led the way into the lecture-room, now filled with tables and hungry people.

Dennis was in a maze, and could scarcely understand her, she was so different from the pensive lady, shrinking from rude contact with the world, that he had expected to meet. He did not realize that there was not a particle of weak sentimentality about her, and that, since now pride was gone, her energetic spirit would make her as truly a leader in scenes like these as in those with which she had been familiar. Much less could he understand that she was hiding a heart brimming over with love to him.

He followed her, however, with much assumed humility. When in the middle of the room, who should meet him squarely but Bill Cronk?

"Hollo!" he roared, giving Dennis a slap on his back that startled even the hungry, apathetic people at the tables.

Dennis was now almost desperate. Glad as he was to see Cronk, he felt that he was gathering around him a company as incongruous as was the supper he had brought home.

If Yahcob Bunk or even the red-nosed bar-tender had appeared, to claim him as brother, he would scarcely have been surprised. He naturally thought that the Baroness Ludolph might hesitate before entering such a circle of intimates. But he was not guilty of the meanness of cutting a humble friend, even though he saw the eyes of Christine resting on him. In his embarrassment, however, he held out the wash-basin in his confused effort to shake hands, and said, heartily, "Why, Cronk, I am glad you came safely out of it."

"Is this gentleman a friend of yours?" asked Christine, with inimitable grace.

"Yes!" said Dennis, firmly, though coloring somewhat. "He once rendered me a great kindness —"

"Well, miss, you bet your money on the right hoss that time," interrupted Bill. "If I hain't a friend of his'n, I'd like to know where you'll find one; though I did kick up like a cussed ole mule when he knocked the bottle out of my hand. Like enough if he hadn't I wouldn't be here."

"Won't you present me, Mr. Fleet?" said Christine, with an amused twinkle in her eye.

"Mr. Cronk," said Dennis (who had now reached that state of mind when one becomes reckless), "this lady is Miss Ludolph, and, I hope I may venture to add, another friend of mine."

She at once put out her hand, that seemed like a snowflake in the great horny paw of the drover, and said, "Indeed, Mr. Cronk, I will permit no one to claim stronger friendship to Mr. Fleet than mine."

"I can take any friend of Mr. Fleet's to my buzzom at once," said Bill, speaking figuratively, but Christine instinctively shrunk nearer Dennis. In talking with men, Bill used the off-hand vernacular of his calling, but when addressing ladies, he evidently thought that a certain style of metaphor bordering on sentiment was the proper thing. But Christine said, "As a friend of Mr. Fleet's you shall join our party at once;" and she led them to the farther end of the room, where at a table sat Dr. Arten, Professor and Mrs. Leonard, Ernst, and the little Bruders, who at the prospect of more eating were wide awake again. After the most hearty greetings they were seated, and she took her place by the side of the little children in order to wait on them. Few more remarkable groups sat down together, even in that time of chaos and deprivation. Professor Leonard was without vest or collar, and sat with coat buttoned tight up to his chin to hide the defect. He had lost his scholarly gold-rimmed spectacles, and a wonderful pair of goggles bestrode his nose in their place. Mrs. Leonard was lost in the folds of an old delaine dress that was a mile too large, and her face looked as if she had assisted actively in an Irish wake. Dr. Arten did the honors at the head of the table in his dress coat and vest that had once been white, though he no longer figured around in red flannel drawers as he had done on the beach. The little round faces of the Bruders seemed as if protruding from animated rag babies, while nothing could dim the glory of Ernst's great spiritual eyes, as they gratefully and wistfully followed Dennis's every movement. Cronk was in a very dilapidated and famished state, and endured many and varied tortures in his efforts to be polite while he bolted sandwiches at a rate that threatened famine. Christine still wore the woollen dress she had so hastily donned with Dennis's assistance on Sunday night, and the marks of the fire were all over it. Around her neck the sparks had burned a hole here and there, through which her white shoulders gleamed. While she was self-possessed and assiduous in her attention to the little children, there was a glow of excitement in her eyes which perhaps Mrs. Leonard understood better than any one else, though the shrewd old doctor was anything but blind.

Dennis sat next to Christine in shirt-sleeves once white, but now, through dust and smoke, of as many colors as Joseph's coat. He was too weary to eat much, and there was a weight upon his spirits that he could not throw off, — the inevitable despondency that follows great fatigue when the mind is not at rest.

Christine darted away and brought him a huge mug of hot coffee.

"Really, Miss Ludolph," he remonstrated, "you should not wait on me in this style."

"You may well feel honored, sir," said Mrs. Leonard. "It is not every man that is waited on by a baroness."

"The trouble with Christine is that she is too grateful," put in the old doctor.

"Now I should say that was scarcely possible in view of — " commenced the professor, innocently.

"I really hope Miss Ludolph will do nothing more from gratitude," interrupted Dennis, in a low tone that showed decided annoyance.

The doctor and Mrs. Leonard were ready to burst with suppressed amusement, and Cronk, seeing something going on that he did not understand, looked curiously around with a sandwich half-way to his open mouth, while Ernst, believing from Dennis's tone that he was wronged, turned his great eyes reproachfully from one to another. But Christine was equal to the occasion. Lifting her head and looking round with a free, clear glance she said, "And I say that men who meet this great disaster with courage and fortitude, and hopefully set about retrieving it, possess an inherent nobility such as no king or kaiser could bestow, and, were I twenty times a baroness, I should esteem it an honor to wait upon them."

A round of applause followed this speech, in which Cronk joined vociferously, and Mrs. Leonard whispered: "O

Christine, how beautifully I learn from your face the difference between dignity and pride! That was your same old proud look, changed and glorified into something so much better."

Dennis also saw her expression, and could not disguise his admiration, but every moment he increasingly felt how desperately hard it would be to give her up, now that she seemed to realize his very ideal of womanhood.

And Cronk, having satisfied the clamors of his appetite, began to be fascinated in his rough way with her grace and beauty. Nudging Dennis he asked in a loud whisper heard by all, which nearly caused Dr. Arten to choke, "The young filly is a German lady, ain't she?"

Dennis, much embarrassed, nodded assent.

A happy thought struck Bill. Though impeded by the weight of an indefinite number of sandwiches, he slowly rose and looked solemnly round on the little group. Dennis trembled, for he feared some dreadful bull on the part of his rough, though well-meaning friend, but Dr. Arten, in a state of intense enjoyment, cried, "Mr. Cronk has the floor."

Lifting a can of coffee containing about a quart, the drover said impressively, and with an attempt at great stateliness:—

"Beautiful ladies and honorable gentlemen here assembled, I would respectfully ask you to drink to a toast in this harmless beverage: *The United States of Ameriky!* When the two great elemental races—the sanguinary Yankee and the pleagmatic German—become one, and, as represented in the blooded team before me" (waving his hand majestically over the heads of Dennis and Christine), "pull in the traces together, how will the ship of state go forward!" and his face disappeared behind his huge flagon of coffee in the deepest pledge. Bill thought he had uttered a very profound and elegant sentiment, but his speech fell like a bomb-shell in the little company.

"The very spirit of mischief is abroad to-day," Dennis groaned. And Christine, with a face like a peony, snatched up the youngest little Bruder, saying, "It is time these sleepy children were in bed;" but the doctor and the Leonards went off again and again in uncontrollable fits of laughter, in which Dennis could not refrain from joining, though he wished the unlucky Cronk a thousand miles away. Bill put down his mug, stared around in a surprised and nonplussed manner, and then said, in a loud whisper, "I say, Fleet, was there any hitch in what I said?"

This set them off again, but Dennis answered good-naturedly, slapping his friend on the shoulder, "Cronk, you would make a man laugh in the face of fate."

Bill took this as a compliment, and the strange party, thrown together by an event that mingled all classes in the community, broke up and went their several ways.

CHAPTER L.

EVERY BARRIER BURNED AWAY.

DENNIS was glad to escape, and went to a side door where he could cool his hot cheeks in the night air. He fairly dreaded to meet Christine again, and, even where the wind blew cold upon him, his cheeks grew hotter and hotter, as he remembered what had occurred. He had been there but a little time when a light hand fell on his arm, and he was startled by her voice,—"Mr. Fleet, are you very tired?"

"Not in the least," he answered, eagerly.

"You must be: it is wrong for me to think of it."

"Miss Ludolph, please tell me what I can do for you?"

She looked at him wistfully and said: "This is a time when loss and disaster burden every heart, and I know it is a duty to try to maintain a cheerful courage, and forget personal troubles. I have tried to-day, and, with God's help, hope in time to succeed. While endeavoring to wear in public a cheerful face, I may perhaps now, and to so true a friend as yourself, show more of my real feelings. Is it too far—would it take too long, to go to where my father died? His remains could not have been removed."

"Alas, Miss Ludolph," said Dennis, very gently, "there can be no visible remains. The words of the Prayer Book are literally true in this case—'Ashes to ashes.' But I can take you to the spot, and it is natural that you should wish to go. Are you equal to the fatigue?"

"I shall not feel it if you go with me, and then we can ride part of the way, for I have a little money." (Dr. Arten had insisted on her taking some.) "Wait for me a moment."

She soon reappeared with her shawl cut in two equal parts. One she insisted on folding and putting around him as a Scotsman wears his plaid. "You will need it in the cool night wind," she said, and then she took his arm in perfect trust, and they started.

In the cars she gave him her money, and he said, "I will return my fare to-morrow night."

"What!" she replied, looking a little hurt. "After spending two dollars on me, will you not take five cents in return?"

"But I spent it foolishly."

"You spent it like a generous man. Surely, Mr. Fleet, you did not understand my badinage this evening. If I had not spoken to you in that strain, I could not have spoken at all. You have been a brother to me, and we should not stand on these little things."

"That is it," thought he again. "She looks upon and trusts me as a brother, and such I must try to be till she departs for her own land; yet if she knew the agony of the effort she would scarcely ask it."

But as they left the car, he said, "All that you would ask from a brother, please ask from me."

She put her hand in his, and said, "I now ask your support, sympathy, and prayer, for I feel that I shall need all here."

Still retaining her hand, he placed it on his arm and guided her most carefully around the hot ruins and heaps of rubbish till they came to where the Art Building had stood. The moon shone brightly down, lighting up with weird and ghostly effect the few walls remaining. They were utterly alone in the midst of a desolation sevenfold more impressing than that of the desert. Pointing to the spot where, in the midst of his treasures of art and idolized worldly possessions, Mr. Ludolph had perished, she said, in a thrilling whisper, "My father's ashes are there."

"Yes."

Her breath came quick and short, and her face was so pale and agonized that he trembled for her, but he tightened his grasp on her hand, and his tears fell with hers.

"O my father!" she cried, in a tone of unspeakable pathos, "can I never, never see you again? Can I never tell you of the love of Jesus, and the better and happier life beyond? Oh, how my heart yearns after you! God forgive me if this is wrong, but I cannot help it!"

"It is not wrong," said Dennis, brokenly. "Our Lord himself wept over those He could not save."

"It is all that I can do," she murmured, and, leaning her head on his shoulder, a tempest of sobs shook her person.

He supported her tenderly, and said, in accents of the deepest sympathy, "let every tear fall that will: they will do you good." At last, as she became calmer, he added, "Remember that your great Elder Brother has called the heavy laden to Him for rest."

At last she raised her head, turned, and gave one long parting look, and, as Dennis saw her face in the white moonlight, it was the face of a pitying angel. A low "Farewell!" trembled from her lips, she leaned heavily on his arm, they turned away, and seemingly the curtain fell between father and child to rise no more.

"Mr. Fleet," she said, pleadingly, "are you too tired to take me to my old home on the north side?"

"Miss Ludolph, I could go to the ends of the earth for you, but you are not equal to this strain upon your feelings. Have mercy on yourself."